SUPERSONIC
FLIGHT

SUPERSONIC FLIGHT

The Story of the Bell X-1 and Douglas D-558

RICHARD HALLION

INTRODUCTION BY MICHAEL COLLINS
AND MELVIN B. ZISFEIN

To Chuck Foster
with all best wishes,
Dick Hallion

Published in association with
THE SMITHSONIAN INSTITUTION
NATIONAL AIR AND SPACE MUSEUM

THE MACMILLAN COMPANY, *New York, New York*
COLLIER-MACMILLAN LTD., *London*

The Macmillan Company
866 Third Avenue, New York, N.Y. 10022
Collier-Macmillan Canada Ltd., Toronto, Ontario

Library of Congress Catalog Card Number: 72-88809

First Printing

Printed in the United States of America

CONTENTS

PART

TWO

THROUGH THE "SOUND BARRIER"

PART

THREE

THROUGH MACH 2

ACKNOWLEDGMENTS

I t would have been impossible to write the story of the XS-1 and D-558 without the generous cooperation of many individuals and organizations. Special thanks are due to the NASA Historical Office and the Smithsonian Institution for their gracious help over the past several years. I am particularly grateful to Dr. Eugene M. Emme, NASA Historian; and Dr. Frank W. Anderson, Deputy NASA Historian; Michael Collins, Director, National Air and Space Museum; and Melvin N. Zisfein, Deputy Director, National Air and Space Museum. I also want to acknowledge the assistance given me by the Air Force Historical Office, Air Force Museum, Air Force Systems Command, NASA Langley Research Center, National Archives, and Naval Air Systems Command. I wish to thank especially Carl Berger, Office of Air Force History; Dr. Donald R. McVeigh,* Historian, Air Force Systems Command; Robert W. Mulac and Neva B. Brooks, NASA Langley Research Center; Dr. Lee M. Pearson, Historian, Naval Air Systems Command; and Ralph Jackson and James Love, NASA Flight Research Center. I especially appreciate the assistance given me by Russell Bourne, Consultant on Special Publications, Smithsonian Institution; Louis S. Casey, Acting Assistant Director, National Air and Space Museum; and Robert B. Wood, National Air and Space Museum.

The faculty of the Department of History, University of Maryland, have always provided patient counseling and thoughtful advice that I have found most helpful. My debt to them is great. I benefited from consultations with Dr. Richard E. Thomas, former Head, Department of Aerospace Engineering, University of Maryland, who directed my initial

* Died 30 April 1972.

research in this area; and with Dr. Jewel B. Barlow, Assistant Professor, Department of Aerospace Engineering. Their advice and encouragement were invaluable.

I wish to thank the following participants in the XS-1 and D-558 research aircraft programs who have assisted me in this reseach through interviews or correspondence.

Milton B. Ames, Jr., Senior Research Associate, Office of Advanced Research and Technology, NASA.

Neil A. Armstrong, Professor of Aerospace Engineering, University of Cincinnati.

John V. Becker, Chief, Hypersonic Vehicles Division, NASA Langley Research Center.

Ralph P. Bielat, High-Speed Aircraft Division, NASA Langley Research Center.

Clinton E. Brown, Chief Scientist, Hydronautics, Inc.

Robert A. Champine, Research Aircraft Flight Division, NASA Langley Research Center.

A. Scott Crossfield, Vice-President, Flight Research and Development, Eastern Air Lines.

Leo J. Devlin, Jr., former Chief Designer, Douglas Aircraft Company (El Segundo).

Capt. Walter S. Diehl, USN (Ret.)

Macon C. Ellis, Jr., Hypersonic Vehicles Division, NASA Langley Research Center.

Paul Emmons, Chief Engineer, Flight Test Operations, Bell Aerospace Company.

Richard H. Frost, President, Frost Engineering Development Corporation.

William G. Gisel, President, Bell Aerospace Company.

Robert R. Gilruth, Director, Key Personnel Development, NASA Manned Spacecraft Center.

Benson Hamlin, Vice-President, Westinair Division, Stinson Aircraft.

Edward H. Heinemann, Vice-President, General Dynamics Corporation.

Robert A. Hoover, Executive Assistant, North American Rockwell Corporation.

Dr. Abraham Hyatt, Aerospace and Systems Group, North American Rockwell Corporation.

Ezra Kotcher, formerly of the Wright Air Development Division, Wright-Patterson AFB.

Axel T. Mattson, Assistant Director, NASA Langley Research Center.

Jean A. Roché, former Army Air Forces Liaison Officer to the NACA Langley Memorial Aeronautical Laboratory.

Dr. L. Eugene Root, former Chief, Aerodynamics Section, Douglas Aircraft Company (El Segundo).

A. M. O. Smith, Chief Aerodynamics Engineer for Research, McDonnell Douglas Aircraft Company.

Stanley W. Smith, Engineer, Vertol Division, The Boeing Company.

Robert M. Stanley, President, Stanley Aviation Corporation.

*John Stack, Vice-President Enginering, Fairchild Industries.

Dr. Floyd L. Thompson, Special Consultant to the NASA Administrator.

Thomas A. Toll, Office of Director for Aeronautics, NASA Langley Research Center.

Gerald M. Truszynski, Associate Administrator for Tracking and Data Acquisition, NASA.

Harold Turner, formerly of the NACA Langley Memorial Aeronautical Laboratory.

Joseph Vensel, former Chief of Operations, NASA Flight Research Center.

Robert A. Wolf, Cornell Aeronautical Laboratory, Inc.

Brig. Gen. Charles E. Yeager, USAF.

* Died 18 June 1972.

INTRODUCTION

Michael Collins, Director, National Air and Space Museum
Melvin B. Zisfein, Deputy Director, National Air and Space Museum

The first supersonic flight and the first trip to the moon had many things in common. Both were produced by the American aerospace industry, both required quantum jumps in many areas of engineering, and both required the utmost in pilot training and human and physical support systems. Most significantly, supersonic flight and space travel were both born of the vision of people who dared to assert that "it could be done," who had to prove repeatedly to doubters that it might be worth doing, and who were harassed, from start to finish (but particularly at the start), by many and variously oriented prophets of failure.

In order to appreciate the X-1 achievement, let us examine the problems of flying faster than sound and review the pitfalls as they might have been foreseen on the "before" side of the achievement. We will find that in the mid-1940s it was not difficult to extrapolate existing knowledge into many fears, few entirely groundless.

We are considering manned powered flight in a lifting vehicle (an airplane) through the air at speeds faster than sound travels through that same air. Of all the possible limiting speeds, there were good reasons to select the speed of sound as the upper limit. Ahead of a lifting wing there is an upwash, a current of air particles moving upward in anticipation of the approach of the wing. This flow pattern prevails at all speeds below the speed of sound. The particles are "informed" by pressure waves emanating from the wing. The pressure waves that move the air ahead of the wing travel at the speed of sound.

If the wing in our example then speeds up, so that it is moving at or above the velocity of sound, the pressure waves that previously "warned" the air ahead of the wing's coming are overtaken by the wing itself.

In the early 1940s this chain of reasoning led to dire predictions about supersonic flight. Pilots blamed the sonic "bunching up" of air for the frightening vibrations airplanes encountered when they dove at nearly sonic speed. Engineers knew that a wing moving at supersonic speed creates shock waves, violent disturbances in the air which move along with the wing as if attached and, in a sense, adjust the airflow for the supersonic wing's lack of advance warning. These shock waves were expected to ruin the air flow, stall the wings, reverse the control forces, and otherwise produce serious mischief. Numerous incidents of near catastrophic high speed buffeting, control loss and upset encounters, as well as some unexplained crashes, seemed to confirm those fears.

Supersonic bullets had been coming out of pistol, rifle, and cannon muzzles for years and (with their shock waves) speeding precisely to their targets. But a bullet is a bullet and a thin skinned, winged, control surfaced airplane seemed to be quite another thing.

There were serious predictions that the pilot's voice would get stuck in his throat when he flew faster than sound, ignoring the fact that in the cockpit the pilot is surrounded by air at rest with respect to him. Some even feared that flying supersonically reversed time and that the pilot would turn into a young boy.

If you were a sober analyst you would have noted that Geoffrey de Havilland died in a disintegrating D.H. 108 while trying to "break the sound barrier." As late as 1959, the Readers Digest conjured up an "invisible wall" in digesting an article from The Royal Air Force Flying Review:

> During the war a British engineer named Frank Whittle invented the jet engine, and deHavilland built the first production-type model. He produced a jet plane named Vampire, the first to exceed 500 m.p.h. Then he built the experimental DH 108, and released it to young Geoffrey for test. In the first cautious trials the new plane behaved beautifully; but as Geoffrey stepped up the speed he unsuspectingly drew closer to an invisible wall in the sky then unknown to anyone, later named the sound barrier, which can destroy a plane not designed to pierce it. One evening he hit the speed of sound, and the plane disintegrated. Young Geoffrey's body was not found for ten days."

The strange buffeting, high structural loads, aerodynamic flow separations, erratically varying control moments, trim changes, and stick forces associated with transonic and supersonic flight certainly indicated that achieving supersonic flight was not merely a problem of packing more power into a stronger airplane. Supersonic flight was known earlier than the 1940s to be fundamentally different. The aerodynamicist recognized that at supersonic speeds many of his time-tested methods were no longer applicable. At the most fundamental level the governing supersonic flow equation was the Wave Equation, not LaPlace's Equation as at subsonic speeds; all supersonic flow solutions were expected to be different. This difference in air behavior certainly was fundamental. An unprecedented zone, in front of a supersonically traveling body, where the approaching body's presence could not be felt, was poetically named by Dr. Theodore von Kármán the "Zone of Silence or Forbidden Signals." (The Tenth Wright Brothers Lecture delivered by von Kármán in 1947 is a monumental paper which summarizes the state of knowledge of supersonics at the dawn of the supersonic era.)

A new aerodynamic force, wave drag, became important at supersonic speeds, adding substantially to the thrust requirements imposed by the more familiar skin friction drag, profile drag, lift-induced drag and interference drag. In the mid 1940s it was impossible to be certain that there were no other transonic and supersonic phenomena as yet unanticipated. Even at the most "practical" level in the 1940s the unnerving thing about supersonic flight was that there were little "hard" supersonic test data. It was difficult to assess the accuracy of the various transonic and supersonic flow solution techniques that the more mathematically oriented aerodynamicists had devised. Any predicted sonic or supersonic load or control force might be off several orders of magnitude. Only experience would change this, and the experience might be costly.

During the middle and late forties, the authors of this Introduction were in school. The fact that about 25 years later they would become responsible for a collection containing the X-1 was in their "zone of forbidden signals." What they learned collectively during this period included a series of analyses and reasoned hypotheses which indicated that, at best, flight faster than sound would be tricky with foreseeable equipment and, at worst, impossible in a practical sense. Let us go back to re-create some of these anticipated problems.

First we have the "sound barrier." What was it? Actually it was no barrier at all, but what might be considered to be a mathematically expressed warning of probable physical difficulties. In one sense the "sound barrier" was a number of subsonic curves of flight parameters that seemed to approach infinity as speed was increased (far beyond the zone of validity of the curves) toward the speed of sound.

Aerodynamicists, particularly those of a mathematical bent, had long been exercising the problem of "compressibility effects," the term frequently used to describe what happened to aerodynamic properties as a vehicle's speed approached and (if possible) exceeded the speed of sound. The term Mach Number (named after the scientist Ernst Mach) was devised to describe the ratio of aircraft speed to the speed of sound. Hence, $M = V/V_s$, or, Mach Number = Vehicle Velocity/Velocity of Sound. Mach 1 is the velocity of sound, Mach 2 we are flying at twice the velocity of sound, Mach 0.95 is 95% of the velocity of sound, etc.

The theoretical aerodynamicists had for some time examined what happens as a vehicle approaches the speed of sound. Prantdl and Glauert derived the approximate factor $1/\sqrt{(1-M^2)}$ as a correction factor for pressure or lift. This term shows that, for a winglike body fixed in an airstream (or an airfoil moving through the air at a given attitude), the pressure or overall lift will increase over the low speed value as velocity is increased, and that the rate of increase will accelerate; so that as we approach the velocity of sound (Mach 1), pressure and lift will approach infinity (as the denominator approaches zero). In 1947, the year of the first supersonic flight, one of the first generally available compressible aerodynamics textbooks was published. Its authors were Liepmann and Puckett. In this text the excellent correlation of (then) recent NACA experiments with the Prantdl-Glauert factor (and with a more refined factor by von Kármán and Tsien) is demonstrated graphically. The 1947 Liepmann and Puckett curve is reproduced here as Figure 1 to show the reader this trend of rising pressure leading into a then unexplored region. This same trend was also evident in a text published several years later by Hilton. His curves are reproduced as Figure 2. Such data were generally available in the aeronautical engineering community well before the X-1 flew.

Unfortunately, during the 1940s, the period when these comparisons were being made and published in reports, their generality was overestimated. Some people inferred that this increase of "everything" toward infinity as Mach 1 was approached could be taken literally (forgetting the limitations of the theoretical derivations, clearly stated by the aerodynamicists) and that vehicle drag would increase to infinity. Hence the "Sound Barrier." Figure 3 shows this increase in drag with Mach Number as it might have been viewed in the mid 1940s in a frightening graph in Hilton's text.

Let us approach the sound barrier notion from a more physical viewpoint. In Figure 4, a lifting wing moving through the air constantly emits pressure disturbances. Each pressure pulse expands outward like ripples in a pool. Each wavefront moves out in all directions at the speed of sound. In Figure 5 the wing is moving at Mach 0.9 and rapidly overtaking the forward moving pressure wavefronts. In Figure 6 the wing is moving at Mach 1.0. Here the pressures from all forward wavefronts pile up in a concentrated front. With a little imagination this front becomes a "pressure wall," and the "sound barrier" concept is given a physical interpretation. In his 1947 Wright Brothers Lecture, von Kármán called this pressure pile up phenomenon the "Rule of Concentrated Action."

The expression "breaking the sound barrier," while dramatically edifying, might better have been phrased as "traverse the transonic tangles and traps." Uncertainty was the key emotion. Because no one really knew the level at which the steadily increasing subsonic force coefficients peaked out to merge with the steadily decreasing supersonic force coefficients, transonic loads were an open question. Doubts about static and maneuvering loads were compounded by additional uncertainties regarding the onset of "shock stall," the possible loss of lift from this phenomenon, and the accompanying incremental buffeting loads. Extreme conservatism was called for, but you can't build an airplane like a bridge and expect it to fly.

The flutter implications of not really knowing the magnitude and distribution of these aerodynamic loads were enormous. Flutter is that aerodynamic-structural phenomenon which results in spontaneous vibrations of members of a flying air vehicle, sometimes growing rapidly to induce catastrophic structural failure. Transonic wing, tail, and control surface flutter predictions were all extremely questionable. A nonlinear variant of flutter, aileron buzz, was a particular nuisance all through the early X airplane programs.

A constant source of danger and a tax on the designer was the expected (and sometimes unexpected) shift of centers of pressure as speed changed from subsonic to supersonic. A center of pressure might be regarded as the application point of any aerodynamic force, such as wing lift. The change in wing center of pressure from about one-quarter of the wing chord (subsonic) to about one-half of the wing chord (supersonic) sounds innocuous. It is not. Particularly with the airplane shapes of 1947, huge changes in trim, stability, control forces, and maneuvering loads could result. The designer was faced with accommodating such changes and foreseeing more capricious variants of these that might be associated with the constantly changing shock wave patterns characteristic of transonic flow.

A principal ingredient in all this uncertainty was the "uncertainty of similitude." We simply were not sure how we should test models or interpret the results of tests. Many experts considered a transonic wind tunnel to be forever impossible. (They did not foresee the invention of the porous or slotted wind tunnel throat.) Even if, in an expensive free-flight transonic rocket test, a shock wave was found to appear on the model, did this mean that one would appear on the full-scale airplane? The academic and industrial research and development communities were seriously at work on all of these questions in 1947, but there were no firm answers and little "hard" data.

Of course there was no impenetrable "sound barrier," and supersonic flight was achieved through the process that forms the bulk of this book. We hasten to point out, however, that the success of the supersonic flight venture leaned heavily on the methodical mathematical aerodynamic studies that constituted the life work of a generation of dedicated scholars. Lest these go unrecognized here, we have added a brief appendix to this report. It is reproduced from the 1947 textbook *Introduction to Aero-*

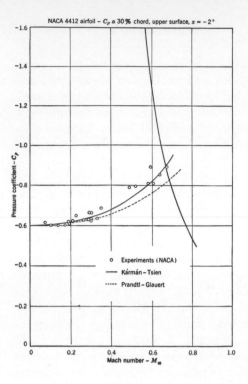

NACA 4412 airfoil – C_p a 30% chord, upper surface, $x = -2°$

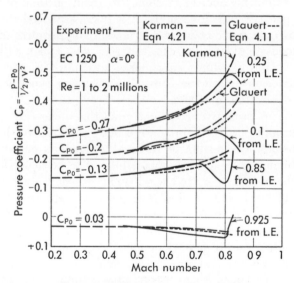

(ABOVE) FIGURE 1. *Pressure coefficient versus Mach number. (Hans W. Liepmann and Allen E. Puckett*, Introduction to Aerodynamics of a Compressible Fluid, © *1947, John Wiley & Sons, Inc., New York)*

(BELOW) FIGURE 2. *Comparison of Kármán and Glauert theories with experiment. (William F. Hilton*, High-Speed Aerodynamics, © *1951, Longmans, Green & Co. Ltd., London)*

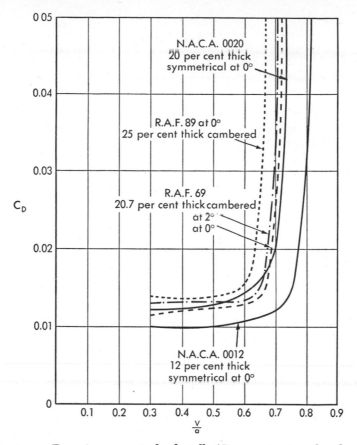

FIGURE 3. *Drag increase at shock-stall. (Curves rise too sharply as they are not corrected for wind tunnel interference.) (William F. Hilton,* High-Speed Aerodynamics, © 1951, *Longmans, Green & Co. Ltd., London)*

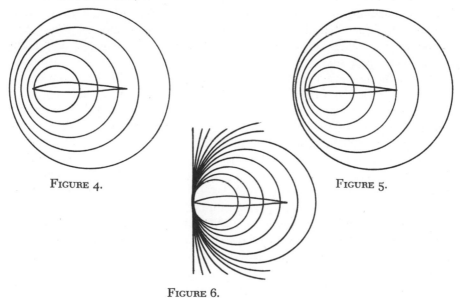

FIGURE 4.

FIGURE 5.

FIGURE 6.

dynamics of a Compressible Fluid by Liepmann and Puckett; it lists an assortment of seminal papers by a distinguished group.

This should in no way detract from the credit due the first supersonic flight teams, or, for that matter, those who followed the initial flights by working for years to extract more and better data from the X-1 and D-558 flight programs. These data were used for everything from the confirmation of total airplane drag prediction methods to the validation of laminar-to-turbulent boundary layer transition point calculations for the prediction of aerodynamic heating rates. Their effect on subsequent design efforts is great. These tests and their output, in addition to generating considerable primary design method validation data, also helped train the first generation of supersonic aircraft designers.

One of the authors of this Introduction had the privilege of working in the midst of the X airplane aerodynamics team during his early years at Bell Aircraft Corporation. Even a few years after the initial X-1 flight, the excitement of flight planning for a new record-setting (and, of course, data-gathering) flight was infectious. Some of the flight planning was desk work, but a good deal of it was centered on two strange looking analog computers. At least one of these was known as the BAPA (Bell Aircraft Performance Analyzer); perhaps both were; they will be called BAPA-I and BAPA-II here although these designations may not be exact. BAPA-I looked like a black girder structure made from some large Erector set. It had dials and knobs on the front and (when operating) a bank of softly glowing light bulbs (for electrical ballast) underneath. BAPA-II was an improved version replacing BAPA-I. It had a shiny gray case, large dials and knobs built into a sloping front, and the general air of a submarine control panel in a low-budget motion picture. Each BAPA run simulated, in accelerated time, a possible X airplane flight, taking into account launch inputs, fuel consumption, empirical lift and drag variation with Mach Number, altitude, etc. From the results of these runs and related calculations, final flight strategies were selected and flight plans were prepared.

At the beginning of a BAPA run the team assembled in front of the machine with about three seated dial-reading knob turners and one flight director. On command the airplane was "launched" and all the personnel hand-controlled their assigned knobs to reflect readings of dials showing changes in such variables as weight, Mach Number, and altitude. One virtue of the machine was that it was *slow*, so that input settings could be readily changed by hand to correspond to constantly changing flight variables. Since all input data (such as lift and drag coefficients) were known only as nonlinearly varying empirical functions of Mach Number and other variables, automatic regulation of machine inputs to correspond to these variables was out of the question. Each "flight" was an odd looking exercise with a four-man (or so) crew with eyes glued on the dials, following the machine readouts and a string of verbal commands as they turned the appropriate knobs. However, this was reasonably sophisticated at a time of relatively low technological sophistication—and the technique worked.

Today our level of sophistication is much higher in the hardware and software of both design and flight. Sometimes higher sophistication leads to higher costs, and usually it leads to a better designed, more reliable product. From the pilot's point of view, today's sophisticated airplanes operate routinely on either side of the "sound barrier," and in fact under some conditions the pilot must check his instruments to determine whether he is in subsonic or supersonic flight. How disappointing to find that the engineers have learned their lessons so well that they have reduced the pilot's awareness of the "sound barrier" to a surreptitious glance at the Machmeter. While this may be true of recent aircraft, such as the "Century Series" fighters, some of the aircraft following closely on the heels of the X-1 were not so well behaved. One of the authors recalls his first trip past Mach One, in a barely supersonic F-86 Sabrejet. The trick here was to climb to high altitude and then go into a near vertical dive. Even with this gravity assist, it was difficult to obtain the telltale jump of the Machmeter which indicated that the shock wave had passed the static port on the side of the fuselage. In fact, individual F-86s showed persnickity differences. Some were easily handled through Mach 1; others developed an uncontrollable roll, and could only make it through into supersonic flight in corkscrew fashion; while some "dogs" would waver right at the threshold, and could not be induced to go beyond Mach 0.96 or 0.97.

But this era in aviation was soon over and, with the advent of the F-100, supersonic level and even climbing flight became commonplace for the military fighter pilot. The bomber pilots even had their supersonic fling with the B-58 and the experimental Mach 3 B-70, which embarrassed the latest fighters by leaving them far behind in a cloud of vapor trails. Then pilots were given a new supersonic option; going straight up on a rocket headed for earth orbit or beyond.

The Mercury, Gemini, and Apollo boosters all have similar launch profiles. Having only slightly more thrust than weight as they leave the launch pad, they get off to the excruciatingly slow start we have all seen, as the missile inches up our television screen. As the fuel load lightens, however, the constant thrust of the engines causes the acceleration to increase rapidly, and supersonic speed is usually achieved in a bit over a minute's time at an altitude of around 35,000 ft. In other words, we find ourselves in the F-86's domain, but heading straight up instead of straight down, and hopefully without any uncontrollable tendencies. As speed and dynamic pressure build, noise and vibration inside the cockpit (of aircraft or spacecraft) also increase, and reach a peak just as Mach 1 is reached. Beyond that, things get quieter and smoother rapidly, especially in the case of the spacecraft, which soon finds itself far above the disturbing aerodynamic properties of the dense atmosphere below.

Although the past twenty-five years have shown amazing progress, even today only a few can visit the supersonic domain. We have deliberately chosen not to attempt commercial supersonic flight at this time, less because of technological difficulties than concern over economic and ecological factors. It is difficult to predict when these impediments may be overcome, but it does seem safe to look past the Concorde to the day when high Mach number flight becomes commonplace.

Chuck Yeager's flight of October 14, 1947, in the Bell X-1 is clearly a major milestone on the road from Kitty Hawk to the moon. We join Mr. Hallion in recognizing this achievement on its twenty-fifth anniversary and in saluting those in industry, government, research institutions, and universities whose combined efforts gave us the knowledge and machines to fly at supersonic speeds.

The following is the appendix to Hans W. Liepmann and Allen E. Puckett, *Introduction to Aerodynamics of a Compressible Fluid*, listing seminal papers. (© 1947, John Wiley & Sons, Inc.)

References

The following table of references is not intended to be a complete list of papers on the subject of compressibility effects in aeronautics. It is rather intended to give a brief list of papers useful for further study of the subject. A very complete list of references can be found in L. R. Michel's *Bibliography on Flow of Compressible Fluids* (Department of Mechanical Engineering, Massachusetts Institute of Technology), 1943–1944.

In addition, the following references are of basic importance.

General

SAUER, R., *Theoretische Einführung in die Gasdynamik*, Springer, Berlin, 1943. Reprinted by Edwards Bros., Inc., Ann Arbor, Mich.

ACKERET, J., *Handbuch der Physik*, Vol. 7, Chapter 5, Springer, Berlin, 1927.

BUSEMANN, A., *Handbuch der Experimentalphysik*, Vol. 4, Part I, Akademische Verlagsgesellschaft, Leipzig, 1931.

KÁRMÁN, TH. VON, "Compressibility Effects in Aerodynamics," *Jour. Aero. Sci.*, 8, 337, (1941).

TAYLOR, G. I., and L. W. MACOLL, "The Mechanics of Compressible Fluids," in Durand's *Aerodynamic Theory*, Vol. III. Reprinted by Durand Reprinting Committee, California Institute of Technology, 1945.

BATEMAN, H., "Report of the Committee on Hydrodynamics," Part IV; *National Research Council Bull. 84*, Washington, D.C., 1945.

KÁRMÁN, TH. VON, "Problems of Resistance in Real Fluids," *Reale Academia d'Italia*, 15th Volta Congress, 1935.

Thermodynamics

EPSTEIN, S., *Textbook of Thermodynamics*, Wiley, New York, 1937.
STODOLA, A., *Steam and Gas Turbines* (translated), McGraw-Hill, New York, 1927.

Methods of Expansion in Powers of the Mach Number

JANZEN, O., "Beitrag zu einer Theorie der stationären Strömung kompressibler Flüssigkeiten," *Physikalische Zeitschrift*, 14, 639 (1913).
RAYLEIGH, LORD, "On the Flow of Compressible Fluid Past an Obstacle," *Philosophical Magazine* (6), 32, 1 (1916), or *Papers*, 6, 402.
HOOKER, S. G., "The Two-Dimensional Flow of Compressible Fluids at Subsonic Speeds Past Elliptic Cylinders," *R. & M.*, British A.R.C., No. 1684 (1936).
POGGI, L., "Campo di velocita in una corrente piana di fluido compressibile," *L'Aerotecnica*, 12, 1519 (1932).
"Caso dei profili ottenuti con representazione conforme dal cerchio ed in particolare dei profili," Joukowsky, *L'Areotecnica*, 14, 532 (1934).

Method of Expansion in Powers of a Thickness Parameter
(Small Perturbations)

GLAUERT, H., "The Effect of Compressibility on the Life of Airfoils," *Proc. of the Royal Society* (A), 118, 113 (1927).
PRANDTL, L., "Über Strömungen, deren Geschwindigkeiten mit der Schallgeschwindigkeit vergleichbar sind," *Jour. Aero. Research Institute of Univ. Tokyo*, No. 6, p. 14 (1930).
GÖRTLER, H., "Der Kompressibilitätseinfluss für dünne wenig gekrümmte Profile bei Unterrchallgeschwindigkeit," *Z.A.M.M.*, 20, 254 (1940).
HANTZSCHE, W., and M. WENDT, "Gasströmungen mit Übergang von Unterschall-zu Überschallgeschwindigkeiten," *Z.A.M.M.*, 22, 72 (1942).
GOLDSTEIN, S., and YOUNG, "The Linear Perturbation Theory of Compressible Flow with Application to Wind Tunnel Interference," *British A.R.C.* 6865, Aero, 2262 FM 601, July 6, 1943.
TSEIN, H. S., and L. LEES, "The Glauert-Prandtl Approximation for Subsonic Flows of a Compressible Fluid," *Jour. Aero. Sci.*, 12, 173 (1945).

Airfoil Theory for Supersonic Motion

ACKERET, J., "Luftkräfte auf Flügel, die mit grösserer als Schallgeschwindigkeit bewegt werden," *ZFM*, 16, 72–74 (1925).
BUSEMANN, A., "Aerodynamischer Auftrieb bei Überschallgeschwindigkeit," *Luftfahriforschung*, 12, 210–220 (1935).
PRANDTL, L., "Theorie des Flugzeugtragflügels im zusammendrückbaren Medium," *Luftfahrtforschung*, 13, 313–319 (1936).
KÜSSNER, H. G., "Allgemeine Tragflächentheorie," *Luftfahriforschung*, 17, 370–378 (1940).

Hodograph Methods

CHAPLYGIN, A., *Gas Jets* (Russian), Moscow, 1904.

DEMTCHENKO, B., "Sur les mouvements lents des fluides compressibles," *Comples rendus*, 194, 1218 (1932); also "Variation de la resistance aux faibles vitessces sous l'influence de la compressibilite," *ibid.*, 194, 1720 (1932); and "Quelques problems d'hydrodynamique bidimensienelle des fluides compressibles," *Pub. scientifiques et techniques du M'inístere de l'Air*, No. 144 (1938).

BUSEMANN, A., "Hodographenmethode der Gasdynamik," *Z.A.M.M.*, 12, 73–79 (1937).

TSIEN, H. S., "Two-Dimensional Subsonic Flow of Compressible Fluids," *Jour. Aero. Sci.*, 6, 399 (1939).

Exact Transonic Solutions

TOLLMIEN, W., "Zum Ubergang von Unterschall in Überschallströmungen," *Z.A.M.M.*, 17, 117–136 (1937).

RINGLER, F., "Exakie Lösungen der Differentialgleichungen einer adiabatischen Gasströmung," *Z.A.M.M.*, 20, 185–198 (1940).

KÁRMÁN, TH. VON, "Compressibility Effects in Aerodynamics," *Jour. Aero. Sci.*, 8, 337 (1941).

Optical Methods of Observation

SCHARDEN, H., *Forschung auf dem Gebiel des Ing.*, 5 (1934).

PROLOGUE

In the summer of 1946, Great Britain abandoned all efforts to develop manned supersonic research aircraft, citing the postwar financial condition for the decision. The Ministry of Supply announced that henceforth Great Britain would use rocket-propelled models to investigate supersonic flight conditions. But a more dramatic and perhaps pertinent reason appeared in a press interview of Sir Ben Lockspeiser, the Ministry of Supply's Director-General of Scientific Air Research. "We have not the heart," he declared somberly, "to ask pilots to fly the high-speed models, so we shall make them radio-controlled."

It is not known what 36-year old Goeffrey Raoul de Havilland, chief test pilot of his father's firm, the de Havilland Aircraft Co., Ltd., thought of the Ministry of Supply's decision. He was busy readying the trim de Havilland D.H. 108 Swallow, a sweptwing tailless aircraft, for an assault on the world's air speed record. Britain actually had two Swallows: the first, serial TG 283, to check the low-speed behavior of sweptwings; and the second, serial TG 306, for high-speed sweptwing research. To complete the two aircraft as quickly as possible, de Havilland had fitted sweptwings and swept vertical tail fins to standard Vampire fuselages containing their Goblin turbojet powerplants. The company had not built the Swallows for transonic or supersonic research, but rather to investigate sweptwing stability and control problems, and to provide data for the proposed D.H. 106 transport. Thus, the Ministry of Supply's decision did not affect company plans to test the two D.H. 108 airplanes.

In his career as a test pilot, Geoffrey de Havilland had already compiled a distinguished record. He flew the first Mosquito bomber his father's company built, the first Vampire jet fighter, and the first de

1

Havilland Hornet long-range fighter. On the coming speed-record runs, he would have to fly the slate gray D.H. 108 #2 over a measured course at an altitude of less than 1,100 feet. On September 7, 1946, Royal Air Force Group Captain E. M. Donaldson, flying a modified Gloster Meteor Mk. 4, raised the world air speed record to 615.778 mph. De Havilland would have to exceed this by at least 1% to establish a new record.

He planned his record attempt for the end of September 1946. Few doubted that de Havilland would break Donaldson's record, and in one small sweepstakes speeds below 640 mph were given little chance of winning. In mid-September he began practicing for the record run. Flying the Swallow at increasingly higher speeds at lower altitudes, he unofficially exceeded the Meteor record even on these trials.

At 5:30 on the afternoon of September 27, Geoffrey de Havilland taxied the D.H. 108 out on the runway at the company's Hatfield Aerodrome, ran up the Goblin turbojet, and, with the engine shrieking at full power, rolled ever faster down the runway and then into the air. The Swallow disappeared from view over the Thames estuary. The flight plan called for a low-level maximum speed run followed by a maximum speed dive. If all went well, the next Swallow flight would be for the air speed record.

The first reports of disaster reached the company 30 minutes after the swift D.H. 108 lifted away from Hatfield. While walking along Canvey Island, an RAF Flight Lieutenant and his wife heard the whistle of a jet, a crackling noise, and saw three bits of wreckage tumble from the sky into the shallow water of Egypt Bay. Other observers saw the Swallow, flying several thousand feet above the Thames estuary at high speed, disintegrate before their eyes. A group of Mosquito pilots spotted wreckage amid the marshland along Egypt Bay. The Swallow had crashed, and Geoffrey de Havilland was missing. Ten days later the pilot's body washed ashore at Whitstable. He was the second of company founder Capt. Sir Geoffrey de Havilland's sons to die while test flying company aircraft.

Accident investigators recovered much of the wreckage, enough to ascertain that the airplane had not exploded. Analysis of retrieved recording instrumentation indicated that the plane had fallen victim to compressibility. Inadvertently, Geoffrey de Havilland had exceeded the Swallow's critical Mach number and, in the dense lower atmosphere, compressibility forces had ripped the D.H. 108 apart. The accident lent credence to then-current dire predictions about the existence of an impenetrable sonic barrier through which no aircraft could fly, and reinforced British determination to avoid manned supersonic research.

For more than a quarter century, the effects of compressibility had been a matter of interest and concern to aerodynamicists and engineers, propeller specialists, airplane and engine manufacturers, high-speed airplane design teams, and pilots. Now all of this interest and study was to culminate soon in the first attempt to exceed the speed of sound in a manned aircraft. For, across the Atlantic Ocean, a group of American scientists and engineers were readying a special breed of research aircraft for their first trial flights. Despite de Havilland's death, they pushed doggedly on, their resolve to lay to rest the myth of the "sound barrier" stiffened all the more.

ONE

The Development of the X-1 and D-558

I

THE NEED FOR
A TRANSONIC
RESEARCH AIRPLANE

Late in 1918, members of the Army Air Service Engineering Division could peer up into the sky above McCook Field, Ohio, and recognize a big 2-place biplane droning above Dayton. This plane, the USD-9, was an "Americanized" version of the British De Havilland D.H. 9 day bomber, itself an outgrowth of the famed D.H. 4. The USD-9 cruised along at 100 mph and had a top speed of 115 mph. Unlike the British D.H. 9, the USD-9 had a 12-cylinder 400 hp Liberty engine turning a large 4-bladed propeller. The USD-9 represented the peak of the 1918 aeronautical state-of-the-art. A rugged aircraft, weighing 4,750 lbs. fully loaded, it was a far cry from the frail open-structure biplanes with which most of the European nations had gone to war in 1914.

To aeronautical engineers, the stimulus of wartime demands had required that they develop aircraft to fly faster, farther, and higher than those of the enemy. Often, they lacked the necessary research equipment to derive useful information that could be incorporated in new or existing designs. Power plant engineers were concerned with wringing every available horsepower out of aircraft engines and then translating it into thrust from the whirling propeller. One question facing them was whether or not existing information on propeller airfoils could be applied to propellers moving much faster. Though the USD-9, for example, flew at 115 mph, the tips of its propeller scythed through the air at 650 mph, close to the speed of sound.[1]

In the fall of 1918, the Army Air Service Engineering Division decided to construct a small wind tunnel, entrusting the design to Frank W. Caldwell and Elisha N. Fales. Both were graduates of the Massachusetts Institute of Technology; Fales received his degree in 1911 and Caldwell his a year later. Upon graduation, both men joined the Curtiss Aeroplane Company in Buffalo, New York. In 1916, Caldwell became foreman of the Curtiss propeller department. A year later, he went to McCook Field. Fales, after a short stint as an assistant professor of mechanical engineering at the University of Illinois, joined Caldwell at the Army airfield in Ohio.[2]

Frank Caldwell was chief of the propeller branch of the Air Service Engineering Division. He and Elisha Fales, working in conjunction with C. P. Grimes, designed the tunnel to operate up to 450 mph so that it could test propeller airfoils at high speeds. The throat section of the tunnel featured a diameter of 14 inches. Both Fales and Caldwell had undertaken preliminary propeller research at MIT from 1909 to 1912, with the assistance of Gaetano Lanza, head of the Department of Mechanical Engineering. Now they built six airfoils with 6-inch spans and 1-inch chords, mounted them in the McCook tunnel, and made observations as the airstream passed around the airfoils at various speeds from 30 mph to 450 mph.[3]

At low airspeeds, air can be treated as an incompressible fluid like water in order to simplify mathematical treatment of airflow. At high airspeeds, however, the compressibility factor has to be taken into consideration. As an airplane moves through the air at high speed, it builds up a pile of air ahead of it. At about 450 mph, the accelerated flow above the wing may become locally supersonic, moving as fast as sound, or even faster.[4] Thus, the plane is in the transonic region, an area of mixed subsonic and supersonic flow. If the speed is increased further, the complete flow around the airplane becomes supersonic, and the plane is in the supersonic region, moving faster than sound. During transonic flight, shock waves form on the aircraft, move back and forth, and violently disrupt the airflow. Critical changes in pressure and loading may occur, and the aircraft undergoes severe structural stress. Total airframe drag rises sharply. The controls sometimes lose their effectiveness. It was for these reasons that, just prior to and during the Second World War, compressibility became such a serious problem to designers of high-speed military aircraft.

During the tunnel tests at 450 mph, Caldwell and Fales unexpectedly stumbled upon the effects of compressibility on airfoil behavior. They discovered two basic phenomena. At high speeds the drag of the airfoil increased abruptly while the lift decreased, resulting in a sharp drop in the lift-drag ratio.[5] Further, the airflow separated from the airfoil because of the mixed subsonic and supersonic flow patterns.[6] Such behavior came as a shock to propeller engineers, who had always assumed that "we could double our propeller speed just as soon as we were able to double our plane speed and strengthen our engine enough to stand the stresses involved."[7]

Caldwell and Fales' pioneering work was next taken up by Dr. Lyman J. Briggs and Dr. Hugh L. Dryden, both of the Bureau of Standards, and Lt. Col. G. F. Hull of the Army Ordnance Department. These men tested the same 6 airfoil sections used by Caldwell and Fales, but at much higher velocities, from 550 fps to 1,000 fps. The tests were made at the General Electric Company's Lynn, Massachusetts, plant, using an air jet from a turbine-driven 3-stage centrifugal compressor. Dryden, a young physicist who had received his Ph.D. from Johns Hopkins in 1919 at the age of 20, performed all data reduction and computations.[8]

The findings of Briggs, Dryden, and Hull confirmed those of Caldwell and Fales. During bad weather tests, the men had covered the airfoils with oil to keep them from rusting. They noted that the oil moved in a pattern indicating separation of airflow at high speeds. Likewise, they observed the decrease in lift and increase in drag at transonic speeds. They concluded that propeller airfoils lost efficiency as the tip speed approached the velocity of sound.[9]

Intrigued by the loss of efficiency, Briggs and Dryden continued their research at the Army's Edgewood Arsenal using a compressor plant formerly used during the First World War to refrigerate mustard gas. They ran tests on airfoils from Mach 0.5 to Mach 1.08, 563 fps to 1,218 fps. Most importantly, Briggs and Dryden fitted the airfoils with pressure orifices to record pressure distribution over the airfoil surface. In these tests the now-familiar separation of flow, drop in lift, and increase in drag occurred at transonic speeds. Most importantly, at Mach 1.08, Dryden and Briggs observed standing shock waves about ½ inch in front of the airfoil models. They reported their findings in the annual report of the National Advisory Committee for Aeronautics for 1926.[10]

The Briggs-Dryden team then began a comparative study of 24 airfoil sections at transonic speeds. In this investigation, they discovered that thin airfoils—airfoils having a low thickness-chord ratio—retained their effectiveness at higher speeds than did thicker airfoils. The thick airfoils, in contrast, showed a marked decrease in lift coefficient.[11] In an attempt to improve airfoil efficiency at transonic speeds, Briggs and Dryden undertook analysis of circular-arc airfoils. They found the circular-arc airfoils, while inefficient at low speeds, featured much greater efficiency at speeds above Mach 0.65 than did conventional airfoils. Briggs and Dryden concluded their propeller research program by recommending that propeller designers incorporate conventional airfoil sections on the inner portion of the blade, but use circular-arc airfoil sections on the outer third of the blade to retain efficiency of the blade at high tip speeds.[12]

Since a propeller airfoil is identical to a wing airfoil, aeronautical engineers realized that an airplane would also encounter a rise in drag, loss of lift, and rearward shift in the center of pressure location if it moved through the air at transonic velocities. But the question seemed an academic one, since existing aircraft did not fly fast enough to encounter compressibility. This feeling changed dramatically in the late summer of 1931. On September 29, Royal Air Force Flight Lt. George Stainforth went aloft in a sleek Supermarine S.6B floatplane to win the Schneider Trophy for Great Britain. When he touched down on the smooth water off Calshot Castle, he had concluded the world's first 400 mph flight. Despite the bulk of its floats and the drag of its bracing struts and wires, the S.6B had made one circuit of the 3 kilometer course at 415 mph.[13] At these velocities, aeronautical engineers could no longer afford to think of air as an incompressible fluid. Stainforth's flight was the first obvious signal that aeronautical research would have to look forward to a time when aircraft were flying at 400 mph and above.

One man who believed that aircraft could be built despite the potential problems of compressibility was a young junior aeronautical engineer employed at the National Advisory Committee for Aeronautics' Langley Memorial Aeronautical Laboratory at Hampton, Virginia. He was John Stack. Stack, who graduated in 1928 with a B.S. in aeronautical engineering from MIT made a study of what sort of airframe configuration would be best suited to high-speed flight where compressibility effects would be encountered. Almost one year to the day after Stainforth's record flight, Dr. George W. Lewis, the NACA's Director of Aeronautical Research, had stated that 500 mph seemed the practical limit for "the airplane of the present day." But he held out the hope that engineers might well add two or three hundred miles per hour to the maximum speed of aircraft over the next decade by refined design techniques and careful streamlining.[14]

John Stack, one year after Lewis' disclosure, came up with one such aircraft. In many respects the proposal was as radical in its day as the X-1 was in 1945. Stack envisaged a propeller aircraft just large enough to house a Rolls-Royce R engine of 2,300 hp. It was a mid-wing monoplane of cantilever construction, with a fuselage of circular cross section. The wing spanned 29.1 feet. The fuselage diameter was 40 inches. The wing had an area of 141.2 square feet, an aspect ratio of 6, and an average wing chord of 4.85 feet. The wing featured a NACA 0018 airfoil section at the root, tapering to a NACA 0009 section at the wing tip. Stack tested a model of the design in the Langley variable-density wind tunnel.

Stack felt the aircraft should be as clean aerodynamically as possible, with a fully retractable landing gear and skin-type radiators. The pilot would see out of the airplane through transparent fuselage skins or by an indirect mirror system. Stack assumed that the propeller, despite tip losses from compressibility, would retain 75 percent efficiency. Thus, the airplane would have an uncorrected maximum speed of about 566 mph, and a landing speed of 103 mph. When Stack took into account compressibility effects, he found that the airspeed of the airplane would drop approximately 40 mph to about 525 mph. Stack optimistically concluded that the paper study—for the airplane was never seriously developed—indicated that aircraft could safely attain much higher airspeeds. He acknowledged that much compressibility research remained to be done in the future.[15]

Not all scientists shared Stack's optimism. British aerodynamicist W. F. Hilton plotted horsepower requirements versus Mach number and found an almost asymptotic relationship; in order to exceed the speed of sound, he concluded, an airplane would require over 30,000 hp. The speed of sound, Hilton gloomily predicted, loomed "like a barrier against future progress."[16]

In September and October 1935, leading aerodynamicists from around the world gathered in Campidoglio, Italy, for the Fifth Volta Congress on High Speeds in Aviation. Benito Mussolini opened the proceedings on a somewhat somber note by announcing the Italian invasion of Abyssinia.[17] The Congress itself devoted its attention to the problems of supersonic flight. The Italian Government showed its guests the Guidonia Laboratory, where technicians were building a Mach 2.7 supersonic wind tunnel patterned after an earlier Mach 2 wind tunnel completed at Zurich, Switzerland, by Jakob Ackeret. Ackeret's wind tunnel was the first modern supersonic wind tunnel in the world.[18]

The Volta Congress had two important influences upon supersonic flight. First, and most importantly, it served to stimulate supersonic research using supersonic wind tunnels. Theodore von Kármán returned to the United States, for example, and immediately began contacting responsible government sources about developing supersonic wind tunnels. Unfortunately, he met with indifference. Abroad, however, supersonic research moved more quickly. Germany, for example, developed a Mach 4.4 wind tunnel that went into operation at Peenemunde in 1941.[19] Second, the most advanced paper presented at the Volta Congress was that of German engineer Adolf Busemann. Its influence, however, was more subtle, and not truly appreciated until after the Second World War. In his paper, Busemann suggested use of "arrow-wings" (sweptwings) to alleviate the onset of high drag rise at transonic speeds. Early in the pioneer days of flying, John W. Dunne employed the sweptwing configuration on a series of British biplane designs as a means of improving stability and control. Busemann's proposal, however, was the first time that the swept configuration appeared in high-speed aerodynamics. The paper went unnoticed by other aerodynamicists, but later stimulated German sweptwing research during the Second World War. The results of this research, together with the wartime research of NACA scientist Robert T. Jones—who was unaware of Busemann's work—greatly influenced postwar American sweptwing aircraft development.[20]

Despite increased awareness of the problems of transonic and supersonic flight, little "hard" data existed on transonic conditions. Most of the existing data came from the propeller tests that gave some indication of the nature of transonic conditions and from drag-test results of bullets and shells decelerating through the speed of sound. Lt. Col. H. Zornig, head of the Army Ballistic Research Laboratories at the Aberdeen Proving Ground, delivered a ballistics lecture in the mid-1930s at Wright Field, Ohio. He presented curves that plotted the drag coefficient of blunt-, medium-, and sharp-nose projectiles versus Mach number. The curves did show the abrupt rise in drag close to the speed of sound. But the transonic drag rise, while high, did not exceed by more than two or three times the low-speed subsonic drag value.[21]

Sitting in the audience was Ezra Kotcher, a senior instructor at the Air Corps Engineering School at Wright Field. Following graduation from the University of California in 1928 with a B.S. in mechanical engineering, he had joined the Army Air Corps as a junior aeronautical engineer. Now, listening to Zornig, Kotcher developed an intuitive feeling that the sonic barrier was "not necessarily a permanent flight barrier, but rather a wind tunnel technique barrier—or a psychological barrier."[22] Zornig's data impressed Kotcher because it gave an inkling of what really happened aerodynamically in the transonic region across the speed of sound.[23]

Kotcher remembered the Zornig lecture. In mid-1939, Capt. T. A. Sims requested that he write a short report on future aeronautical research and development problems for transmittal to the Kilner-Lindbergh board that Air Corps Chief Maj. Gen. Henry H. "Hap" Arnold had established on May 5, 1939, to investigate military aircraft development. Kotcher prepared the report and submitted it in August 1939. The Air Corps Engineering Section passed it on to Maj. Gen. Arnold and the NACA.

It was noteworthy in several respects. Kotcher stated that in order to achieve significant advances in high-speed performance it would be necessary to undertake extensive transonic research. He advocated "comprehensive flight research programs" to correlate wind tunnel data with full-scale performance. He suggested that gas turbine or rocket propulsion systems be developed eventually to replace propeller propulsion systems because of compressibility limitations upon propeller aircraft at high speeds.[24]

Kotcher's strong advocacy of gas turbine or rocket propulsion came at a time when neither was in serious consideration. In the same month that Kotcher submitted his report, Erich Warsitz completed the world's first turbojet flight, in the Heinkel He-178 in Germany. But in the United States, scientists did not seriously consider the turbojet engine until the formation of the Durand Special Committee on Jet Propulsion by the NACA in March 1941.[25] Indeed, in 1938, a Navy board of engineers had concluded that gas turbines were unsuited for aircraft.[26] At the time of Kotcher's report, the Army had just awarded the Guggenheim Aeronautical Laboratory of the California Institute of Technology a $10,000 contract for research into both solid- and liquid-fuel rocket engines for takeoff assistance.[27] The Army, however, was not interested in rockets for propulsion. Right through the war Kotcher remained the staunchest of the few advocates pure rocket propulsion had within the Army Air Corps.

The chief importance of the Kotcher report, however, lay in its call for a high-speed flight research program. Kotcher stressed the importance of a full-scale flight research program as a necessary check on available wind tunnel data. The wind tunnels at this time were of the closed-throat type and, as the speed of the airflow approached that of sound, the tunnels "choked." Shock waves forming off the test model and its supports would reflect off the tunnel walls, inhibiting accurate measurement of flow characteristics and behavior around the model. This condition persisted from about Mach 0.7 to about Mach 1.3. At Mach numbers below 0.7 or above 1.3, smooth airflow through the tunnel once more existed, and aerodynamicists could make accurate measurements. Thus, the very area in which scientists were interested, the transonic region between subsonic and supersonic flight, remained a closed area in which the wind tunnel could not operate with precision. In coming years, wind tunnel advocates became the strongest supporters of a transonic research airplane pending advances in wind-tunnel technology that would eliminate the choking phenomenon and open up the transonic region to ground-based researchers.[28]

The choking phenomenon led to the first NACA interest in transonic research vehicles. At NACA's Langley Laboratory, John Stack brought up the idea of a research airplane in conferences with NACA's Director of Aeronautical Research, Dr. George W. Lewis, when Lewis visited Langley on several occasions in 1941.[29] Stack had foreseen the need for a full-scale flight vehicle for transonic research in 1940, when it became apparent that wind tunnels were hampered by choking, and no advance in wind-tunnel technology appeared likely in the near future.[30] Following his earlier configuration research, Stack kept in close touch with the compressibility problem through a concerted program of propeller research. In 1933, he had constructed a 24-inch high-speed tunnel capable of more than 500 mph and driven from the pressure tank of the Langley variable density tunnel.[31] In 1941, he and his associates at Langley began research on propeller configurations for 500 mph operation at 25,000 feet, using the Langley 500 mph 8-foot high-speed tunnel that had gone into operation in 1936. In short order they evolved a 6-bladed contra-rotating propeller capable of converting 90 percent of its engine power into thrust at 500 mph, an almost unbelievable efficiency in 1941.[32]

Up until 1941, compressibility had really remained the problem of the aerodynamicist. But now it dramatically became the problem of the pilot. Lockheed Aircraft Corporation engineer Clarence L. "Kelly" Johnson had designed a new Army twin-engine interceptor, the P-38 Lightning. It began its flight testing in January 1939. Lockheed lost the first prototype in a landing accident following a cross-country flight, and a second prototype did not take to the air until late 1940. A year later the Army Air Corps already had the first production models, the P-38D and P-38E, in service. The P-38 was an extremely high-powered and clean design. It picked up speed rapidly in a dive, and became the first American aircraft to encounter the dangers of compressibility in flight.

Some pilots, after nosing the P-38 into a dive, suddenly found the plane began buffeting and shuddering, with a tendency to tuck under. Disconcertingly, the control column froze as if implanted in concrete. Sometimes, after diving to lower, denser altitudes, shaken pilots discovered that the P-38 mysteriously nosed up and recovered. But on several occasions, the dive continued until the aircraft broke up. The P-38's compressibility problem did not come as a complete surprise to Lockheed engineers. Clarence Johnson and Hall L. Hibbard, as early as 1937 and 1938, had stated that compressibility would present a serious problem at speeds approaching and above 500 mph.[33] Accordingly, Lockheed began a compressibility investigation using 2 specially modified P-38E aircraft. One, P-38E serial 41-2048, featured a longer fuselage to accommodate a flight test observer and special research instrumentation. The other, P-38E serial 42-1986, had its tail booms aft of the coolant radiators swept upwards so as to place the horizontal stabilizer 30 inches higher. Hopefully, this latter modification would place the horizontal tail above the wing wake, thus retaining elevator effectiveness.[34]

One morning Lockheed test pilot Ralph Virden took off from Lockheed's Burbank facility in the P-38 with upswept booms. He planned a dive test in the airplane, followed by a low-altitude demonstration before watching Army officials. Observers on the ground heard the snarling whine of a P-38 at full power. The noise built up to a strident crescendo suddenly broken by the awful thump of an airplane striking the earth.

Investigation showed that when Virden attempted to pull the P-38 out of its dive, the airloads had exceeded the structural strength of the tail and ripped it from the plane.[35]

In December 1941, a few weeks following Virden's death, the Army requested that the NACA investigate the cause of the P-38's problems. A month later, a P-38 arrived at Langley laboratory where a team of engineers under John Stack mounted and tested it in the Langley 30- by 60-foot full-scale wind tunnel. Langley engineers also tested a ⅙ scale P-38 model in the Langley 8-foot high-speed tunnel at speeds up to 500 mph. The 8-foot tunnel tests revealed that loss of wing lift due to shock waves forming on the upper surface of the wing at about Mach 0.675— 445 mph at 36,000 feet—caused a loss of downwash on the horizontal stabilizer that, in turn, put the P-38 in an increasingly steeper dive. The violently disturbed airflow from the wing flailed the tail and, in Virden's case, tore it off.[36]

Under the pressure of wartime development—for the United States and its allies were fighting with their backs to the wall in spring 1942— Langley engineers found a cure for the P-38 by March 4. They suggested installation of a dive flap on the lower surface of the wing, which would permit the wing to retain lift at high Mach numbers, thus enabling the pilot to retain sufficient control of the aircraft to pull it out of high speed dives. Langley turned over the P-38 dive-flap investigation to the NACA Ames Aeronautical Laboratory at Moffett Field, California, where engineers under the direction of Albert L. Erickson checked out the flap in the Ames 16-foot tunnel.[37] The flap idea proved sound, and Lockheed flight-tested them on P-38E serial 41-2048. Lockheed test pilots Milo Burcham and A. W. "Tony" LeVier found the dive flaps corrected the P-38's behavior during the course of many high-speed dives, including one by LeVier to over Mach 0.7 followed by a 7½ g pullout at 1,000 feet.[38] Lockheed subsequently installed dive flaps as standard production equipment on Lightnings beginning with the P-38J-25-LO series.

Though the flap cured the P-38's difficulties, it did not spell the end of the problem of compressibility. It simply raised the aircraft's critical Mach number so that the aircraft could fly faster without encountering loss of control due to compressibility effects. The problem of developing new aircraft capable of flying safely at transonic speeds remained. With the advent of turbojet propulsion, the problem took on new urgency.

In March 1941, because of reports of German research into reaction powerplants, the Army requested the NACA study jet propulsion; NACA Chairman Vannevar Bush established the Durand Committee in response. In the meantime, the Air Corps chief, General Arnold, journeyed to Great Britain and learned, to his great surprise, that the British were preparing to flight-test a turbojet engine, the Whittle W.1. He returned to the United States, subsequently arranging for development of the Whittle engine in this country under the direction of the General Electric Company.[39] This ultimately resulted in the Army placing a contract with the Bell Aircraft Corporation on September 30, 1941, for the United States' first turbojet airplane, the XP-59A.[40]

The turbojet engine held great promise in permitting aircraft to attain higher airspeeds and it eliminated the problems associated with propeller efficiency at high speeds since it did not employ a propeller. Within a month of the formation of the Durand Committee, one NACA scientist, Eastman N. Jacobs, predicted at a committee meeting that with the NACA's new family of high-speed airfoils, he believed it possible to attain approximately the speed of sound in flight.[41] Then the P-38 encountered its compressibility difficulties. To aeronautical engineers, it seemed as if the propulsion limitation on high-speed flight had disappeared, only to be replaced by a design problem of equal magnitude.

In mid-1942, faced with a lack of reliable wind-tunnel data at Mach numbers between 0.7 and 1.3, several NACA engineers formed together to investigate alternative methods of research. One idea that came up in discussions was the concept of a transonic research aircraft, an idea that John Stack had suggested to George Lewis in 1941. Stack established a small team of Langley engineers consisting of himself, Milton Davidson, Harold Turner, and Walter Williams. This small group began studying possible research aircraft configurations.[42] Prior to this time, Eastman N. Jacobs, head of the Langley Airflow Research Division, had initiated a study of possible transonic aircraft designs with Milton Davidson and Harold Turner.[43] From the start, Jacobs and Stack were enthusiastic supporters of the research airplane concept.

In the Jacobs group, Jacobs assumed overall direction of research. Milton Davidson performed the calculations and Harold Turner did the drafting of the proposals. Jacobs, Davidson, and Turner investigated possible configurations using the proposed Westinghouse 19A engine, but concluded the configurations were so underpowered that they would be incapable of transonic flight. One of the earliest configurations studied incorporated a sweptwing planform and landing skids. The group did not investigate the possibility of rocket propulsion.[44] Later, however, the Stack team investigated both turbojet and rocket-propelled configurations, and ran wind-tunnel studies on them.[45]

The Stack and Jacobs studies generally concentrated on air-breathing propulsion systems using conventional ground takeoff.[46] Starting in 1939, Jacobs had experimented with the Campini propulsion system, in which a conventional gasoline engine drove a compressor. Fuel then mixed with the airstream and ignited in a burner. Jacobs and his two assistants, Macon C. Ellis, Jr., and Clinton E. Brown, had high hopes for the Campini system. They built an operating Campini test bed at Langley that consumed 3 pounds of gasoline per second, producing a gigantic and spectacular blow torch from the burner that impressed—and often terrified—viewers.[47] Jacobs felt that the Campini system could be incorporated in military aircraft to give them performance superior to that of existing propeller aircraft, as well as long loiter times.

Macon Ellis and Clinton Brown conducted a study of the Campini engine system that later resulted in design of a Campini-powered aircraft by Ellis, Brown, and F. Daum. This design proposal featured a Pratt and Whitney R-1535 radial engine, a tricycle landing gear, a high shoulder-wing, and a Vee tail. It had a 15 percent-thick wing spanning 41.4 feet, with an area of 215 sq. feet. The design team estimated gross weight of the plane at 9,780 lbs. The design team could not estimate the maximum speed of the aircraft owing to uncertain values for drag at speeds over 550 mph due to compressibility effects.[48] What interested the design team members most, aside from the apparent advantages of the Campini system, was that when the aircraft attained Mach 0.75, the engine would be producing 3 times the amount of thrust necessary to reach that velocity. They did not know what stability and control problems might be encountered above Mach 0.75, but knew that with the available thrust, as one team member recalled, "we could have really barreled into the transonic region."[49]

In October 1942, the Langley Campini engine was progressing satisfactorily. The Durand Committee expressed interest in the power plant, and called Eastman Jacobs to arrange for a demonstration run at Langley. The appointed day arrived, the committee members stationed themselves 200 yards behind the burner, and the test crew lit the engine. Perversely, the test run was disappointing, marked by unstable combustion that had plagued trials of the Campini engine at Langley in 1941. A week after the demonstration, word came from NACA Headquarters to suspend all work on the Campini project. The disappointing test run, together, perhaps, with official concern over the huge amounts of precious gasoline being burned in an apparently fruitless attempt to develop a reliable propulsion system, killed the Campini investigation.[50] All hopes of developing a Campini airplane that might prove useful for transonic research vanished.

By early 1943, compressibility had assumed critical importance in NACA, Army, and Navy wartime aeronautical research. Some indication of how prominently it figured in NACA planning can be seen in the formation of a Compressibility Research Division at Langley in 1942 under the direction of John Stack, and in the increasing amount of correspondence between Langley staff members concerning compressibility research at this time. Army Air Forces and Navy combat squadrons suddenly found that their aircraft faced a new and frighteningly mysterious danger aside from the enemy. An epidemic of tail failures during dives appeared in three production high-speed aircraft, the Republic P-47

Thunderbolt, the Curtiss SB2C Helldiver, and the Bell P-39 Airacobra. Extensive tests at Langley and Ames laboratories resulted in recommendations to manufacturers to strengthen the tails to withstand high air loads at high speed. In the case of the Helldiver, a new Navy dive bomber, compressibility effects distorted the wing surface, causing separation of flow. The turbulent wake induced severe flutter of the horizontal tail, finally exceeding the tail's structural limits and destroying it. NACA recommended stiffening of the wing to prevent distortion, and strengthening of the tail to withstand 13g loads.[51]

The problem of compressibility became all the more vexing because of the complete inability of wind tunnels at the time to serve the needs of the aeronautical engineer in his search for reliable and useful aerodynamic data at Mach numbers between Mach 0.75 and 1.3. Now that the turbojet appeared as a means of overcoming propeller limitations, the only remaining barrier to high-speed flight—including flight faster than the speed of sound—appeared to be a knowledge barrier, where aerodynamicists could not predict with certainty what occurred in the turbulent speeds of transonic flight. The immediate problem facing aerodynamicists was how to arrive at accurate research tools and methods to derive needed data and strip the mystery from compressibility and transonic aerodynamics.

In mid-December 1943, William S. Farren, director of the British Royal Aircraft Establishment, arrived in the United States to present the Seventh Wright Brothers Lecture before the Institute of Aeronautical Sciences in Washington, D.C., on December 17. To people in aeronautics, December 17 assumed the stature of a national holiday because it was the anniversary of the Wright Brothers flight at Kitty Hawk, North Carolina, in 1903. Government and industry aeronautical representatives always came to Washington for the lecture, and the NACA committee—the representatives appointed by the President— always held a special meeting.[52]

The topic Farren chose for his talk was "Research for Aeronautics— Its Planning and Application."[53] In the lecture, Farren acknowledged the problem of compressibility and stated that if aeronautical engineers planned on attaining high speeds, they would have to devote considerable effort to "avoiding or reducing the effect of compressibility."[54] In keeping with the spirit of the talk, Dr. William F. Durand, the chairman of the NACA Special Committee on Jet Propulsion, called a special conference the next day at NACA Headquarters in Washington on jet propulsion in England.[55] Among the approximately 20 people at the meeting was Robert A. Wolf, an engineer with the Bell Aircraft Corporation at Buffalo, New York.

Since the beginning of 1943, the idea of a high-speed research airplane had been germinating in Wolf's mind. Wolf had served as technical adviser and designer of the airframe, cabin pressurization, and propulsion system of the Bell XP-59 Airacomet, the United States' first turbojet aircraft. In July 1943, he journeyed to England to review the progress being made there in turbojet propulsion. While abroad, the vision of more powerful turbojets with greater thrust stimulated his interest in designing transonic aircraft, provided that the stability and control problems facing high-speed aircraft could be solved.[56]

At the December 18 meeting, Durand asked essentially one question: What should the United States do with the turbojet propulsion concept brought to this country from Great Britain? In the discussion that followed, Wolf suggested that the country had the opportunity to construct a special high-speed research airplane to provide transonic aerodynamic data for aircraft manufacturers. The data was urgently needed, since jet aircraft would soon encounter in level flight the transonic speeds now being approached by propeller aircraft in dives. He then suggested a basic plan of development, in which the Army, Navy, NACA, and aircraft industry would define the type of aircraft needed, the military would procure it, the industry would develop it under contract, and the NACA would conduct the flight research and disseminate information.[57]

Wolf's proposal was but one of many ideas suggested in outline form at the roundtable discussion. Fearing that his proposal might be distorted or lost in the meeting minutes, he wrote to Dr. George W. Lewis on December 29, again stressing the need for a transonic research aircraft. In his letter he stated:

> It appears quite possible to construct a single engine aircraft based on available gas turbine jet power plants which will fly at speeds in level flight exceeding the critical Mach numbers of currently used types of wings. If this aircraft were designed with enough inherent versatility to changes in control surfaces, wings, etc., it should be possible to develop usable control surfaces such as ailerons, dive control flap, tail surfaces, etc., which would work satisfactorily at or above the critical speeds of the wings. Furthermore, this could be done in level flight and would not be subject to the dangers and difficulties associated with the high accelerations encountered in current dive programs.[58]

Lewis responded by writing Wolf that the NACA was highly interested in procuring a turbojet research aircraft for investigating compressibility and aircraft stability and control at high speeds, and was giving the matter "our very serious consideration."[59]

Simultaneously with Wolf's suggestion, the Army Air Forces were renewing interest in transonic flight research. British intelligence reports indicated that Nazi Germany had rocket and jet-propulsion research projects in an advanced state of development. Now, over four years after Ezra Kotcher's original suggestion for transonic flight research in the fall of 1939, the AAF decided to act upon his recommendations. In mid-January 1944, the Development Engineering Branch of the Materiel Division at AAF Headquarters, Washington, issued Confidential Technical Instruction 1568 that authorized "the initiation of a study of the possible development of an experimental article for the purpose of investigating aerodynamic phenomena in the range of 600-650 mph."[60]

Kotcher, after 1939, had become chief of the Vibration and Flutter Unit of the AAF Aircraft Laboratory at Wright Field. Following Pearl Harbor, he was called to active duty as an army captain and in late 1942 was introduced to the jet-propelled P-59. In 1943, the Engineering Division selected him as project officer on the proposed Northrop XP-79 rocket-propelled flying wing interceptor. The rocket-powered XP-79 program never reached the hardware stage. A manned scale prototype of the XP-79, the Northrop MX-324, did make a rocket flight on July 5, 1944, the first flight of an American rocket aircraft designed from the outset for rocket propulsion.[61] Yet the XP-79 program did subsequently influence American transonic research aircraft developments.

The proposed powerplant for the XP-79 was a 2,000-lb-thrust rocket engine being developed by Aerojet Engineering Corporation. This engine, dubbed the Rotojet, used red fuming nitric acid and aniline for propellants. When in contact, the two ignite violently, making an ignition system unnecessary. Aerojet designed the engine with four chambers having canted nozzles. The nozzles imparted rotation to the engine that drove a gear train that powered fuel pumps supplying the propellants to the engine. Naively, Northrop designed the basic structure of the XP-79 of magnesium, which, when in contact with nitric acid, "fizzed like a piece of zinc in hydrochloric acid."[62] Most importantly, however, Aerojet planned a 6,000-lb-thrust engine, also using acid and aniline as propellants, and rotation to drive fuel pumps, as a follow-on to the 2,000-lb-thrust engine designed for the XP-79. This engine was being developed under Project MX-121, in anticipation of a superperformance airplane.[63]

In early 1944, Kotcher decided to make a comparative investigation of the merits of rocket and turbojet propulsion for a transonic research aircraft. This resulted in the so-called Wright Field "Mach 0.999" study. The "Mach 0.999" facetiously referred to the "impenetrable sonic barrier" of popular imagination. Kotcher requested that the Design Branch of the Aircraft Laboratory at Wright Field investigate two configurations, one using a General Electric TG-180, an axial flow turbojet of about 4,000-lb thrust then under development, and the other using the proposed 6,000-lb-thrust Aerojet rocket engine.[64]

By April 1944, the Design Branch had completed the comparative designs. From every performance standpoint, the rocket-powered aircraft appeared the better way to attempt transonic research. Its chief advantage was its high speed, which rendered dives to high Mach numbers unnecessary. The high thrust of the rocket engine provided good high-altitude performance, in contrast to existing turbojets, whose thrust was marginal. Additionally, the rocket powerplant provided flight researchers with added testing time. Instead of diving earthwards, at great risk to the test plane and pilot, for about 30 seconds, the rocket offered the possibility of high-speed level flight for around 2 minutes.[65] In light of subsequent developments, the "Mach 0.999" rocket-research aircraft the Design Branch configured makes an interesting comparison with the Bell XS-1. Both aircraft featured bullet-shaped fuselages, mid-wing design, conventional tail surfaces—though the Wright Field design had the horizontal surfaces mounted on the fuselage and not on the vertical fin, as did the XS-1—a smoothly faired cockpit canopy, and a liquid-fuel rocket engine of 6,000-lb thrust.

Kotcher showed the rocket design to Theodore von Kármán, director of the Guggenheim Aeronautical Laboratory, California Institute of Technology (GALCIT), and acting scientific consultant to General Arnold. Kármán concurred in the feasibility of building such an aircraft, approved the design, and calculated the craft's lift-to-drag ratio at three.[66] When Kármán examined the "Mach 0.999" proposal, he already knew about AAF efforts to investigate high-speed flight. In 1943, Brig. Gen. Franklin O. Carroll, chief of the Engineering Division at Wright Field, had asked Kármán if it would be possible to design an airplane to fly at Mach 1.5. After spending a weekend in thought and calculations, Kármán concluded it could be safely done.[67] In 1944, General Carroll, as Kotcher's commanding officer, both recognized the need for a transonic research aircraft and endorsed Kotcher's approach.[68]

While Wolf's proposal was stimulating interest in the NACA and at Bell and while Kotcher's design studies were emerging from the drafting boards at Wright Field, NACA scientists were investigating alternative stopgap methods of transonic research. What resulted became an attempt at an international cooperative effort into transonic research. W. S. Farren, after presenting the Wright Brothers lecture, had discussed the transonic wind-tunnel research problem with NACA representatives at Wright Field. One solution both the British Royal Aircraft Establishment and the American NACA had experimented with had been dropping weighted bodies from high altitudes. The bodies would then attain velocities equal to or faster than that of sound. Radar and visual tracking from the ground could determine the speed and path of the falling body. In subsequent discussions between the NACA and British Ministry of Supply, British and American representatives agreed to undertake joint falling-body investigations.[69] The NACA Executive Committee authorized falling body research in March 1944, and actual falling-body tests began in May, using a B-29 Superfortress carrier aircraft lent by the Army and a Navy supplied SCR-584 radar tracking unit.

At about the same time, fighter pilots putting North American's sleek P-51 in dives found they sometimes could see shock waves streaming from the Mustang's wings. To one NACA Langley engineer, the accelerated airflow over the wing of a P-51 seemed to offer a satisfactory substitute for the wind tunnel. Robert R. Gilruth, a young engineer in charge of flight research under Melvin Gough, chief of the Flight Research Division, realized that when a Mustang dove to about Mach 0.75, the accelerated airflow over the Mustang's wing reached about Mach 1.2. Gilruth reasoned that he could use this accelerated flow to test airfoils. He devised a small balance mechanism to fit within the P-51's gun compartment, and then mounted the test airfoil vertically above the P-51 wing. Though Gilruth encountered skepticism from wind-tunnel advocates, his wing-flow method proved useful in deriving transonic data on airfoil shapes and the effects of aspect ratio, thickness, sweepback, and airfoil section.[70]

The falling-body and wing-flow methods—together with the later rocket-propelled model work under Gilruth at NACA's Pilotless Aircraft Research Division on Wallops Island—provided vital data on drag variation through the speed of sound. But these methods had their limitations as well, in expense and work involved to achieve limited results. In wind-tunnel testing, the scientist develops a feel for what occurs to the test model. He can take pressure distribution measurements and look through the tunnel port and see shock-wave formation. This was lost in the falling-body and rocket-model program.[71] Pending the development of transonic wind tunnels and wind-tunnel techniques, the research airplane appeared as the best possible alternative method of transonic research. The British had also recognized that the research airplane concept appeared the best method of attempting transonic research pending wind-tunnel developments. In 1943, the Air Ministry issued specification E24/43, calling for development of an experimental aircraft capable of attaining 1,000 mph at 36,000 feet. Miles Aircraft, Ltd., responded by initiating development of a turbojet design, the M.52.[72]

On March 15, 1944, representatives of the Army Air Technical Service Command, Navy Bureau of Aeronautics, and the NACA gathered at Langley Laboratory. They held two conferences, one chaired by Capt. Walter S. Diehl, USN, and the other chaired by Col. Carl F. Greene, AAF liaison officer at Langley. Both dealt with development of a possible transonic research aircraft.[73] Captain Diehl, who in effect acted as the Navy Bureau of Aeronautics representative to the NACA, had earlier discussed the research airplane concept with John Stack and

Comdr. Emerson Conlon of the BuAer's Structures Branch. Like Stack and Kotcher, Captain Diehl felt, as early as 1942, that the research airplane appeared the only way to convince people that the "sonic barrier" was just a steep hill, drawing upon transonic shell data to support his contention.[74]

These two March 15 meetings tied together, for the first time, Army, Navy, and NACA interest in the research airplane concept. Gen. Oliver P. Echols, assistant Chief of Staff at AAF Headquarters, had questioned the wisdom of the AAF procuring a nonmilitary research airplane solely as an Army Air Forces project; in response, Ezra Kotcher drafted a letter for transmittal to Dr. George W. Lewis, suggesting joint AAF-NACA participation in developing a research aircraft to support the NACA research mission.[75] The NACA, in December 1943, formed—at Lewis' suggestion—a special five-man panel to coordinate NACA high-speed research. This panel consisted of John Stack, Russell G. Robinson, H. Julian Allen, R. E. Littell, and Eastman N. Jacobs. At the initial panel meetings, Stack suggested that NACA sponsor rocket- or turbojet-propelled transonic research aircraft.[76] Now at the March meeting, NACA representatives suggested a joint NACA-military development program to construct a turbojet-powered research airplane.

The NACA, in consultation with Navy Bureau of Aeronautics representatives, decided to detail Milton Davidson, a NACA engineer familiar with the research airplane concept, to the Navy Bureau of Aeronautics in Washington. Davidson would collaborate with Ivan Driggs, head of BuAer's Aviation Design Research Branch on configuring and preparing specifications for a Navy-sponsored transonic research aircraft.[77] NACA's suggestions for a joint program came logically, since the NACA did not possess the facilities, nor the administration, to handle such a program on its own.[78] Stack urged Col. Carl F. Greene and Jean Roché of the Army Air Forces liaison office at Langley to convince the Army to develop a transonic research aircraft, citing the prominent role the Army had played in procuring the P-59, the United States' first turbojet aircraft.[79]

Despite the low-thrust values for existing turbojet engines, NACA engineers generally favored turbojet propulsion over rocket propulsion. Their reasoning did not stem from an unwillingness to innovate, but rather from the cautious approach that was a hallmark of NACA research. They recognized that rocket technology was in its infancy, and that rocket engines, circa 1944, were often tricky, unreliable, and dangerous. Above all, they did not like the idea of a manned research aircraft, heavily loaded with explosive fuels and test instrumentation, lifting from a runway with the pilot relying on a rocket to keep him aloft.[80] They realized that if the rocket cut out, even fractionally, the transonic research airplane program would end in a tower of smoke above a crater off the end of the runway. Some of the NACA research pilots at Langley did not support the idea of a transonic research aircraft in the first place— they felt they were being asked to risk their lives because wind-tunnel researchers were unable to do the necessary work on the ground.[81] Now, on the question of rocket propulsion, NACA flight researchers stated emphatically that no NACA pilot would ever fly a rocket airplane.[82]

In early May, the Army Air Forces Materiel Command Head- quarters at Wright Field ordered Ezra Kotcher to Langley Laboratory to discuss high-speed research with the NACA. Kotcher attended a May 15 meeting at Langley, and presented the results of the Wright Field "Mach 0.999" study, including a drawing of the rocket aircraft. At this meeting, NACA representatives agreed to submit a transonic aircraft design to the AAF for approval and construction. NACA did submit a design proposal to Wright Field two months later, on July 10. The design was turbojet-powered, and had provisions for 400 lbs. of research instru- mentation similar to an installation on a NACA P-51 Mustang flying at Langley in a compressibility research program involving high-speed dives.[83] Bell Aircraft Corporation had sent Eastman N. Jacobs and Dr. George W. Lewis a 3-view drawing of a tentative turbojet-powered re- search aircraft in April 1944; it is unclear whether or not this proposal influenced in any way the subsequent NACA proposal submitted to the AAF in July. In any case, the AAF rejected the NACA turbojet design out of hand as being too conservative in design, particularly since the turbojet engine did not give the airplane good high-speed capabilities.[84] By mid-1944, then, Kotcher had succeeded in persuading the AAF to support a rocket-propelled design.

In addition to his role in developing a transonic aircraft, Kotcher directed other Army combat aircraft development programs. He served as project officer on the P-59, XP-79, and Lockheed P-80, and even supervised a program on flight-refueling Boeing B-17 Flying Fortresses by Consolidated-Vultee B-24 Liberator tankers.[85] Late in June 1944, Gen. Franklin O. Carroll appointed Kotcher project officer on the JB-2 missile project, an attempt to copy the German pulsejet-powered V-1 "buzz-bomb" robot missile. This occupied Kotcher over the next several months until a climactic launching at Eglin Field, Florida, on October 12, 1944. After working all night readying a JB-2 for a scheduled demonstration before assembled officials including Theodore von Kármán and Hugh L. Dryden, Kotcher gave the firing order and the JB-2 took off in a cloud of smoke with a loud hiss, flying several miles before splashing into the Gulf of Mexico. Kotcher then returned to Wright Field and resumed his deliberations on transonic aircraft development. He began looking for a likely contractor to develop the aircraft.[86]

Meanwhile, a Bureau of Aeronautics engineer had taken steps to

AAF Wright Field "Mach 0.999" Study for Transonic Airplane, April 1944

initiate a Navy-sponsored high-speed research airplane. First Lieutenant Abraham Hyatt, a Marine Corps officer and graduate of the Georgia Institute of Technology with a B.A. in aeronautical engineering, had worked before the war with the Curtiss, Martin, and McDonnell aircraft companies. In 1944, he entered the Marines on assignment to the Navy Bureau of Aeronautics Aviation Design Research Branch, working under Ivan Driggs.[87] As had Kotcher, Wolf, Stack, Diehl, and others before him, Hyatt saw that the lack of high-speed aerodynamic knowledge posed a serious handicap to the aircraft designer. Likewise he saw the research airplane conception as the most feasible and convenient method of acquiring high-speed data. He concluded that the Navy should sponsor such an aircraft in order to ensure that American naval aviation would retain its high standard of world leadership.

Accordingly, on September 22, 1944, Hyatt issued a memorandum on a proposed turbojet-propelled high-speed research airplane for circulation through the Bureau of Aeronautics. Such an aircraft, the memo stated, could furnish knowledge on transonic drag, flight loads, and stability and control. Further, the turbojet configuration would permit acquisition of data on engine thrust and duct inlet design. Evaluation flights by Navy and Marine combat pilots could yield useful tactical information for future high-speed Navy combat aircraft.[88]

In part the memo read,

> All branches of aeronautical engineering are confronted with a serious lack of knowledge of engineering laws which govern the design of airplanes at speeds above 500 miles per hour.
>
> The present trend of military airplanes is toward super speeds. Even greater competition in super speed airplane design will exist among nations as the war progresses and after the termination of the present war.
>
> It is proposed that the Bureau of Aeronautics take the necessary steps to obtain an airplane with the following specifications:
>
> (a) Minimum high speed of 650 miles per hour at sea level.
> (b) As clean as special care in manufacturing can accomplish.
>   1. Extra heavy covering for wings, tail and fuselage.
>   2. Special care in scaling.
> (c) All around vision sacrificed for cleanliness by making pilots enclosure contained in fuselage.
> (d) Low thickness ratio of wings—possibly 10% at root section.
> (e) All armament and equipment other than required by pilot to fly in vicinity of airfield be eliminated.
> (f) Fuel capacity determined by maximum time aloft required for a given test.
> (g) Landing and take-off limited by ability to do so from a class "AA" airport only.
> (h) Provision for complete instrumentation for flight characteristics and flight loads.
> (i) Design yield load factors of 10 to 12 and high strength tail.
> (j) Jet propelled.

Hyatt's proposed airplane represented a more conservative approach towards the problem of high-speed research, an approach more in keeping with the views of NACA engineers. Ezra Kotcher, on the other hand, favored a more radical rocket-propelled aircraft. Both men agreed that the research aircraft should be overstrength to withstand high load factors, and unencumbered by military requirements. But they differed considerably on the desired propulsion and performance characteristics of the aircraft. Hyatt wanted turbojet propulsion and 650 mph—Mach 0.85—performance. Kotcher wanted rocket propulsion and 800 mph, so that the aircraft could exceed the speed of sound. At 35,000 feet, the altitude Kotcher felt desirable for flight testing, the rocket aircraft would attain just under Mach 1.2.

So it was that as the end of 1944 approached, both the Army and Navy sought to develop separate transonic research aircraft projects. They both relied on the advice and suggestions of the NACA in guiding and establishing their programs. But since the two services would finance and procure the aircraft, the ultimate selection of configuration and structural details lay with the service and the contractor. On the choice of propulsion, for example, the Navy chose to abide by the advice of the NACA. The Army, however, chose to develop a more radical rocket-propelled airplane, against the general feeling within the NACA favoring air-breathing engines.[89]

Over 20 years had passed since the first tentative high-speed aerodynamic research on propeller airfoils by Caldwell, Fales, Briggs and Dryden. The speeds of the new turbojet aircraft were over 4 times those of the fastest World War I fighters and bombers. As a sampling, the intervening years between 1918 and 1945 witnessed the introduction of the controllable-pitch propeller, the retractable landing gear, cantilever construction, the NACA cowling, and the turbojet—all of which increased high-speed aircraft performance. In 1944, new turbojet-propelled fighter aircraft attained level flight speeds that could only be reached by propeller-driven fighters during a maximum power dive. The military services, the NACA, and the aircraft industry suddenly realized that the designer needed reliable information so he could reduce or overcome the effects of compressibility, and thereby design more efficient high-speed aircraft. Pending the development of satisfactory transonic wind tunnels, the best immediate solution seemed the development of a transonic research aircraft. With this decision in mind, the research-aircraft advocates within the Army, Navy, and NACA now turned to finding a contractor willing to take on the task.

NOTES

1. F. W. Caldwell and E. N. Fales, *Wind Tunnel Studies in Aerodynamic Phenomena at High Speeds*, NACA Technical Report No. 83 (1920), p. 77.

2. Wayne W. Parrish, ed., *Who's Who in World Aviation, 1955* (Washington, D.C., 1955), pp. 49, 99–100.

3. NACA Technical Report No. 83.

4. At sea level, the speed of sound is approximately 1,116 feet per second (fps). It varies with altitude, dropping off to approximately 968 fps at altitudes between 36,000 and 66,000 feet. The common unit of measurement for the speed of sound is *Mach number*, in honor of the Austrian physicist Ernst Mach. The Mach number is the ratio of the speed of an object to the speed of sound. Thus, Mach 0.5 is half of the velocity of sound, Mach 1 is the velocity of sound, and Mach 2 is twice the speed of sound.

5. NACA Technical Report No. 83.

6. *Ibid.* Also, letter, Ezra Kotcher to author, 23 Jan. 1972.

7. NACA Technical Report No. 83.

8. L. J. Briggs, G. F. Hull, and H. L. Dryden, *Aerodynamic Characteristics of Airfoils at High Speeds*, NACA Technical Report No. 207 (1924), p. 465.

9. *Ibid.* Also Hugh L. Dryden, "Supersonic Travel Within the Last Two Hundred Years," *The Scientific Monthly*, LXXVIII, No. 5, (May 1954), 289–95.

10. Briggs and Dryden, *Pressure Distribution Over Airfoils at High Speeds*, NACA Technical Report No. 255 (1926), pp. 581–82.

11. Briggs and Dryden, *Aerodynamic Characteristics of Twenty-Four Airfoils at High Speeds*, NACA Technical Report No. 319 (1929), p. 346.

12. Briggs and Dryden, *Aerodynamic Characteristics of Circular-Arc Airfoils at High Speeds*, NACA Technical Report No. 365 (1931).

13. Don Vordeman, *The Great Air Races* (Garden City, 1969), p. 415.

14. "How Fast Can We Fly?", *The Sunday Star*, 11 Sept. 1932.

15. John Stack, "Effects of Compressibility on High Speed Flight," *The Journal of the Aeronautical Sciences*, Vol. I, January 1934, 40–43.

16. Walter T. Bonney, "High-Speed Research Airplanes," *Scientific American*, Vol. 189, No. 4, (October 1953), 36–41.

17. Dryden, "Supersonic Travel Within the Last Two Hundred Years," p. 293. Theodore von Kármán with Lee Edson, *The Wind and Beyond: Theodore von Kármán, Pioneer in Aviation and Pathfinder in Space* (Boston, 1967), pp. 219–20.

18. *Ibid.*: Dryden, p. 293; Kármán, pp. 221–22.

19. *Ibid.*: Dryden, p. 293; Kármán, pp. 223–25.

20. Kármán, *Aerodynamics* (New York, 1963), pp. 133–34. The influence appeared notably in the design of the North American F-86 and Boeing B-47.

21. Letter, Ezra Kotcher to author, 23 Jan. 1972.

22. *Ibid.*

23. *Ibid.*

24. Air Corps Materiel Division Engineering Section Memorandum Report 50-461-351 (Aug. 18, 1939), pp. 5, 6, 11, 14. Content transmitted in letter, Ezra Kotcher to author, 23 Jan. 1972.

25. Robert Schlaifer and S. D. Heron, *Development of Aircraft Engines and Fuels* (Boston, 1950), pp. 378–79, 457–58.

26. Letter, Ezra Kotcher to author, 23 Jan. 1972. Also, Kármán, *The Wind and Beyond*, p. 225.

27. Robert L. Perry, "The Ancestors of the X-1," p. 10 (Rough draft, June 1965, in NASA Historical Archives files).

28. Later, the development of the X-1 and D-558 spurred efforts to develop efficient transonic wind tunnels. The choking phenomenon was not alleviated until the introduction of the "slotted throat" tunnel after the Second World War.

29. Interview of John Stack by the author, 19 May 1971.

30. *Ibid.*

31. Dryden, "Supersonic Travel Within the Last Two Hundred Years," p. 294.

32. George W. Gray, *Frontiers of Flight: The Story of NACA Research* (New York, 1948), pp. 213–14.

33. Martin Caiden, *Fork-Tailed Devil: The P-38* (New York, 1971), p. 49.

34. Le Roy Weber, *The Lockheed P-38J-M Lightning*, Profile Publication No. 106 (Surrey, Eng.; 1966), pp. 4–5.

35. Tony LeVier and John Guenther, *Pilot* (New York, 1954), p. 133.

36. Gray, *Frontiers of Flight* pp. 150–51.

37. *Ibid.*, p. 153. Also Edwin P. Hartman, *Adventures in Research: A History of Ames Research Center 1940–1965* (Govt. Printing Office, Washington, 1970).

38. LeVier, *Pilot*, pp. 142–48.

39. Schlaifer and Heron, *Development of Aircraft Engines and Fuels*, pp. 457–58, 461–62.

40. Ronald D. Neal, "The Bell XP-59A Airacomet: The United States' First Jet Aircraft," *Journal of the American Aviation Historical Society*, Vol. XI, No. 3, (Fall 1966), 155–78.

41. Minutes of Meeting of Special Committee on Jet Propulsion, 22 April 1941, p. 5, NASA Historical Archives.

42. Stack interview, 19 May 1971.

43. Interview of Harold Turner by the author, 11 Nov. 1971.

44. *Ibid.*

45. Stack interview, 19 May 1971.

46. Statement of John Stack at AIAA History Session, San Francisco, Calif., 28 July 1965, NASA Historical Archives.

47. *Ibid.* Also interview of Clinton E. Brown by the author, 12 May 1971.

48. Macon C. Ellis, Jr. and Clinton E. Brown, *NACA Investigation of a Jet-Propulsion System Applicable to Flight*, NACA Technical Report No. 802 (1943), pp. 498–501. Also, Brown interview, 12 May 1971.

49. *Ibid.*

50. Schlaifer and Heron, *Development of Aircraft Engines and Fuels*, pp. 450–51, 468. Brown interview, 12 May 1971.

51. Gray, *Frontiers of Flight*, pp. 161–65.

52. Interview of Milton B. Ames, Jr., by the author, 26 July 1971.

53. W. S. Farren, "Research for Aeronautics—Its Planning and Application," *Journal of the Aeronautical Sciences*, Vol. XI, No. 2, (April 1944), 95–109.

54. *Ibid.*, p. 103.

55. "Beginnings of the X-1," n.d., in NASA Historical Archives.

56. Letter, Robert A. Wolf to author, 4 April 1972.

57. *Ibid.*

58. Quoted in "Beginnings of the X-1," p. 3.

59. *Ibid.*

60. Data transmitted from Ezra Kotcher to author, 23 Jan. 1972.

61. "MX-324—Step to Manned Rocket Flight," *Aeronautics and Astronautics*, Vol. II, (Oct. 1964), 55. Northrop redesigned the aircraft as the XP-79B, powered by two Westinghouse 19B turbojets. It went out of control and crashed on its first flight, Sept. 12, 1945, killing Northrop test pilot Harry Crosby.

62. Statement of Ezra Kotcher at AIAA History Session, San Francisco, Calif., 28 July 1965, NASA Historical Archives.

63. Letter, Ezra Kotcher to author, 24 July 1971. Also, letter Kotcher to William Lundgren, 4 Nov. 1953.

64. Letters, Ezra Kotcher to author, 10 Sept. 1971 and 23 Jan. 1972. Also, letter, Kotcher to Lundgren, 4 Nov. 1953, and Kotcher statement at AIAA History Session, 28 July 1965.

65. *Ibid.*

66. *Ibid.*

67. Kármán, *The Wind and Beyond*, pp. 233–34.

68. Letter, Kotcher to Lundgren, 4 Nov. 1953.

69. F. L. Thompson, "Flight Research at Transonic and Supersonic Speeds With Free-Falling and Rocket Propelled Models," Paper presented at the Institute of Aeronautical Sciences—Royal Aeronautical Society meeting, May 1949, pp. 1–4, NASA Historical Archives. Also, interview of Floyd L. Thompson by author, 31 May 1972. The British program gained the dubious nickname "Undropped body program." British plans to initiate a falling-body program became tied up in committee and no research resulted.

70. Letter, Robert R. Gilruth to author, 27 Jan. 1972. Also interview of Robert R. Gilruth by Michael D. Keller, 26 June 1967, NASA Historical Archives. See Gray, *Frontiers of Flight*, pp. 336–37.

71. Interview of John V. Becker by the author, 12 Nov. 1971.

72. "The Miles Supersonic," *The Aeroplane*, LXXI, No. 1842, (Sept. 13, 1946), 295–96.

73. *Air Force Supersonic Research Airplane XS-1 Report No. 1*, 9 January 1948, p. 5, NASA Historical Archives. Also Ames interview, 26 July 1971, and letter, Walter S. Diehl to author, 6 Jan. 1972.

74. Letter, Walter S. Diehl to author, 6 Jan. 1972.

75. Letter, Ezra Kotcher to author, 7 Nov. 1971.

76. Joseph A. Shortal, *History of Wallops Station: Origins and Activities Through 1949* (comment edition, n.d.), pp. 11–12, NASA Historical Archives.

77. Letter, Walter S. Diehl to author, 6 Jan. 1972. Ames interview, 26 July 1971.

78. Stack interview, 19 May 1971.

79. Ames interview, 26 July 1971.

80. Thompson interview, 31 May 1972.

81. Ames interview, 26 July 1971.

82. Becker interview, 12 Nov. 1971.

83. Air Materiel Command Correspondence Summary of Project MX-653 History, 14 Jan. 1947, p. 1. Transmitted to author by Ezra Kotcher. Also letters, Ezra Kotcher to author, 23 Jan. 1972 and 22 Feb. 1972.

84. *Ibid.* Also, "Beginnings of the X-1," p. 3, and William R. Lundgren, *Across the High Frontier: The Story of a Test Pilot—Major Charles E. Yeager, USAF* (New York, 1955), p. 31.

85. Data from Kotcher Biographical File, National Air and Space Museum, Smithsonian Institution (hereafter cited as NASM).

86. *Ibid.* Also, letter, Kotcher to author, 7 Nov. 1971, and Thomas A. Sturm, *The USAF Scientific Advisory Board: Its First Twenty Years, 1944–1964* (Washington, D.C., 1967), p. 4. Letter, Kotcher to Lundgren, 4 Nov. 1953.

87. Parrish, *Who's Who in World Aviation, 1955*, pp. 154–55. Also letters, A. M. O. Smith to author, 31 March 1972 and 17 April 1972.

88. Abraham Hyatt, *Proposed High Speed Research Airplane*, Memorandum Aer-E-225-AH, 22 Sept. 1944. Transmitted to author from A. M. O. Smith, 17 April 1972.

89. NACA continued this preference for air-breathing propulsion well after the X-1 entered development. In 1944, Eastman N. Jacobs, Arthur Kantrowitz, Macon C. Ellis, Jr., Clinton E. Brown, and Coleman du Pont Donaldson investigated ramjet propulsion. The results of this research culminated, in December 1945, in a NACA Advance Confidential Report in which Brown and Ellis outlined a ramjet supersonic research aircraft proposal. The aircraft was designed for 3 to 5 minute endurance at Mach 1.4. It would carry a pilot and data recording instrumentation, though it could also be developed as an unmanned aircraft. It would have been either air launched or towed to altitude. Rocket boosters would have accelerated it to transonic speeds, where the ramjet would take over. The aircraft received very serious consideration within NACA—John Stack, for one, feels it was unfortunate that it was not developed. But the proposal did not emerge from the conference stage, and was not pursued further. The principle statistics for the aircraft were:

Maximum speed:	Mach 1.4
Landing speed:	100 mph
Length:	34 feet 6 inches
Height:	7 feet .85 inches
Wingspan:	20 feet 3.36 inches
Wing area:	68.5 square feet
Takeoff weight:	2,500 pounds
Empty weight:	1,450 pounds

Aside from its unique ramjet power plant, the aircraft featured wings of 3.5 percent thickness-chord ratio having wedge airfoil sections and raked wing tips. Sources: Interview of Macon C. Ellis, Jr., by the author, 12 Nov. 1971. Brown interview, 12 May 1971. Stack interview, 19 May 1971. Thompson interview, 31 May 1972.
Also: Arthur Kantrowitz and Coleman duP. Donaldson, "Preliminary Investigation of Supersonic Diffusers," NACA ACR L5D20 (May 1945). Macon C. Ellis, Jr., and Clinton E. Brown, "Analysis of Supersonic Ram-Jet Performance and Wind-Tunnel Tests of a Possible Supersonic Ram-Jet Airplane Model," NACA ACR L5L12 (December 1945). Macon C. Ellis, Jr., and Clinton E. Brown, "Proposal of Supersonic Ram-Jet Missiles," NACA Memorandum Report, 30 Jan. 1945. Stack statement at AIAA History Session, 28 July 1965.

II

THE DESIGN
DEVELOPMENT
OF THE BELL XS-1

F ew American aircraft companies could lay stronger claims to crea-
tive ingenuity and expertise than the Bell Aircraft Coporation. One
of the newer aviation concerns, Bell traced its origins back to the
Consolidated Aircraft Corporation. When Consolidated's president,
Reuben Fleet, decided to move the firm west to San Diego, one of the
vice presidents, Lawrence D. Bell, elected to remain at Buffalo, New
York, and head his own firm. So it was that on July 10, 1935, Bell, together with former Consolidated officers Robert J. Woods and Ray P.
Whitman, formed the Bell Aircraft Corporation.[1]

Within 2 years the firm ran up sales totaling nearly 2 million dollars,
mostly from Consolidated subcontracts. The firm soon displayed a flair
for the radical, the unconventional, and the untried. This tendency,
imparted upon company engineers, stemmed from the character of Bell
and Woods themselves. Lawrence Bell entered the airplane business in
1912 as a 17-year-old mechanic to 2 exhibition pilots. One was famed
stunt pilot Lincoln Beachey. The other was his brother Grover Bell, who

perished in an accident a year later. Bell considered leaving aviation after his brother's death, but decided to remain with it. He developed a makeshift bomber for Pancho Villa, the Mexican revolutionary general, then joined the Glenn L. Martin company. In succession he became factory superintendent, general manager, and later Martin vice-president. In 1925, he went with Consolidated, staying with that firm for the next decade.[2]

When Lawrence D. Bell formed the Bell Aircraft Corporation in July 1935, Robert J. Woods was a 31-year-old project engineer with Consolidated. He immediately left and joined Bell. Woods graduated from the University of Michigan with a B.S. in aeronautical engineering in 1928. In August 1928, he joined the NACA at Langley Laboratory, working in the variable density tunnel.[3] He shared the same desk with John Stack, and the 2 men struck up a friendship that lasted until Woods' death in 1956.[4] Woods soon left the NACA, however, for he was eager to develop some of his own designs and see them fly. He went with the Towle Aircraft Company in Detroit and developed a twin-engine amphibian. After a brief stint with the Detroit Aircraft Corporation and the Lockheed Aircraft Company, he left for Consolidated. There he designed a 2-seat fighter, the Y1P-25 powered by a Curtiss V-1570-27 engine equipped with a supercharger. Consolidated developed this aircraft into the A-11 attack plane and the later P-30, P-30A, and PB-2 series.[5]

After joining Bell in 1935, Woods' engineering talent flourished. In June 1936, together with Harlan M. Poyer, Woods began development of what became the P-39 Airacobra, a single-seat fighter with the engine behind the cockpit driving the propeller via an extension shaft. Obsolescent when the Japanese attacked Pearl Harbor, the P-39 nonetheless served well as a ground strafer and fighter bomber, both with the air forces of the United States and the Soviet Union. In 1937, the Woods-designed Bell FM-1 appeared, an unorthodox five-place twin-engine fighter powered by two Allison V-1710 engines driving pusher propellers. One 37mm cannon projected from the front of each pusher engine nacelle. The FM-1 Airacuda did not enter active Air Corps service, but it anticipated the development of the long-range escort fighter and the more recent "gunship."

During the war, Bell not only produced and developed its own aircraft, but those of other manufacturers as well. A Bell plant at Marietta, Georgia, assembled Boeing-designed B-29 Superfortresses, and the Bell Buffalo plant turned out Boeing B-17 parts and assemblies. Bell produced advanced versions of its P-39, as well as a new fighter, the P-63 Kingcobra—most of which went to Russia under Lend-Lease. The company also retained its interest in the radical and the unorthodox. It furnished the Army with the P-59, the first American turbojet. Woods designed a prototype experimental lightweight fighter, the XP-77. In 1943, the company began development of the XP-83, an attempt to produce a successful long-range turbojet-powered escort fighter.

On November 30, 1944, Robert J. Woods stopped at Maj. Ezra Kotcher's office at Wright Field after hours. Woods did not know of Bell engineer Robert Wolf's research-aircraft proposal to NACA Director of Aeronautical Research Dr. George W. Lewis eleven months earlier, and Wolf, chief research engineer for Bell, was now occupied in the problems of helicopter development.[6] Kotcher, since coming back to Wright Field from the JB-2 tests at Eglin Field, Florida, had been searching for contractors to develop an Army-sponsored transonic research airplane. As engineers passed through Wright Field to discuss new fighter proposals, Kotcher asked them whether or not their firms would be interested in developing a research airplane, preparatory to developing new advanced combat aircraft. All of them agreed that such a program was desirable, but they emphasized to Kotcher that their firms were production-oriented, and would not undertake such a "one-off" program.[7]

What began as a friendly chat between two engineers unexpectedly developed into a serious discussion on the problems of high-speed aircraft. Cautiously, Kotcher advanced the research-aircraft concept, asking Woods if he might be interested. When Woods evinced an interest to involve the company, Kotcher responded by outlining the concept in order to give Woods an appreciation of what he would be getting the Bell company into. Kotcher told Woods that the AAF wanted a special nonmilitary-type high-speed airplane, unencumbered by military requirements and overstrength for safety. Such a plane, Kotcher said, should be rocket-powered for maximum performance. It should be capable of attaining 800 mph at 35,000 feet with an endurance of 2 minutes. If Bell accepted the offer to develop the aircraft, the company would only have to guarantee a safe and controllable airplane up to Mach 0.8. Beyond that, the Army would not hold the Bell company responsible for aircraft behavior. Right then, Woods agreed to commit Bell to develop the airplane.[8] The Army had found its contractor.

Woods' action caught the company president by surprise. After leaving Kotcher's office, Woods telephoned Lawrence Bell, who was in Louisville, Kentucky, and said, "You'd better sit down and relax. I've got some news. I've just committed you to the production of an 800 mph plane."[9] There was no answer. Finally, Woods said, "Operator, I've been cut off." Bell replied, "No, I just said what have you done?"[10] Between the two men were strong bonds of mutual respect for the other's ability, as well as personal friendship. Bell decided to let the commitment stand. The next day, Woods informed Kotcher that the Bell Aircraft Corporation would begin design studies of a transonic research aircraft for the Army.[11]

Though Ezra Kotcher recommended rocket propulsion for the airplane, Robert Woods favored turbojet propulsion. The first sketches Woods drew of the proposed airplane incorporated a turbojet General Electric I-16 (J-31) power plant. Considering possible long-term benefits from the research airplane, Woods also included provisions for guns, should the Army be interested in a possible combat aircraft development. Kotcher showed Woods intelligence reports on the German rocket-propelled Me 163 *Komet* that by the winter of 1944 was occasionally engaging American bombers over Germany. Here was a combat aircraft that demonstrated successful rocket-engine operation. Woods reluctantly agreed to evaluate the Aerojet 6,000-lb-thrust rocket engine then under development as the possible power plant for the Bell research airplane.[12]

Woods returned to Buffalo by train, drawing sketches of various configurations on the way. On his return, Robert Stanley, Bell engineer, called together a design team for the airplane.[13] The team consisted of Stanley, Benson Hamlin, Paul Emmons, Stanley W. Smith, and Roy Sandstrom. Each of the team members had broad experience in aircraft design and operation. For example, Robert M. Stanley, a former Navy pilot and holder of a B.S. in aeronautical engineering from the California Institute of Technology, had been the first American to fly a turbojet aircraft. He served as test pilot on the Bell P-59 program, making the nation's first turbojet flight on October 1, 1942. Before then, he worked as a sales demonstrator and test pilot with the United Aircraft Corporation.[14] Benson Hamlin, who held a B.Ae.E. from Rensselaer Polytechnic Institute, had been one of six outstanding engineering students selected from across the nation in 1937 to work with Chance Vought Aircraft. Hamlin's specialty was flight testing; he served as flight test engineer with Boeing and the Vega Aircraft Corporation on B-17 production. He joined Bell in 1942, and had managed Bell's flight test activities on the turbojet P-59 at Muroc Dry Lake, California, during 1943.[15] Stanley W. Smith received a B.S. in aeronautical engineering from the University of Michigan, and also had been the National Soaring Champion for 1933. He worked as a designer for the Bowlus-du Pont sailplane firm, then as a teacher and supervisor of the New York state aviation schools from 1936 to 1939. He then joined Bell as a stress analyst and preliminary design engineer.[16]

In December 1944 the AAF, Bell, and the NACA prepared final general specifications for the transonic research aircraft. In a joint AAF-NACA conference held at Langley Laboratory on December 13 and 14, the AAF reemphasized its support of developing a rocket-propelled rather than turbojet-propelled aircraft.[17] At the same time, Langley instrumentation engineers prepared specifications for the instrumentation that the aircraft should carry. They concluded the plane should carry 500 pounds of instrumentation equipment, comprising 370 pounds of instruments and approximately 130 pounds of wiring and tubing. The instrumentation should fit within a space allotment of 9 cubic feet, and would include 60-cell manometers, control position and control force recorders, an accelerometer, and a Miller 12-element recording oscillograph that would replace the two 60-cell manometers when it was used.[18] This specification formed the basis for the future instrumentation package installed in both the future XS-1 and D-558 aircraft.

On December 20 and 21, Kotcher met with Bell representatives Robert Woods, Paul Emmons, Benson Hamlin, and Dr. Vladimir Morkovin at Air Technical Service Command headquarters at Wright Field. They discussed the instrumentation requirements of the plane, and agreed that the airplane should be as relatively uncomplex and straightforward as possible. They decided that the pilot should be seated and not lie prone, as in the proposed XP-79, and that the airplane should be capable of taking off at 150 mph within 5,000 feet of a 7,000-foot runway, and land at 90 mph.[19] Both the NACA and the Air Force insisted that the aircraft be designed for an 18g ultimate load factor; this figure represented a 50 percent higher load factor above existing fighter aircraft, and largely reflected ignorance of what aerodynamic loads the aircraft might experience in the transonic region. The NACA and AAF Aircraft Laboratory decided to build for a higher load factor to ensure the plane would hold together during its turbulent passage from subsonic to supersonic flight. This requirement complicated the already difficult task facing Bell engineers of designing a transonic flying laboratory.[20]

Bell began development of the research airplane under project designation MX-524.[21] The first task for the team was assembling adequate data from which to draw up a suitable airframe. Accordingly, Benson Hamlin, design engineer, and Paul Emmons, project aerodynamicist, left Buffalo and toured the research institutions in the United States that might have developed suitable data or that would be able to give the Bell team advice. Among the installations Emmons and Hamlin visited were the California Institute of Technology—where they discussed the project with Dr. Clark B. Millikan—and the Army Aberdeen Proving Grounds. The trip was a disappointment. At each facility, Emmons and Hamlin asked what wing section they should use, what type of control surface, what wing and fuselage shape. Each time they received a new set of answers. "Various people told us the various thoughts that they might have," Hamlin recalled later, "But every single one of them also added in the same breath, 'we really can't tell you because we really don't know.' "[22] At Aberdeen, Army scientists suggested that the two men visit the Ballistics Laboratory at Wright Field, so Hamlin and Emmons left for Ohio.

The two Bell engineers had earlier concluded that the only objects they knew that moved at supersonic velocities all the time were bullets. They wondered why a .50 cal. bullet had the shape it did. At Wright Field they asked ballistics experts why the standard .50 cal. bullet had the shape it did, and what its transonic drag values were. The ballisticians did not know the drag characteristics of the bullet, but they did explain the reasoning behind the shape. What mattered was the dispersion pattern of the bullets. In tests where researchers fired bursts of bullets from a machine gun at a target, bullets having an ogival shape produced the best pattern. The .50 cal. bullet had such a shape, selected because of the test results. Hamlin and Emmons obtained some Schlieren photographs and sketches of decelerating .50 cal. bullets for use in designing the Bell research airplane.[23] Then the two engineers returned to Buffalo. The trip convinced both men that Bell was strictly on its own in developing the airplane; no one really had any concrete knowledge of how to design a transonic research vehicle.[24]

The Bell design team made this feeling clear in a team conference held on January 15, 1945. The subsequent report stated:

> Generally, the reaction from most people approached is that very little is known about design or conditions for supersonic flight, especially stability and control problems. All felt that a project similar to MX-524 is highly desirable and the need for it is keenly felt throughout the industry. Such a flying laboratory would be in great demand by nearly all research and development groups as an aid in studying many different individual problems and phases of research.
>
> Insofar as concrete information and suggestions have not been forthcoming we should continue our design studies based on our own ideas and at the same time keep abreast of any information which may be of value.[25]

Benson Hamlin now began tentative designs of various configurations. The first configuration he investigated was a research airplane powered by an I-16 engine for climb to altitude, but using the Aerojet 6,000-lb-thrust rocket engine for transonic and low supersonic research. After the pilot completed the research portion of the flight he could return to base on the power of the turbojet alone. As the study progressed, Hamlin and the rest of the Bell team concluded that the plane would have a poor rate of climb due to a decrease in turbojet performance at altitude. This required additional turbojet fuel, which added to the size and weight of the airplane. The plane attained the test altitude of 35,000 feet at low airspeed, requiring large amounts of rocket fuel to accelerate to transonic velocities. This also added to the size of the plane, and the combination turbojet and rocket installation resulted in an extremely complex design. Hamlin decided to abandon this configuration and investigate other possible layouts.[26]

Hamlin next studied possible configurations using all-rocket propulsion. He determined the shape, the weight, and loadings of the aircraft and made a step-by-step analysis of its performance capabilities. The configurations he chose he termed "super airplanes." The first two designs did not achieve the desired performance requirements. But "super airplane No. 3" did. The No. 3 design had a gross weight of 21,000 lbs., and utilized a 6,000-lb-thrust rocket engine with 6.5 minutes worth of fuel. On takeoff, the thrust of the engine would be augmented by 4 assist rockets that the pilot would jettison after takeoff. The assist rockets boosted the weight to 24,640 pounds. Hamlin's performance calculations indicated that the aircraft could take off in about 3,060 feet, climb to altitude at a climb rate of between 16,000 and 20,000 feet per minute—a figure 5 times higher than that of existing aircraft—and attain 35,000 feet with 171 seconds of rocket time remaining.[27]

When Robert Woods saw Hamlin's performance estimates, he still expressed reluctance to develop an all-rocket aircraft. He requested that Hamlin investigate an all-turbojet research airplane. Hamlin and the Bell design-team members investigated a turbojet aircraft, and ultimately derived a configuration capable of attaining 725 mph at sea level. This figure was still below the 800 mph the Army wanted. Further, the performance of the aircraft fell off at altitude, so that any transonic flight tests of this turbojet configuration would have to be made at low altitudes where the air loads on the aircraft were highest. Hamlin considered this "very dangerous," and Bell engineers searched for ways to improve engine performance so that tests could be run at a higher, safer altitude. In particular, team members held meetings with General Electric representatives and asked whether G.E. could boost the thrust of its projected TG-180 turbojet to increase performance potential of a transonic turbojet-propelled research aircraft. G.E. declared that such a boosting was not possible. This led Bell to drop all thought of using turbojet propulsion in the research aircraft.[28] Bell did not give consideration to ramjet propulsion since the Army desired that the plane should be capable of taking off under its own power, and incorporation of ramjet propulsion would require some form of booster propulsion until the aircraft attained sufficient velocity for the ramjet to operate. Further, ramjets were an unknown quantity, and engineers knew little about their characteristics and design.[29]

The NACA and the Air Technical Service Command decided two other questions the firm's design team had. The first was what wing section to use on the airplane. Engineers within the NACA were split as to whether or not a thick or a thin wing was more desirable. Aerodynamicists at Ames Laboratory in California favored a wing of about 12 percent thickness-chord ratio in order to attain the critical Mach number more quickly and create transonic flow. But Robert Gilruth of NACA's Langley Laboratory strongly disagreed. Using his wing-flow method of research, Gilruth found that thick wings lost their lift in the transonic region, while thin wings retained their lift in the transonic region. Gilruth realized that the success of the transonic research aircraft depended on a thin wing section. The decision on which section to use, either a thick section or a thin one, rested in the judgment of Floyd L. Thompson, Assistant Chief of Research at Langley Laboratory. Dr. Lewis, NACA's Director of Aeronautical Research, had clamped a lid of secrecy on early wing-flow-test results. Discussions on the data were awkward because only Gilruth and Thompson knew of the results at that time.

Thompson examined the data collected by Gilruth and concurred that a thin wing would be more desirable. So he rejected the thick wing option, and pressed for use of a thin wing section. Thin wing advocates suggested using wings of 5 percent thickness-chord ratio, but Langley engineers decided on a compromise, whereby the research airplane would have two sets of wings. One set would have a thickness-chord ratio of 8 percent; the other would have a thickness-chord ratio of 10 percent. Research studies could be made on both. In conferences with Bell, NACA representatives reported their decision on the thickness question. Some observers, while accepting the aerodynamic reasons for selecting the configuration, had little confidence that Bell designers could fabricate an 8 percent wing with the desired 18g load factor.[30]

The second question decided for Bell was that centering around the Aerojet 6,000-lb-thrust "Rotojet." The Rotojet would utilize red fuming nitric acid and aniline as propellants. These two were hypergolic, meaning that whenever they mixed, they reacted violently, thus obviating the necessity of providing an ignition system for the engine. Wondering just how violently the two liquids reacted, members of the Bell design team purchased a bottle of each from a drug store. They taped the bottles together, went to the gun butts at the Buffalo plant where armorers sighted-in the machine gun installations on Bell airplanes, and threw the two bottles against a rock. The glass shattered, and the contents erupted in flame. Shaken by what they had seen, the Bell engineers returned to their drawing boards. All they could envision was the plane having a mishap, or having to land with propellants aboard, and then the fuel tanks bursting on landing, instantaneously obliterating the pilot, plane, and anything else close by. It meant that Bell would have to design the plane to extreme requirements to prevent such a possibility from occurring, an almost insurmountable task.[31] At the same time, the Army Air Technical Service Command was having second thoughts about the Aerojet engine. Its development was not moving smoothly due to technical

complications, and, like Bell, the AAF recognized the hazardous characteristics of using a hypergolic fuel combination on a manned aircraft. The
Aerojet 6,000-lb-thrust engine dropped from consideration.[32]

Fortunately, a substitute for the Aerojet engine was already at hand.
This was a 6,000-lb-thrust engine being developed for the Navy by
Reaction Motors, Inc., of Pompton Plains, New Jersey. The Reaction
Motors company was truly a "shoestring" operation. Four pioneers of
early American rocketry had formed the organization in December 1941,
shortly after Pearl Harbor. These men were Lovell Lawrence, Jr., H.
Franklin Pierce, James H. Wyld, and John Shesta, members of the
American Rocket Society. Interestingly, in 1939, James Wyld had worked
together with John Stack at Langley Laboratory on high-speed airfoil
research. The company first set up shop in a garage in North Arlington,
New Jersey, but moved to a rented store—"Pat's Tailor Shop"—in Pompton Lakes. By 1943, the firm had again moved, this time to a former
night club located in Pompton Plains.[33]

In the same way that the Army had contracted with GALCIT for
development of assist rockets, the Navy contracted with the tiny firm of
Reaction Motors for the same purpose. Drawing on their previous American Rocket Society experience, RMI members developed a 1,000-lb-
thrust rocket engine and tested it in November 1942. By May 1943, they
had a 3,400-lb-thrust engine undergoing test.[34] While at Pompton Plains,
RMI personnel began development of a 6,000-lb-thrust engine, the LR-8,
for the Navy. Navy Comdr. C. Fink Fischer, an active supporter of naval
rocket research, had prepared the specifications for the latter engine.[35]
Fischer himself, in May 1942, made a rocket-assisted takeoff trial from
Anacostia Naval Air Station in a Brewster F2A-3 Buffalo using five
British solid-fuel antiaircraft rockets.[36]

The RMI engine consisted of four separate rocket cylinders, each of
which produced 1,500-lb thrust. The company designation of the engine
was 6000C4—6,000-lb thrust, 4 cylinders. The propellants were liquid
oxygen and water-alcohol. Each cylinder consisted of an igniter and
combustion chamber, and the engine, with the exception of the controls,
piping, and wiring, was of welded stainless steel construction. The operator could not throttle the engine, but could ignite or shut down each
cylinder separate from the others. Thus, the engine could run at 25
percent, 50, 75, or 100 percent power. So effective was the engine's regen-
erative cooling system that the external cylinder temperature rarely
exceeded 140° Fahrenheit, though the internal temperature attained
4,500-5,000° Fahrenheit.[37]

Lovell Lawrence met with Ezra Kotcher and promised a demonstration of the 6,000-lb-thrust engine, which RMI engineers had disassembled
and placed in storage. Engineers hurriedly assembled the engine,
equipped it with a new ignition system, propellant lines, and valves, and

painted it black. The demonstration came off without difficulty, and RMI was now the prime developer of the Bell research airplane's rocket engine.[38] Hamlin had learned of the RMI corporation early in 1945. The Bell Aircraft Corporation detailed Bell engineer William M. Smith to the RMI firm to work with RMI engineers in making the engine flight-worthy.[39] The decision to use the RMI engine removed the anxiety that had surrounded the Aerojet engine and its hypergolic fuel combination. The RMI engine propellants, liquid oxygen and alcohol, were safe to handle, nonhypergolic, and readily available. Bell had already rejected such propellants as hydrogen peroxide, which requires special handling, and nitromethane, whose detonation characteristics were not fully under-stood. Bell considered and rejected a gasoline and liquid oxygen fuel system, for gasoline was not suitable for regeneratively cooled engines, and the plane would have required a tank of water to aid in cooling.[40]

On March 10, 1945, the Army Air Technical Service Command noti-fied the NACA that the Army was awarding Bell a contract to develop a rocket-propelled straight-wing research airplane using a NACA 66-series airfoil section. The NACA and the Army would work out joint guidelines for performance, stability and control requirements, wind-tunnel testing, flight testing, radar tracking, and instrumentation.[41] Six days later, the Army issued contract W33-038-ac-9183, covering design and construction of three transonic research aircraft under project designation MX-653.[42] The Army assigned the aircraft the designation XS-1: Experimental Sonic-1.

It is interesting to note that the contract stipulated a straight-wing configuration. This reflected the wishes of Air Technical Service Com-mand personnel. By March 1945, the Army ATSC already knew of the advantages of wing sweep as a means of alleviating compressibility shock. This knowledge did not come from Busemann's pioneering paper in 1935 but rather from the research of NACA scientist Robert T. Jones. He dis-covered the theory of sweep while investigating slender-wing theory. At the time, both Jones and Ezra Kotcher were working on the JB-2 project, and Jones discussed his theory with the Army engineer. Kotcher, in turn, explained the wing-sweep theory to Theodore von Kármán, who by now was heading the AAF Scientific Advisory Group (SAG) that General H. H. Arnold had formed on Nov. 7, 1944. Von Kármán and Kotcher discussed the principle with his assistant, Dr. Hsue-shen Tsien. Both Kármán and Tsien thus learned of wing sweep roughly six months before they toured the shattered remnants of Germany's wartime aircraft indus-try and discovered German sweptwing research. In February 1945, Jones discussed the sweep theory with Jean A. Roché of the AAF ATSC liaison office at Langley.[43]

The reason why the AAF did not employ sweep on the XS-1, or at least let the contractor choose between a swept and nonswept configura-

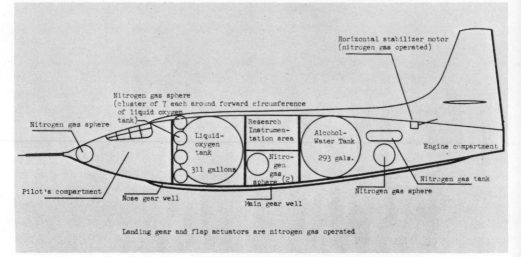

Bell X1 #1 Cutaway Showing Internal Details

tion, is that the Air Technical Service Command desired the XS-1 to provide data applicable to conventional aircraft design as typified by the Lockheed P-80-type fighter. The sweptwing, while promising performance improvement, was still an unknown quantity, not verified by experimental application. The AAF still considered the straight wing configuration as a viable high-speed aircraft planform in the future. Thus, the Air Technical Service Command requested that the XS-1 have a straight wing configuration.[44]

The NACA had developed basic design criteria for a transonic research aircraft, such as the decision to employ a thin wing section and approximately 500 pounds of research instrumentation. One of the most important design criteria NACA established for the Bell transonic research airplane centered on the design of the horizontal tail surfaces. John Stack concluded that the horizontal stabilizer should have a lower thickness-chord ratio than the wing. The reason was that if the wing encountered severe compressibility effects, the horizontal tail would not experience the same problems simultaneously with the wing. By using a thinner airfoil section on the tail, the critical Mach number of the tail— the velocity where high drag rise occurred—would be higher than the critical Mach number of the wing. Thus, if the pilot encountered severe stability and control problems, he could retain control over the airplane until the plane decelerated to safer lower Mach number. If both the wing and the tail had the same airfoil section, both would experience the problems of compressibility simultaneously and with equal severity, and the pilot might find he had no control over the aircraft, possibly resulting in loss of the pilot and airplane.[45]

To ensure adequate longitudinal control during transonic flight, Stack, Gilruth, and others further suggested that the horizontal tail be all-moving. In other words, rather than have a fixed horizontal stabilizer surface with a movable elevator, NACA recommended that the stabilizer itself be adjustable by the pilot while in flight. Thus, for ordinary subsonic flight, the pilot could control the aircraft through the elevator. But if the need arose, he could move the stabilizer as well as the elevator, in effect making the horizontal tail all-moving.[46] NACA likewise furnished Bell with a "very definite" location for the location of the horizontal stabilizer.[47] NACA believed that one of the principal difficulties facing the airplane in transonic flight would be impingement of the wing wake upon the horizontal tail surfaces. NACA asked Bell to place the horizontal tail as high as possible to position it above the wing wake. This resulted in Bell placing the horizontal stabilizer high on the vertical fin.[48]

Aside from general guidelines for the design of the airplane—for example, the type of propulsion, type of wing configuration, and desired performance goals and load factor—the Army wanted to give Bell complete freedom in designing the airplane. When the Army wrote up the XS-1 specification, therefore, it stipulated that the standard specifications for aircraft design would not apply to the design of the XS-1. This included the designers' "bible," the *Handbook of Instructions for Airplane Designers*, 8th Edition, July 1, 1936, commonly referred to as the "Handbook."[49] The Bell Aircraft Corporation design team had to develop a configuration that had enough excess power to pass quickly through the speed of sound, was strong enough to withstand transonic buffeting, and with more control power than conventional aircraft.[50]

Hamlin and Emmons, using the data they had accumulated on .50 cal. bullets, began design of the XS-1 aircraft. They decided to shape the fuselage just like the bullet. With this decision behind them, they next devoted attention to the design of the cockpit. From a drag standpoint, a protruding cockpit seemed undesirable. It would create a shock wave, and from a design standpoint it seemed a good idea at least to have a similar protrusion below the fuselage for symmetry. After serious consideration, Hamlin and Emmons decided to eliminate these protrusions from the airplane and incorporate a cockpit canopy mounted flush with the ogival surface of the nose. This led to yet another problem, this one from a pilot's standpoint. The flush canopy design furnished very poor forward visibility for the pilot on takeoff and landing. So Bell built a wooden cockpit mockup, and Hamlin and Emmons asked Bell test pilot Jack Woolams, XS-1 project pilot, to sit inside and decide whether he had sufficient visibility from the airplane on takeoff and landing. Woolams approved the canopy design, but Bell did modify the window shape to improve the visibility from the pilot's standpoint. The modifications did not change the ogival shape of the nose.[51]

Benson Hamlin considered the design of the XS-1's wings possibly the greatest difficulty that the Bell design team faced. Hamlin wanted to design the wings to a 7g load limit, but the requirements set forth by the NACA and the AAF stipulated an 18g loading. Since the XS-1 was to have two wing sections, one plane with 10 percent-thick wings and the other two with 8 percent-thick wings, Hamlin doubted that the required strength could be built into such thin wings.[52] On the final aircraft, Bell managed to incorporate the 18g load factor. The wing skins of the plane were exceptionally thick, tapering from ½ inch at the wing root to conventional thickness at the tip. The thick skins provided a stiff structure, as well as retaining accurate surface contours. The formation of the wing skins did prove difficult, however.[53]

Early in the design of the aircraft, Bell considered developing the first XS-1 with a conventional tail, and the second XS-1 with a Vee tail. NACA studies indicated that the Vee tail might alleviate the problems associated with wing wake interference on the horizontal tail surfaces. However, Bell dropped the Vee tail from consideration and decided to develop the airplanes with conventional tail surfaces. In conformance with Army wishes, Bell wanted to keep the aircraft as simple as possible, so that it could return information useful to conventional-type aircraft. For this reason Bell rejected other possible layouts—including canard configuration and wing sweep.[54]

One question that raised some disagreement among Bell engineers was whether to design the XS-1 for air launching. From the start, Benson Hamlin wanted to design the airplane with skids, so that a mother launch airplane could carry it aloft, launch it, and the pilot could fly the mission and then come in for a landing on the skids. Hamlin believed that air launching was the best way of getting high performance, since the rocket airplane would not need to consume rocket propellants during the climb to the 35,000-foot test altitude. He felt it unnecessary to design the airplane with a retractable landing gear, since the gear would occupy valuable space and contribute undesirable weight. Stanley and others agreed that the skid landing gear seemed the best technical approach.[55]

Robert J. Woods, however, disagreed. Woods was interested in the X-1 as a possible first step towards development of a manned rocket-propelled interceptor. He wanted to include a retractable landing gear so that the airplane could take off from the ground. At meetings with the NACA at Langley Field, Hamlin expressed his desire to incorporate a skid landing gear; Woods disagreed.[56] At the same time, a new factor entered the air launch controversy. This factor was the question of safe aircraft operation. Robert Stanley recognized that the first few seconds after takeoff would be extremely hazardous, inasmuch as the rocket plane would be heavily laden with a full fuel load, at low altitude, and at low airspeed. He recommended in discussions with Ezra Kotcher at Wright Field that the airplane be air launched from a mother launch plane, such as a Douglas C-54 Skymaster transport. Woods did not favor the launch aircraft idea, stating that it would not produce an operational-type airplane.[57] The controversy remained unresolved until arbitrated by the company president, Lawrence D. Bell.

Bell decided both in favor of a retractable landing gear and Stanley's arguments in favor of air launching the airplane. Bell transferred Woods to the company's corporate staff. Development of the XS-1 continued under Robert Stanley and Benson Hamlin. Robert Woods subsequently went to Germany after the surrender to examine the German aircraft industry for American air technical intelligence. The European mission removed him from the crucial detail design of the XS-1, which took place over the summer of 1945.[58]

Before it even flew, the Bell XS-1 program advanced aeronautical technology. It accomplished this by stimulating development of new wind-tunnel techniques. The principal reason behind the development of the XS-1 and D-558, of course, was the inability of existing wind tunnels to furnish satisfactory and reliable transonic aerodynamic data. But the development of the XS-1—and later the development of the D-558—stimulated the development of new methods of wind-tunnel research, particularly since both aircraft required the best knowledge available. Actually, the quest for better wind tunnels had begun about 1943 at the NACA's Langley Laboratory. In 1944, during one of John Stack's frequent visits to the Langley 16-foot wind tunnel, John V. Becker, head of the tunnel and holder of a B.S. in mechanical engineering from New York University, suggested using a "splitter plate" support system in the tunnel to permit accurate wing model testing to above Mach 0.9. This method furnished useful data for high-speed turbojet bomber development.[59]

In 1945, spurred on by the XS-1 and D-558 programs, Langley engineers hastened their efforts to develop satisfactory methods of transonic wind-tunnel research. Adopting Gilruth's wing-flow methods, wind-tunnel researchers constructed specially shaped plaster throats to generate accelerated flow. This method became known as the transonic bump technique. They also developed an entirely new method of testing model high-speed airplane configurations using special sting supports with internal balances. By using small models and the nonchoking sting support system, Langley engineers could test the XS-1 and D-558 almost up to the speed of sound. Thus, before the XS-1 flew, NACA engineers had new methods of acquiring data that went far beyond anything possible in the 1930s. Eventually, with the development of the slotted-throat wind tunnel, Langley engineers solved the transonic experimental problem on the ground, but with the stimulus of having the XS-1 and D-558 in the picture. Its design required sound development, which in turn added urgency to the efforts of ground researchers to develop adequate wind-tunnel techniques.[60]

By May 1945, Bell had the design of the XS-1 well in hand. Bell engineers had established the general configuration and layout of the aircraft, though detail design of the plane was not yet complete. The design team had already predicted the performance of the aircraft based on a launch weight of 13,034 lbs. and a fuel load of 8,160 lbs. The estimates were far beyond the performance capabilities of any existing aircraft. If ground launched, Bell estimated the airplane could attain 1,100 mph at approximately 65,000 feet. If air launched with the same 8,160 lb. fuel load, it could streak to over 1,600 mph at the same altitude.[61]

As originally planned, the XS-1 design featured two large cylindrical fuel tanks, one forward of the wing for liquid oxygen, and one aft of the wing for the alcohol. Bell planned to incorporate a turbine-driven fuel pump to feed the propellants to the engine. But now technical difficulties arose to threaten the whole XS-1 program. The Bell design team had long recognized that the turbopump was "one of the items most likely to interfere with the early flight of the airplane."[62] By late April, the turbopump was falling rapidly behind schedule. Robert Stanley realized that continued reliance upon the turbopump would necessitate delays in delivery of the aircraft and initiation of flight testing. Rather than risk delay, Stanley decided to drop, at least temporarily, the proposed turbopump installation. Instead, Bell would install a pressurized fuel system, in which high pressure gas forced the liquid oxygen and alcohol into the engine under pressure. The AAF received notice of the Bell decision on May 3, 1945.[63]

The decision to switch to a pressurized fuel system automatically necessitated air launching the aircraft. Whereas previously air launching had emerged primarily as a safety consideration, now it became a necessity because of a marked decrease in the XS-1's estimated performance. The decision to use a pressurized fuel system necessitated storing a pressurized gas under high pressure to force the fuel into the rocket engine. Bell selected nitrogen for the pressurized system, requiring nitrogen storage tanks. Since the fuel tanks holding the liquid oxygen and alcohol now required pressurization to expel their contents into the engine, they had to be constructed to withstand the pressure. This necessitated that they be of spherical shape rather than cylindrical shape, with extremely thick strong tank skins. Likewise, the nitrogen gas had to be stored in spherical high-pressure storage bottles. The effect of the pressurized fuel system decision upon the XS-1's design was twofold. The landing weight jumped by one ton, and the volumetric reduction in available propellants—caused by the nitrogen bottles and spherical propellant tanks, both of which took up or wasted space—reduced the fuel load from a maximum of 8,160 lbs. to 4,680 lbs. This cut engine time from 4.1 to 2.5 minutes.[64]

If the XS-1 now flew from the ground, the smaller fuel load gave the plane only subsonic performance, thus not meeting the contract requirements. Air launching now became an absolute necessity.[65] With air launching, Bell estimated that the airplane could attain just over 900 mph at 50,000 feet. Absolute ceiling dropped from around 140,000 feet to 87,750 feet. Both airspeed and altitude capabilities were still well within those desired by the NACA and the Air Force, and still remained about double those of existing aircraft. However, to attain this performance, the XS-1 had to be air launched. Any thought of going back to ground takeoff would mean that the aircraft could not fulfill its design mission of transonic-flight research.[66]

Subsequent events proved Stanley's decision to utilize a pressurized fuel system as sound. Bell decided to complete the first two XS-1 aircraft with the pressurized fuel system, but delay completion of the third XS-1 until a low-pressure turbopump installation could be incorporated. Eventually, the third aircraft, the X-1-3, emerged in mid-1951 with a turbopump installation. It featured much higher performance capabilities than its two sister ships, but development of a reliable turbopump had consumed five years of research. By the time the X-1-3 entered flight testing, the original two MX-653 aircraft were grounded, their flight test programs complete.[67]

By August 1, 1945, design team members had completed detail design of the aircraft.[68] During early discussions with AAF representatives, a question had arisen on the availability of a suitable launch aircraft while the war raged on. The AAF needed every available Boeing B-29A Superfortress bomber—the first choice for launch aircraft by Stanley and Hamlin—and the second choice, the Douglas C-54 Skymaster transport, was in demand by the AAF Air Transport Command. But when the two atomic bombs and the subsequent Japanese surrender ended the war in the Pacific, the problem of securing a suitable launch aircraft disappeared amid the hundreds of B-29's returning to the United States for scrap or storage.[69]

The smooth bullet contours of the XS-1 design hid an extremely crowded fuselage. The fuselage contained 2 propellant tanks, 12 nitrogen spheres, the pilot's pressurized cockpit, 3 pressure regulators, a retractable landing gear, the wing carry-through structure, the rocket engine, and the flight research instrumentation. It was of semi-monocoque 24ST aluminum construction. Ahead of the XS-1's wing was the spherical liquid oxygen tank. It could hold 311 gallons—2,920 lbs.—of the supercold liquid. Bell designed it of annealed stainless steel 3/16 inch thick to avoid the danger of embrittlement at −300° F. and to withstand an internal pressure of approximately 350 psi. The alcohol tank, designed to hold 293 gallons—2,100 lbs.—of fuel, did not have to withstand the same low temperatures as the liquid oxygen tank, so Bell designed it from normalized SAE 4130 steel, with a wall thickness of ⅛ inch. To prevent fuel sloshing from affecting the plane's center of gravity location, Bell engineers designed the tanks with transverse baffles inside the tanks.[70]

The nitrogen pressurization system gave the Bell design team the greatest difficulty in design. Engineers discovered that liquid oxygen readily absorbed gaseous nitrogen. This meant that Bell had to design the nitrogen system for a higher pressure in order to ensure that the XS-1 had sufficient nitrogen on board to force the liquid oxygen and alcohol into the rocket engine. The design team found it necessary to incorporate a 4,500 psi storage pressure. Bell designed sufficient tankage to contain 17.5 cubic feet of nitrogen at 4,500 psi, a total of 301 lbs. Engineers stored the nitrogen in 12 pressure spheres scattered throughout the fuselage, their location depending on available internal space. Bell planned to fabricate the spheres from steel ranging in thicknesses from ¼ to ⅝ inches depending on the size of the tank. Engineers placed one nitrogen sphere directly ahead of the cockpit, clustered 7 in a ring behind the cockpit and in front of the liquid oxygen tank, installed 2 more below the wing behind the liquid oxygen tank, and placed 2 behind the alcohol tank.[71]

Engineers designed a common manifold system connecting the 12 nitrogen storage vessels together, using welded high-pressure joints rather than detachable fittings in order to prevent leakage. They incorporated 3 pressure regulators in the aircraft to reduce the 4,500 psi source pressure to usable levels. The regulator development posed additional design difficulties due to the extreme pressure and low temperature requirements that the system had to satisfy. One regulator reduced the 4,500 psi source pressure to 1,500 psi for operation of the landing gear and wing flaps, simplifying operation of the airplane and removing the need to incorporate batteries or hydraulic pumps for these functions. Two other regulators each reduced the 4,500 psi source pressure to 340 psi before it entered the propellant tanks to pressurize the propellants. The XS-1 pilot could control the 3 regulators from the rocket airplane's cockpit.[72]

Adding to the difficulties of designing the nitrogen pressurization system was the fact that nitrogen is sold commercially in cylinders at no more than 2,200 psi pressure. Bell had to have nitrogen at twice this pressure. The gas had to be uncontaminated by oil droplets, or else Bell ran the risk of having an explosion when the contaminated nitrogen mixed with the liquid oxygen. The requirement for pure nitrogen ruled out existing methods of deriving pressurized nitrogen. Bell engineer Lloyd Bevin solved the problem by developing a nitrogen evaporator. The evaporator boiled off liquid nitrogen as a high pressure gas. Liquid nitrogen passed out of a 36-inch sphere, then boiled off as a gas that could be piped into the plane's nitrogen tanks at the requisite 4,500 psi pressure. The 36-inch sphere, heart of the evaporator unit, consisted of two hemispheres fabricated from 3-inch-thick stainless steel. Bell technicians hydrostatically tested the sphere to 9,000 psi. During tests with nitrogen, engineers noted liquid dropping from the frosted lines through which the liquid nitrogen flowed. They puzzled over the phenomenon before discovering that the cold nitrogen lines were condensing liquid oxygen out of the air.[73]

Interestingly, the Bell XS-1 design team also used nitrogen pressurization to pressurize the cockpit. This required that the pilot wear an oxygen mask at all times while flying the airplane. Bell designed the airplane to maintain an internal pressure of 3 psi above the atmospheric pressure in order to ensure the safety of the pilot at high altitude. The pressure cabin of the airplane leaked no greater than 1 psi per hour, a completely satisfactory figure in light of the planned short duration of the XS-1 flights. Before launch from the B-29, the rocket pilot would enter the XS-1 through a small hatch located on the right side of the fuselage nose. An assistant would lock the hatch panel itself in place, sealing the XS-1 cabin pressurization.[74]

The XS-1 design contained a number of other interesting features besides the pressurization system. One was the thin wing planform, whether of 8 percent thickness-chord ratio or of 10 percent thickness-chord ratio. The 8 percent wing was only 5.94 inches thick at the wing root, and the 10 percent wing but little larger at 7.42 inches. It was difficult enough for Bell to design such a thin wing in 1945, particularly for an 18g load factor. The NACA further complicated the task by asking Bell to cut 240 pressure orifices and install 12 strain gauges in the left wing to acquire pressure distribution and air loads information. The construction of the wings with their heavy milled aluminum wing skins was a laborious task, more easily said than done. As might be expected, the thicker 10 percent wings were ready before the thinner 8 percent wings.[75]

Bell did not boost the control surfaces, for design-team members felt that the small size of the airplane made high stick forces unlikely. The adjustable horizontal stabilizer Bell designed for the airplane could move through an angle of 15° at a rate of 1° per second if needed for transonic control to overcome rapid trim changes. An electric motor operated a screw jack to change the angle of attack of the stabilizer. Instead of incorporating a traditional fighter-type control stick, the team designed the XS-1 to use a control wheel, a method more commonly employed on bombers or transports. Bell incorporated the wheel control so that, if the need arose, the pilot could use both hands on .the wheel for greater effectiveness. Accordingly, engineers installed all the major controls— thrust selector, instrumentation switches, stabilizer control, and power shutoff—on the control wheel so that the pilot could operate them without taking his hands from the wheel.[76]

After completing design of the airplane, Bell engineers constructed a wooden mockup of the proposed airplane, showing the internal structure of the XS-1 and serving as a check on the engineering drawings. On October 10, 1945, Bell held the mockup inspection on the design, with representatives of the AAF Air Technical Service Command and NACA attending. No major changes resulted from this inspection, though Bell engineers believe some minor technical changes in the design may have occurred as a result of mockup inspection comments.[77] The mockup inspectors approved the design; the Bell company now turned to fabricating the airplanes, virtually handcrafting each one.

Just as Bell began construction on the XS-1s, interest in sweptwings reached a height following the discovery of sweptwing research in Germany. It had a side effect upon the XS-1: some individuals criticized NACA for not recommending wing sweep on the rocket airplane, and Bell engineers studied a possible sweptwing modification of the basic XS-1 design. Robert Stanley called Benson Hamlin from Wright Field one day, and asked him to start work immediately on a sweptwing version of the XS-1. Try as he might Hamlin could not develop a workable swept version, for the sweptwings created an entirely new center wing section—to say nothing of the plane's completely new aerodynamic characteristics— and necessitated rearrangement of the propellant system. He continued his abortive attempt to modify the XS-1 until it became obvious that the task was impossible. He told Stanley that Bell would have to develop an altogether new aircraft from the start. Bell decided to approach the AAF on an entirely new aircraft, featuring rocket propulsion, air-launch capability, and a sweptwing planform. This ultimately resulted in the development of the supersonic X-2.[78]

By mid-December 1945, the airframe of the first XS-1 neared completion. The AAF had assigned a block of serials for the three aircraft; the first was 46-062, the second 46-063, and the third 46-064. Reaction Motors, Incorporated, did not have the first of the 6000C4 rocket engines —Army designation XLR-11—ready for installation in the airplanes, so Bell completed the XS-1 #1, serial 46-062, without the engine. Technicians then painted the bare aluminum aircraft a gleaming yellow-orange, stenciling "6062" in black on the vertical fin above the horizontal stabilizer. On December 27, 1945, the Bell XS-1 #1 rolled out of the Bell plant, looking like a long sleek orange bullet with thin knife wings.[79] From the nose jutted a long pitot tube for the pilot's instruments. Another airspeed head for the research instrumentation emerged from the left wing tip, while a boom from the right wing tip supported a sideslip angle transmitter.

Though the XS-1 had a generally conventional planform, it displayed a marked contrast to the propeller-driven Bell P-39 and P-63 fighters, and even the turbojet P-59 and P-83. All of its smoothly flowing lines bespoke of hidden power and speed, an effect heightened by the low-slung position the plane assumed on its tricycle landing gear. The coming weeks would witness whether or not the plane fulfilled its promise. Indeed, just the conception and construction of the XS-1 had provided challenge enough, as one Bell engineer later recalled:

> It required an unhesitating boldness to undertake a venture so few thought could succeed, an almost exuberant enthusiasm to carry across the many obstacles and unknowns, but most of all a completely unprejudiced imagination in departing so drastically from the known way.[80]

Meanwhile, 2,000 miles from Buffalo, a group of equally dedicated and imaginative Douglas Aircraft Company engineers in California were busy developing another transonic research airplane, this one for the Navy. The project's company designation was D-558. Unlike Bell's rocket speedster, the "558" had turbojet propulsion, and took off from the ground.

NOTES

1. *Aeronautical Engineering Review*, XVI, No. 1 (January 1957), p. 21. Also, Bell biographical file, NASM.

2. *Ibid.*

3. *Aeronautical Engineering Review*, XVI, No. 1, (January 1957), p. 22, Works Projects Administration, *Who's Who in Aviation, 1942–1943* (New York, 1942), p. 475.

4. Stack interview, 19 May 1971.

5. See note 3.

6. Letter, Robert A. Wolf to author, 4 April 1972.

7. Kotcher letter to Lundgren, 4 Nov. 1953.

8. Letter, Ezra Kotcher to author, 22 Feb. 1972.

9. Lundgren, *Across the High Frontier*, p. 33.

10. Kotcher statement at AIAA History Session, 28 July 1965.

11. Lundgren, *Across the High Frontier*, p. 33.

12. Kotcher statement at AIAA History Session, 28 July 1965. Also letter, Kotcher to Lundgren, 4 Nov. 1953.

13. Letter and recording, Benson Hamlin to author, 19 April 1972.

14. Winfield Scott Downs, *Who's Who in Engineering, 1948* (New York, 1948), p. 1887. Also, *Who's Who in Aviation, 1942–1943*, p. 408.

15. Downs, *Who's Who in Engineering, 1948*, p. 820.

16. *Ibid.*, pp. 1851–52.

17. Eugene M. Emme, *Aeronautics and Astronautics: An American Chronology of Science and Technology in the Exploration of Space, 1915–1960* (Washington, D.C., 1961), p. 49.

18. NACA LMAL, "Estimate of Instrument Requirements for Experimental Airplane," Dec. 27, 1944. In Langley Research Center files (Hereafter cited LaRC files).

19. Lundgren, *Across the High Frontier*, pp. 34–35. In the XP-79, the pilot flew the plane from the prone position. The AAF Aeromedical Laboratory at Wright Field concluded that the prone position would enable the pilot of the XP-79 to best withstand the expected 12g accelerations he would experience.

20. Apparently the AAF, NACA, and Bell independently arrived at the 18g figure. Lt. Col. Carl Reichert of the Aircraft Laboratory derived the figure for the AAF. Stack suggested it to the NACA. At Bell, the same figure was arrived at "pseudo-scientifically," according to former XS-1 personnel. See Walter T. Bonney, "The Research Airplane," *Pegasus*, XVIII, No. 6, (June 1952), 1–16. See also Stack interview, 19 May 1971. Letter and recording, Benson Hamlin to author, 19 April 1972. Letter, Robert M. Stanley to author, 1 March 1972. Letter, Paul Emmons to author, 31 May 1972.

21. Lundgren, *Across the High Frontier*, p. 33. It is unclear whether MX-524 referred only to the proposed Bell research aircraft or to high-speed flight in general. Ezra Kotcher attended a conference in June 1945 under MX-524 to discuss a Lockheed P-80 test program. Yet the development project designation for the P-80 was MX-409. Additionally, by this time (June '45) the XS-1 was being developed under project designation MX-653. Letter, Ezra Kotcher to author, 7 Nov. 1971.

22. Letter and recording, Benson Hamlin to author, 19 April 1972.

23. *Ibid.* Schlieren photographs are taken by a process in which the differing refractive properties of varying air densities are used to show shockwave formation and flow patterns. The term Schlieren is from the German *Schliere*, meaning a flaw or streak in glass.

24. *Ibid.*

25. Quoted in "Beginnings of the X-1," p. 6.

26. Letter and recording, Benson Hamlin to author, 19 April 1972. R. M. Stanley and R. J. Sandstrom, "Development of the XS-1 Airplane," in *Air Force Supersonic Research Airplane XS-1 Report No. 1*, 9 January 1948, pp. 7–8. An earlier version of the Stanley and Sandstrom article appeared in the IAS journal. See R. M. Stanley and R. J. Sandstrom, "Development of the XS-1 Supersonic Research Airplane," *Aeronautical Engineering Review*, VI, No. 8, (August 1947), 22–26, 72. It is not as complete (presumably for security reasons) as the later version.

27. Letter and recording, Benson Hamlin to author, 19 April 1972.

28. *Ibid.*

29. Stanley and Sandstrom, "Development of the XS-1 Airplane," 9 January 1948, p. 7.

30. Letter, Robert Gilruth to author, 27 Jan. 1972. Letter, Robert Stanley to author, 1 March 1972. Thompson interview, 31 May 1972. Also Shortal, *History of Wallops Station: Origins and Activities Through 1949*, p. 13. Shortal states that Langley completed specifications for the Bell transonic aircraft in January 1945.

31. Letter and recording, Benson Hamlin to author, 19 April 1972.

32. Letter, Kotcher to Lundgren, 4 Nov. 1953.

33. George F. Bush, "Early American Rockets," *Aerospace Historian*, XVI, No. 4, (Winter 1969), 28–32.

34. Perry, "The Ancestors of the X-1," p. 24. Also statement of Edward N. Seymour at AIAA History Session, San Francisco, Calif., 28 July 1965, NASA Historical Archives.

35. Lloyd Mallan, *Men, Rockets and Space Rats* (New York, 1958), pp. 23–24. This engine, however, was not being developed for the D-558-2. The D-558-2 was not conceived until August 1945, and not developed until 1946.

36. Emme, *Aeronautics and Astronautics*, p. 43.

37. John Shesta, "RMI's Rocket Engine Which Powers Supersonic XS-1," *Aviation*, XLVI, No. 1, (January 1947), 44–46.

38. Mallan, *Men, Rockets and Space Rats*, p. 25.

39. Letter and recording, Benson Hamlin to author, 19 April 1972. Also Lundgren, *Across the High Frontier*, pp. 69, 159–60.

40. Stanley and Sandstrom, "Development of the XS-1 Airplane," 9 January 1948, p. 10.

41. Air Materiel Command, Correspondence Summary of Project MX-653 History, 14 Jan. 1947, p. 1. Transmitted to author by Ezra Kotcher.

42. Date from *Air Force Supersonic Research Airplane XS-1 Report No. 1*, p. 5.

43. Letter, Ezra Kotcher to author, 7 Nov. 1971. Also, letter, Robert T. Jones to Ernest O. Pearson, Jr., 2 Feb. 1960; Navy Department Record of Invention, 10 April 1946; Robert T. Jones, "The Shaping of Wings to Minimize the Formation of Shock Waves," 27 Feb. 1945; Robert T. Jones, Memo for Chief of Research (Lewis), 5 March 1945. All in NASA Historical Archives.

44. Letter, Ezra Kotcher to author, 7 Nov. 1971. Kotcher statement at AIAA History Session, 28 July 1965. The need for a separate sweptwing research aircraft led to the Bell XS-2 (X-2).

The discovery of wholesale sweptwing research in Germany contributed to a feeling that the straight wing configuration was obsolete. This thinking pervaded both the Army and the NACA immediately after the war. Interestingly, some AAF officials later regretted that the AAF had not obtained sweptwing data in time to change the design of the XS-1. Brig. Gen. Alden R. Crawford, Chief, Production Division, AAF, wrote Dr. Jerome Hunsaker, NACA Chairman, on 24 Oct. 1945 stating that the NACA's withholding of sweptback information that could have resulted in a sweptwing XS-1 design delayed the XP-86 and XB-47 programs. Langley Assistant Chief of Research Floyd L. Thompson replied that at the time the sweptwing planform had not been experimentally verified and to recommend a sweptwing configuration on the XS-1 might have resulted in a "blunder of the greatest magnitude." See Shortal, *History of Wallops Station: Origins and Activities Through 1949*, p. 74A.

45. Stack statement at AIAA History Session, 28 July 1965.

46. *Ibid.*

47. Letter and recording, Benson Hamlin to author, 19 April 1972.

48. *Ibid.*, also Stanley and Sandstrom, "Development of the XS-1 Airplane," 9 January 1948, p. 7.

49. Kotcher statement at AIAA History Session, 28 July 1965. Also Bell Aircraft Corporation specification for XS-1 Airplane, prepared by Benson Hamlin, 1 March 1945, Report 44-947-001, p. 1. Transmitted to author by Ezra Kotcher, 21 Aug. 1971.

50. J. van Lonkhuyzen, "Problems Faced in Designing Famed X-1," *Aviation Week*, LIV, No. 1, (Jan. 1, 1951), 22–24.

51. Letter and recording, Benson Hamlin to author, 19 April 1972.

52. *Ibid.*

53. Stanley and Sandstrom, "Development of the XS-1 Airplane," 9 January 1948, p. 14. Letter, Paul Emmons to author, 31 May 1972.

54. Letter and recording, Benson Hamlin to author, 19 April 1972. Stanley and Sandstrom, "Development of the XS-1 Airplane," 9 January 1948, p. 7. The Vee tail held favor in the mid-1940s as a method of retaining control at high speeds. For example, the Ellis-Brown Campini aircraft featured a Vee tail. NACA also conducted wind-tunnel studies of a model of Republic's proposed XF-91 featuring a Vee tail.

55. Letter and recording, Benson Hamlin to author, 19 April 1972.

56. *Ibid.*

57. Kotcher statement at AIAA History Session, 28 July 1965. Also Kotcher letter to Lundgren, 4 Nov. 1953.

58. *Ibid.*, also letter, Robert M. Stanley to author, 1 March 1972; letter and recording, Benson Hamlin to author, 19 April 1972. While in Germany, Woods headed an air technical intelligence team that investigated the Messerschmitt Oberammergau research facility. He discovered the incomplete Messerschmitt P.1101 developed by Dr. Woldemar Voigt, and subsequently shipped it to the United States. The P.1101 provided an inspiration for Woods' later variable-geometry research. It served as a static test article for the later Bell X-5 variable-sweep aircraft, which it inspired. See Robert Perry, "Variable Sweep: A Case History of Multiple Re-Innovation," RAND study P-3459, October 1966, pp. 3–6.

59. Interview with John V. Becker, 12 Nov. 1971. Also memo, J. V. Becker to Langley Assistant Director for Administration, 16 May 1968, transmitted to the author Nov. 1971.

60. Becker interview, 12 Nov. 1971. In addition to wind-tunnel research, however, one of the principal sources of information on the XS-1 and D-558 designs came from wing-flow tests of wing and body shapes. Letter, Robert R. Gilruth to author, 27 Jan. 1972. Also, interviews with Axel T. Mattson, 10 Nov. 1971 and 6 June 1972. The first sting support systems used external balances, which were not sensitive enough for the small models. This spurred development of internal balances. Mattson ran tests using the sting support system and a special plaster throat in the 8-foot high-speed tunnel. He could test to above Mach 0.9, then jump to Mach 1.2.

61. Stanley and Sandstrom, "Development of the XS-1 Airplane," 9 January 1948, p. 10, Figure 6.

62. Stanley and Sandstrom, "Development of the XS-1 Airplane," 9 Jaunary 1948, p. 11.

63. *Ibid.* Also letter, Robert M. Stanley to author, 1 March 1972. Air Materiel Command, Correspondence Summary of Project MX-653 History, 14 Jan. 1947, p. 2. Transmitted to author by Ezra Kotcher.

64. Stanley and Sandstrom, "Development of the XS-1 Airplane," 9 January 1948, pp. 11–14. Also interview of Richard Frost by the author, 25 May 1972.

65. *Ibid.*

66. Stanley and Sandstrom, "Development of the XS-1 Airplane," 9 January 1948, pp. 4, 9, 11, 12.

67. The X-1-3 was lost on November 9, 1951 during a ground explosion and fire. It had not yet begun powered flight tests. The second of the original XS-1's, the X-1 #2, was grounded awaiting replacement of its propellant tanks. The loss of the X-1-3, together with the loss of the X-1D two months earlier, served as the catalyst for modifying the X-1 #2 as the X-1E.

68. Date from information supplied to NASM. Found in X-1 Series #2 File, NASM.

69. Stanley and Sandstrom, "Development of the XS-1 Airplane," 9 January 1948, p. 9.

70. *Ibid.*, pp. 11–13. Also Robert McLarren, "XS-1: Design and Development," *Aviation Week*, XLIX, No. 4, (July 26, 1948), 22–27.

71. *Ibid.*, (Stanley and Sandstrom), pp. 3, 4, 13.

72. *Ibid.*, p. 13.

73. *Ibid.*, pp. 13–14. Also McLarren, "XS-1: Design and Development," p. 26.

74. *Ibid.* This use of nitrogen to pressurize the cockpit nearly led to the loss of the X-1 #1 in 1949, when the pilot plugged his oxygen mask into the nitrogen outlet rather than oxygen outlet. He was able to rectify the error before he passed out from lack of oxygen.

75. Letter, Robert M. Stanley to author, 1 March 1972. Letter, Paul Emmons to author, 31 May 1972.

76. Letter and recording, Benson Hamlin to author, 19 April 1972. Stanley and Sandstrom, "Development of the XS-1 Airplane," pp. 7, 14–15.

77. Letter and recording, Benson Hamlin to author, 19 April 1972. Letter, Paul Emmons to author, 31 May 1972. Letter, Robert M. Stanley to author, 1 March 1972. Also *Air Force Supersonic Research Airplane XS-1 Report No. 1*, p. 5.

78. Letter and recording, Benson Hamlin to author, 19 April 1972. The boldness of this conception can be seen in the design goal of Bell's proposal. The company estimated Mach 3 speed. The ultimate planned research mission of the aircraft became aerodynamic heating. The X-2 did not make a powered flight until 1955, having been delayed seven years due to developmental difficulties, especially with the Curtiss-Wright XLR-25-CW-1 15,000-lb-thrust engine. On September 27, 1956, it became the first piloted aircraft to exceed Mach 3, but on the same flight it went out of control and crashed, killing the pilot, Capt. Milburn G. Apt, USAF.

79. Date from information supplied to NASM. Found in X-1 Series #2 File, NASM.

80. J. van Lonkhuyzen, "Problems Faced in Designing Famed X-1," p. 22.

CHAPTER

III

THE DESIGN
DEVELOPMENT
OF THE DOUGLAS D-558

Abraham Hyatt's September 1944 memorandum recommending procurement of a Navy-sponsored transonic research airplane had crystallized the sentiments expressed in the Navy's March 1944 meeting with the NACA at Langley Laboratory that the research necessary for development of high-speed aircraft and missiles required procurement of a special transonic research airplane. In mid-December 1944, Comdr. Emerson Conlon of the Bureau of Aeronautics' Structures Branch drafted a letter to the NACA asking for more high-speed aerodynamic data. Capt. Walter S. Diehl, a supporter of the research airplane concept since 1942, added two paragraphs asking that the NACA give high priority to a long list of projects including a new test station at Wallops Island, Virginia, a new 6-foot supersonic wind tunnel, and a research airplane. The letter, which the Bureau of Aeronautics sent on December 19, 1944, informed the NACA that the Bureau of Aeronautics believed that procurement of a research airplane should be expedited, and that the Navy would take steps to procure the aircraft once the

Bureau of Aeronautics had received drawings and specifications from the NACA. The BuAer request came three days after Hitler threw three armies into Belgium and Luxembourg, opening the last great German offensive of the war, the Battle of the Bulge. The suddenly worsening war situation "brought forth orders to BuAer to leave no stone unturned in the development of new and improved weapons."[1]

In March 1944, the Navy and NACA had agreed to detach NACA engineer Milton Davidson from Langley Laboratory to Washington to work with Ivan Driggs in the Bureau of Aeronautics on the preparation of specifications for a proposed transonic research aircraft. Fighting a global war, the Navy did not think it could justify a pure research aircraft, while the NACA was research minded. Davidson disclosed to other NACA engineers that the Navy favored an aircraft capable of meeting military requirements. NACA favored turbojet propulsion and, like the later XS-1, a 500-lb instrument package. Additionally, NACA engineers felt that the plane should be as efficient aerodynamically as possible. NACA felt that the plane should have a simple nose intake for the turbojet engine. The Navy, on the other hand, favored side inlets so as to free the nose for a possible armament installation.[2]

One of the prime contractors for naval aircraft was the Douglas Aircraft Corporation of California, under the leadership of Donald W. Douglas. Douglas had attended the U.S. Naval Academy, but transferred to the Massachusetts Institute of Technology, receiving a B.S. in aeronautical engineering in 1914. In 1916, he joined the Martin company, hired by Lawrence D. Bell. After serving as chief civilian engineer with the U.S. Signal Corps during the First World War, he formed the Douglas Aircraft Corporation in 1920. Since then the company had designed a number of notable airplanes, including the World Cruisers that had flown around the world in 1924, the DC-2 and DC-3 transports, and the A-20 attack bomber. During the Second World War, the company turned out over 10,000 C-47 Skytrain transports, military versions of the DC-3, as well as over 6,000 A-20 Havocs, 5,500 SBD Navy dive bombers, as well as producing B-17's and B-24's designed by Boeing and Consolidated-Vultee. Some of the company's aircraft became almost legendary. One such was the DC-3/C-47 series of transports, which, by 1945, were serving in every war theater as the logistics backbone of the Air Transport Command.

Another was the SBD dive bomber. It was the SBD that had presented the United States with its victorious turning point in the Pacific war, the Battle of Midway. Singlehandedly, SBD's from the carriers *Enterprise, Hornet,* and *Yorktown* sunk the core of Japan's naval strength, the four carriers *Akagi, Kaga, Soryu,* and *Hiryu,* as well as the cruiser *Mikuma.* The Japanese never recovered from the shock of the loss, particularly in the loss of well-trained and combat-tested naval airmen. Since that epochal battle in June 1942, the SBD's had continued to serve as the key naval air weapon. So efficient was this aircraft, that naval dive bomber squadrons displayed a marked preference for it over its chosen successor, the Curtiss SB2C Helldiver.

The secret of Douglas' success as an aircraft manufacturer lay in the high-quality engineers and designers that the firm employed. One such individual was Leonard Eugene Root, holder of M.S. degrees in mechanical and aeronautical engineering from the California Institute of Technology. After graduation from Caltech, L. Eugene Root joined Douglas as assistant chief of the aerodynamics section at Douglas' Santa Monica plant, working under Dr. W. Bailey Oswald. In 1939, he became chief of the aerodynamics section at the Douglas El Segundo plant, working under the plant's chief engineer, Edward H. Heinemann.[3]

For many years, Douglas had been a contractor of naval dive bombers and by 1944 the company realized that the high speeds attained by new combat designs in dives, particularly turbojet aircraft, made it possible for aircraft to encounter severe compressibility effects, particularly general instability and control reversal. Like the Army, Navy, NACA, and Bell, the Douglas engineers felt it desirable to have an aircraft capable of exploring in level flight the high-speed range expected to be encountered in the future by new aircraft designs.[4] Since 1941, when the Army first asked Douglas to study supersonic flight, the company had evaluated high-speed aerodynamics, principally under the direction of Frank N. Fleming of the Douglas Santa Monica Division. In 1944, the company held several conferences with representatives of the AAF Air Technical Service Command on the general aspects of supersonic flight.[5]

As part of his duties at Douglas El Segundo, L. Eugene Root consulted with the NACA, AAF, and Navy to obtain ideas on what areas of aeronautics to develop next. On one trip to Washington late in 1944, Root dropped in on the Bureau of Aeronautics to visit with Capt. Walter S. Diehl, Ivan Driggs, Abraham Hyatt, and Comdr. Bill Sweeney. Sweeney, a Caltech alumnus and old friend of Root's, headed up the Bureau of Aeronautics' VF (Fighter) Desk. During the discussion, Sweeney reached into a drawer and pulled out a very preliminary research airplane specification that Driggs, Hyatt, and Sweeney were studying. He asked Root if Douglas would be interested in working on it. "I said, 'You bet,'" Root later reminisced, "grabbed it, and ran with it."[6]

Back at El Segundo, Root broached the Navy study to chief engineer Edward H. Heinemann, Leo J. Devlin, A. M. O. Smith, and Robert C. Donovan. Heinemann, after serving as a draftsman with Douglas and the International Aircraft Corporation in the 1920's, went with Northrop Aircraft as a design engineer, then with Douglas El Segundo in 1932. In 1936, he became chief engineer of the El Segundo plant and supervised the design of the A-20 and A-26 attack bombers

Douglas D 558 Configuration with Straight Wings and Tail

and the Navy SBD Dauntless. Devlin held a M.E. in aero engineering from Stanford University and was a member of the NACA aerodynamics committee. A. M. O. Smith, while a graduate student at Caltech, belonged to the original Caltech rocket research group of Frank Malina, Weld Arnold, John Parsons, Edward Forman, and Hsue-Shen Tsien. Then he left for Douglas, but in 1942 joined Aerojet as chief engineer, staying until 1944 when he rejoined Douglas as assistant aerodynamicist at El Segundo under L. Eugene Root. Robert C. Donovan, a former associate with Ben O. Howard in the design of racing planes, had served as project engineer on the Douglas XA-26 Invader attack bomber development program.[7]

Navy and NACA specifications for the airplane did not constitute design requirements as much as general guidelines for Douglas to follow in designing their aircraft. Like Bell and the AAF, the Navy specifications generally allowed Douglas a free hand in the design. The general guidelines stipulated that the airplane should not be designed as a combat or service type, that it should be capable of taking off and landing under its own power and have such good low-speed handling characteristics that data gained from its flight program could be directly applied to the design of combat aircraft, that the aircraft should be manned and capable of carrying 500 lbs. of research instrumentation, and that it should be able to attain the maximum velocity possible using available powerplants.[8]

The Douglas El Segundo plant decided to develop a tentative design for the aircraft and submit it to the Navy for approval. Heinemann headed up the design effort, with Leo Devlin as his assistant. L. Eugene Root served as head of the aerodynamics department, with A. M. O. Smith as project aerodynamicist. Donovan acted as project engineer.[9] The team favored a small airplane "wrapped . . . around the largest engine we could find."[10] A. M. O. Smith, in charge of establishing the general planform and appearance of the airplane, selected three wing configurations for test.[11] The basic wing section was a NACA 65-110 airfoil with a 10 percent thickness-chord ratio, but two other sections chosen for the design were a NACA 16-008 section at the root tapering from 8 percent thickness-chord ratio to a 6 percent thickness-chord ratio NACA 16-006 section at the wing tip, and a NACA 2417 airfoil at the root (17 percent thickness-chord ratio) to a NACA 2413 airfoil at the wing tip (13 percent thickness-chord ratio).[12]

The design team decided to incorporate a General Electric TG-180 turbojet—then under development for the AAF—as the basic engine for the planes. Team members felt that the Navy should procure six aircraft, equipped with various wings and engine duct configurations. These six aircraft could acquire aerodynamic data in level flight to approximately Mach 0.89. Then, at a later time, Douglas would install Westinghouse 24C turbojets and supplementary rocket propulsion units in two of the aircraft and fly them at level flight speeds approaching Mach 1.[13] Because of then-current interest in flush and semiflush air intakes, the team configured the basic airplane with a semiflush air intake with an alternate arrangement where the airplane had a simple nose intake.[14]

Douglas gave the proposed airplane the designation Douglas Model 558 High Speed Test Airplane, referring to its company development number. Early in January 1945, Douglas engineer Robert G. Smith, a talented aeronautical artist as well as designer, laid out and drew up the preliminary design of the aircraft.[15] The design spanned 25 ft., with a length of 35 ft. The fuselage was just large enough to fit around a TG-180 turbojet, which obtained its air supply from two semiflush intakes located on either side of the fuselage just aft of the cockpit. The pilot sat ahead of the engine with a small semibubble canopy protruding slightly above the fuselage for vision. The instrument payload was ahead of the cockpit section, and the nose tapered down to a bullet point. The straight wing had pronounced dihedral and emerged low from the fuselage sides. The design featured a conventional tail assembly, with the horizontal stabilizer located roughly in line with the top of the fuselage.[16]

The Douglas company transmitted preliminary engineering proposals to the Bureau of Aeronautics and the NACA in early February 1945. A. M. O. Smith and Leo Devlin then journeyed to Washington and attended several conferences chaired by Comdr. Emerson Conlon where they presented the Douglas proposal. At the second conference, they discussed the availability of the AAF-developed TG-180 to the Navy and its development status. Four days later, at the third conference, February 28, 1945, Smith and Devlin met with the Navy and with John Stack and Milton Davidson of the NACA and again discussed the proposed Model 558 airplane. Smith and Devlin stated that Douglas could submit the first airplanes with TG-180 engines, nose and side intakes, airbrakes, and 10 percent thickness-chord ratio wings. As a second step, the company could submit a new airplane for Mach 1 performance. Douglas company pilots would demonstrate both the Mach 0.89 and Mach 1 aircraft. The Navy and NACA responded that Douglas should demonstrate the aircraft to its maximum level flight speed, and a structural loading of 8g at a lower Mach number.[17]

Early in March 1945, the NACA replied to the Navy's December 19, 1944, letter in which the Bureau of Aeronautics requested that NACA submit drawings and specifications for a transonic research airplane so that the Navy could expedite procurement of such an aircraft. The NACA recommended that the Navy procure the Douglas D-558 proposal in both its turbojet and turbojet-rocket forms. The committee letter further stated:

> The Committee is certain that the procurement of these two models of high-speed research airplanes will permit making a large advance in aerodynamic knowledge in the transonic region of flight and every attempt should be made to make these airplanes available to the NACA for flight research as soon as possible.[18]

Slightly over a month later, on April 13, 1945, Douglas submitted a contract proposal to the Bureau of Aeronautics outlining a three-phase development program. In the first phase, Douglas would construct six TG-180-powered aircraft to obtain aerodynamic data to Mach 0.89. In the second phase, Douglas would modify two for Westinghouse 24C turbojet engines and rocket propulsion so that these two airplanes could investigate aerodynamic conditions around Mach 1. In the third phase, Douglas would prepare engineering proposals and construct a mockup of a combat-type aircraft using results gathered during the testing of the six original D-558 aircraft. As with Bell and the XS-1, Douglas would follow traditional design specifications and criteria only where practicable. The company estimated total cost of the program at $6,888,444.80.[19]

The company did not set firm delivery dates for the airplanes because of the highly experimental nature of the project. Nevertheless,

Douglas representatives believed that the first aircraft could be ready for flight one year after the date of contract with the other five aircraft available six months thereafter. In its conclusion to the proposal, Douglas urged the Bureau of Aeronautics to take prompt action on the proposal, stating, "The urgent need for reliable data covering airplane speeds at high Mach numbers and the importance of this data in connection with current as well as future military aircraft cannot be overemphasized."[20]

The company's preliminary design met with quick BuAer approval. On April 26, 1945, Capt. Theodore C. Lonnquest, USN, director of the Engineering Division, recommended the procurement of the six research aircraft, stating that the Model 558 proposal represented a "well conceived and practically executed design."[21] He did suggest that the proposed rocket-propelled phase be delayed pending further information on the structural details of the rocket installation. Likewise, he advised that the third phase, design and mockup of a proposed fighter developed from the D-558 program, be set aside until the Navy and Douglas acquired flight test information from the phase one research aircraft.[22]

Lonnquest formulated a two-phase flight research program in which both Douglas and the NACA would fly the airplanes. The Douglas company pilots would seek data directly applicable to the design of fighter and dive bomber aircraft. The NACA research pilots would concentrate on acquiring basic and fundamental aerodynamic data at high Mach numbers, such as information on air loads, aircraft stability and control, flutter, and power plant behavior.[23] Lonnquest advocated procurement of all six D-558 airplanes to perform the various research investigations with a minimum of delay. But he also stated gravely, "Furthermore, when flying experimental airplanes into the high Mach number region, there is an almost certain probability that one or more airplanes will be lost as evidenced by the loss of three XFR-1 and several P-80 airplanes."[24]

On May 9, 1945, the Bureau of Aeronautics and the Assistant Secretary of the Navy (Air) formally approved the Douglas proposal.[25] To ensure that the program did not duplicate the Army XS-1 program, the Bureau maintained close contact with Army personnel at Wright Field.[26] For its part, the NACA had little doubt it could justify development of both the XS-1 and D-558. The Navy airplane represented a more conventional design than did the XS-1, and had significant differences in design detail, propulsion, and planform.[27] On June 22, 1945, the Navy Bureau of Aeronautics issued a letter of intent to Douglas for the development of the D-558 aircraft under Contract NOa(s) 6850, which provided for construction of six model D-558 "Phase One" aircraft of alternate configurations, including two alternate wing sections and two alternate nose configurations. Phase Two provided for rocket-boost modification, and Phase Three concerned the proposed design and mockup of

D-558 Model in the Langley 8-Foot High-Speed Tunnel

a combat-type aircraft.[28] Later that month, Douglas began tests of a ¼-scale model of the D-558 in a wind tunnel at the California Institute of Technology for low-speed stability and control data.[29]

In May 1945, L. Eugene Root and A. M. O. Smith had temporarily left El Segundo to go to Germany as part of the Naval Technical Mission, Europe, and evaluate German wartime aeronautical developments. Kermit E. Van Every, holder of an M.E. in aero engineering from Stanford and assistant chief of the aerodynamics section at El Segundo, took the place of both men on the D-558 design team. Strangely, Root's and Smith's trip to Germany had an extremely important impact upon the D-558 program and led directly to the D-558-2.[30]

As early as March 1945, the Douglas design team had fixed the basic design of the airplane. The plane would have an ultimate load factor of 18g, a design gross weight of 7,500 lbs, an overall length of 35 ft. 10 in., a wingspan of 25 ft., an aspect ratio of 4.2, and a wing area of 150 sq. ft. The pure-jet models would have a maximum airspeed of 625 mph at sea level, and Mach 0.84 at 25,000 ft. The plane's fuel supply would be carried in an integral wing tank, the pilot's compartment would be pressurized to an equivalent altitude of 15,000 ft. when the airplane was flying at 30,000 ft, and the whole nose could be jettisoned from the remainder of the aircraft in case the pilot had to abandon the airplane in flight. The fuselage was designed so that alternate wing and tail surfaces could be installed and tested, and the aircraft could be flown with a nose air intake or side air inlets. Finally, the airplane would have an adjust-able horizontal stabilizer for increased control at high speeds.[31] Douglas planned to construct the aircraft as follows:

Airplane	Engine	Nose scoop	Side scoop	Wing	Model
1	TG-180	No	Yes	65-110	558JS1
2	TG-180	Yes	No	65-110	558JN1
3	TG-180	No	Yes	65-110	558JS1
4	TG-180	No	Yes	65-110	558JS1
5	TG-180	No	Yes	2417-13	558JS3
6	TG-180	No	Yes	16-008 (to-006)	558JS2

Note: N = nose scoop.
     S = side inlets.
     J = turbojet (two would have been converted to rocket—R).
     1 = NACA 65-110 airfoil section on wing.
     2 = NACA 16-008 at root, 16-006 at tip.
     3 = NACA 2417 at root, 2413 at tip.

Now, the Douglas design team, minus Root and Smith, devoted their attention to the detail design of the airplane. Team members gave considerable thought to methods of pilot escape at high speed. They doubted that the pilot could survive by the traditional method of jettison-ing the cockpit canopy and then falling clear of the airplane. At first, the team considered incorporating an ejection seat, but found that the force needed to throw the seat and pilot clear of the high vertical fin would be in excess of human physiological limits. Then Heinemann con-ceived using a jettisonable nose capsule, the only possible alternative. After separating from the airplane, the capsule would decelerate to a lower speed—Douglas estimated no faster than 350 mph—enabling the pilot to make a normal bail-out from the nose section.[32] At first, Douglas investigated slowing the capsule with speed brakes or a suitable drag parachute, but dropped both suggestions because the brakes added com-plexity and no suitable high-speed parachute existed. Finally, the team chose a simple jettisonable nose that would slow due to aerodynamic drag. The pilot pulled a release handle located above the instrument panel, which released four "bombrack" type hooks that disengaged, separating the nose section from the rest of the airplane.[33]

Incorporation of the jettisonable nose seriously complicated design of the airplane's control system, but design team members displayed considerable ingenuity in coping with this problem. The difficulty in-volved designing control lines and electrical lines that would separate cleanly when the nose left the airplane. Douglas engineers equipped the electrical lines with quick disconnect pullout plugs. The push-pull controls were more complex, since Douglas engineers had to retain the movement of the cable, yet equip it so it could separate in an emergency. The design team devised grooved drums on a common shaft that passed through the fuselage bulkhead into the nose section of the plane. Thus, one drum was in the nose section, and the other was in the rest of the plane, behind the fuselage bulkhead. The drums translated the linear motion of the push-pull controls into rotary motion. Then, on the other side of the fuselage bulkhead, the other drum translated the rotary motion back into linear motion. Douglas designed the drum shaft with a tongue and groove so that, if the pilot jettisoned the nose, the shaft would separate.[34]

The design team constructed a mockup of the D-558 airplane, and held the first mockup inspection on July 2, 3, and 4, 1945. Among the personnel who attended this mockup meeting was NACA's chief pilot, Melvin Gough.[35] At this meeting, NACA expressed criticism concerning the design strength of the Douglas canopy configuration, feeling it to be less than the 18g load limit for the airplane itself. Additionally, the NACA felt that cockpit vision was unsatisfactory. The only really important change as a result of this first mockup conference, however, was the dropping of side inlets from the program. NACA suggested the design incorporate only a nose inlet, since the aerodynamics of this configuration were better known and understood than those of side inlets.[36] A month later, from August 14 through 17, 1945, Heinemann held a second mockup conference in his offices at El Segundo.

In contrast to the transonic capabilities of the airplane under consideration, the trip to Douglas by Navy and NACA representatives took many hours. For example, Milton B. Ames, Jr., on the technical staff of NACA Headquarters, left Washington with a group of Navy representatives aboard American Airlines' DC-3 "Mercury" flight. The plodding DC-3—another Douglas product—would drone along for several hundred miles, land and refuel, and then take off again. "We flew all night, and we were bushed the next day," Ames recollected, "but we went right out to the plant and checked over the mockup. The job I had there was to see that the cockpit and canopy changes were made in accordance with the NACA's requirements, to provide high visibility yet be safe enough to withstand the high wind loads. The visibility was okay. I remember sitting in it, and I had to be propped up to seat level to check visibility."[37]

The second mockup conference also gave rise to the branching of the D-558 program into a straight-wing turbojet aircraft—the original D-558 conception—and into a sweptwing turbojet- and rocket-propelled design called the D-558-2. The sweptwing airplane came about as a result of sweptwing research both in the United States and abroad, particularly in Germany. The straight-wing turbojet-propelled airplane, now designated the D-558-1, continued under development. The two aircraft retained structural similarities, but differed markedly in appearance, capabilities, and design mission. It is impossible to discuss the two aircraft and their development simultaneously.

THE D-558-1

Once the D-558 design team had decided to develop a minimum size airplane utilizing the most powerful turbojet available, the next question became one of ensuring that the airplane and its components had high critical Mach numbers, in order to delay high-speed drag divergence. This required designing the wing, the fuselage, and the wing-fuselage fillet with high critical Mach numbers. With the assistance of the NACA and the Navy Bureau of Aeronautics, Douglas selected a NACA 65-110 section for the wing because of its proven high Mach number for drag divergence—compressibility effects—and because adequate reliable flight data for the 65 airfoil series existed since it was used on existing aircraft, notably the Douglas A-26. With the airfoil shape selected, the design team turned to the planform of the wing itself. They chose a "relatively low" aspect ratio of 4.17 to save weight and ensure satisfactory low-speed flying qualities, and avoided wing twist to minimize aerodynamic and structural problems at high speeds. The chief problem in designing the fuselage was keeping the frontal area of the body at a minimum in order to retain a high fineness ratio, and choosing a body shape that would not produce accelerated airflow in the vicinity of the wing. The design team selected a cylindrical body shape just large enough to enclose a TG-180 turbojet, thus keeping frontal area at a minimum. At the same time, the straight cylindrical section above the wing minimized velocity increases. In designing the wing-fuselage fillet, Douglas engineers had to choose a configuration that would have a critical Mach number as high as the wing, but that would not degrade the plane's stalling characteristics at low speed. After exhaustive tests in NACA and Caltech wind tunnels, Douglas engineers finally evolved such a configuration, though at some penalty in maximum lift coefficient.[38]

On NACA's recommendation, Douglas placed the horizontal stabilizer of the D-558-1 high on the vertical fin to remove it from the wing wake, following results of NACA wake survey tests made for development of high-speed bombers. The NACA recommendation resulted in Douglas locating the stabilizer higher than on the original tentative D-558 design. Likewise, to retain control effectiveness at high speeds, the stabilizer airfoil section on the airplane was thinner than the wing section. The D-558-1 had a NACA 65-110 wing section, but a 65-008 stabilizer section. Finally, the D-558-1's stabilizer was adjustable in flight, just like the XS-1's for increased control effectiveness in the transonic region.[39]

As part of the development program, Douglas and the NACA at Langley Field initiated extensive wind-tunnel tests of the proposed aircraft shape. Douglas constructed several ¼-scale models and tested them for low-speed stability and control characteristics, engine intake airflow behavior, tip tank aerodynamic characteristics, and characteristics of various proposed flap configurations. The company tested the models in the Caltech Southern California Cooperative Wind Tunnel (CWT). Additionally, Douglas technicians built a special 1/50-scale model nose of the D-558 and A. M. O. Smith, recently returned from his trip to Germany, tested the configuration in the company's Airflow Generator to obtain force data and film records of flight paths.[40] The company also constructed a ⅙-scale high-speed model of the D-558 nose and tested it in the Cooperative Wind Tunnel.[41] All in all, over the 6 months from May through October 1945, Douglas ran more than 223 hours of tests on the D-558-1 in the Caltech Cooperative Wind Tunnel.[42] NACA, deeply committed to the D-558 program, tested six 1/16 solid wood models of the D-558 configuration in the Langley 8-foot high speed tunnel using the new sting support system. The Langley Flight Research Division made wing-flow tests using D-558 models mounted on the wings of P-51 fighters. Finally, NACA engineers used a spin model of the Bell XS-1 configuration to simulate the D-558 in tests in the Langley Spin Tunnel.[43]

Satisfied with the progress of the D-558 design, the Navy Bureau of Aeronautics followed up their June 1945 letter of intent with a formal contract issued on March 28, 1946, calling for construction of six D-558's.[44] With the detail design of the airplanes complete, Douglas now began construction of the first three aircraft, the three D-558-1's.[45] Following company policy, Douglas gave the D-558-1's the appellation "Skystreak."

The Douglas design team had to grapple with a number of technical problems during the construction of the Skystreak. Despite the team's avowal to adopt a conventional approach to avoid any difficulties that might arise from an unconventional or radical design, they often had to find unorthodox solutions. One such problem concerned landing-gear storage. With the fuselage crowded by the engine, flight-research instrumentation, controls, and cockpit, the team found only sufficient remaining space to stow the retractable nose landing gear. The main landing gear would have to go into the wings, even though the wings were—for their day—very thin, and not readily suited to gear storage. The design team had the Goodrich Corporation develop special 20 × 4.4-size

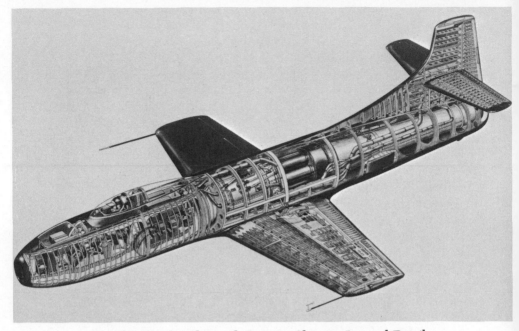

Douglas D-558-1 Skystreak Cutaway Showing Internal Details

wheels with eight-ply nylon tires. Though much smaller and thinner than what Douglas would have desired for a plane of the Skystreak's size and weight, these special wheels could fit within the 10 percent-thick wing, avoiding the undesirable alternative of fuselage or wing redesign.[46] To solve the problem of fuel storage, the design team decided to make the forward 50 percent of the wing fuel-tight so that the wing could act as an integral fuel tank. Technicians coated the inside of the wing with a synthetic rubber sealer that required five weeks for curing and drying. But thus sealed, the Skystreak's wing could carry 230 gallons of kerosene fuel. Additionally, the plane had provisions for additional fuel in jettison-able wing-tip tanks.[47]

Of semimonocoque construction, the Skystreak's fuselage consisted of aluminum alloy frames without stiffeners or stringers, covered by a heavy magnesium alloy skin approximately 1/10 inch thick. This method of fuselage construction increased usable internal space, provided a smoother external surface due to the heavy gauge skin and countersunk rivets, and resulted in a weight saving of 60 lbs. The wings and tail surfaces used conventional rib and stringer construction fabricated from high-strength 75S aluminum alloy. Because the wing had insufficient space for conventional lead aileron balance weights, Douglas engineers selected heavier tungsten alloy counterweights that could fit in the small space available. To ensure that the external surface of the aircraft would be as smooth as possible, the company constructed exceptionally rigid assembly jigs. Technicians fitted the wing and fuselage skins to contour frames, then assembled the internal structure directly to the skin, thus reducing surface irregularities.[48] All the Skystreak's flight controls operated without power boost, aerodynamic balance, or use of control tabs. The setting of the horizontal stabilizer could be adjusted by electric actuators controlled by a switch on the pilot's control wheel. Like the Bell XS-1 design team, Douglas chose a control wheel rather than a control stick for the pilot, presumably—as with the XS-1—to allow the pilot to use both hands effectively should the need arise. To minimize the danger of control surface flutter, the Skystreak incorporated hydraulic dampers for all control surfaces.[49]

Though the NACA had primary responsibility for Skystreak instrumentation, Douglas prepared their own instrument package for the first D-558-1, to be used in a contractor evaluation program. Douglas cut 400 pressure orifices into the wing and tail surfaces to record pressure distribution patterns on a special pressure-measuring system of automatically recording manometers developed by the NACA.[50] Strain gauges would measure air loads on the wing and tail, and Douglas had the William Miller Corporation of Pasadena develop a specially built 30-channel oscillograph to record control forces, flight operating conditions, and data from the power plant installation.[51] To ensure satisfactory operation of the instrumentation under flight conditions, Douglas subjected all the instrumentation to vibration tests and 12g accelerations in a centrifuge at the University of Southern California.[52]

The design team also developed a complex but highly efficient refrigeration system to provide cool air to the cockpit and instrumentation compartment. The efficiency of this equipment was such that it took air from the engine compressor at 450° F. and cooled it to 60° F. before discharging it into the cockpit. Likewise, technicians painted the interior of the Skystreak's fuselage with heat-reflecting paint to prevent absorption of engine heat.[53]

The Bureau of Aeronautics assigned the three D-558-1 aircraft the serials 37970, 37971, and 37972, and by October 1946 all three aircraft were well into construction, being respectively 90 percent, 70 percent, and 60 percent complete.[54] By this time, Douglas had completed design development of the airplane. The design team made some final design changes to the plane, including installation of speed brakes. Early in the design, the team made provisions for speed brakes to permit the pilot to decelerate to slower, safer airspeeds if he encountered severe compressibility effects. Subsequently, as a result of wind tunnel tests, Douglas dropped the brake idea, since the tests indicated that the efficiency of the brakes disappeared at high speeds. But, in further discussions between the El Segundo engineering department and company test pilots, the pilots expressed a strong desire for the brakes as an added safety feature, and requested that the engineers design them to slow the airplane by 50 mph in 15 seconds at maximum speed. Because of the advanced development of the plane, the engineers had to add the brakes externally on either side of the fuselage just aft of the wing. They designed the brakes to open 60° in 3 seconds at Mach 0.9 at 25,000 ft. They had a "blow-back" feature so that they would open partially if the air loads were too high for full opening. NACA tested the brake configuration in the Langley 8-foot high speed tunnel. As a result of static load tests on the Skystreak, Douglas added local spanwise stiffeners to the stabilizer, a very difficult modification since technicians had completed installation of pressure tubing to the pressure orifices in the stabilizer.[55]

On April 10, 1947, the first D-558-1 Skystreak, BuAer No. 37970, arrived at Muroc Dry Lake from El Segundo for its initial flight tests.[56] Company technicians had painted the plane a rich glossy red for high visibility. The Skystreak's coloration made it the most visually exciting of the research airplanes. Lacquered and polished to a high gloss, the sleek research plane possessed the illusion of flying while on the ground. Its long cylindrical fuselage joined a well-faired tail assembly. A long streamlined clear cockpit canopy surmounted the red fuselage. Aft of the wing, the crisp blue and white of the national insignia's star and bar overlapped the speed brakes. The nose bore the legend "Douglas Skystreak." The scarlet fuselage ended abruptly in a gleaming silver tail cone for the jet exhaust. Only the three spindly landing struts with their extremely small wheels broke the clean lines of the airplane. Tests in coming months would reveal whether the attractive airplane could withstand the rigors of transonic flight or whether it, like Geoffrey de Havilland's ill-fated Swallow, would wind up a mass of twisted wreckage.

THE D-558-2

The story of the sweptwing D-558-2 Skyrocket has its origins in both American and German sweptwing research. The catalyst for the Douglas-Navy-NACA decision to construct a sweptwing research airplane came from the trip L. Eugene Root and A. M. O. Smith took to Germany to investigate wartime German aeronautical research. In May 1945, Root and Smith left El Segundo for Europe; they were under contract from Douglas to the Bureau of Aeronautics to join the Naval Technical Mission in Europe (NavTechMisEu).

Root and Smith first joined the mission in Paris, then left for Germany under orders to investigate aerodynamic reports from the Göttingen laboratory, the *Aerodynamische Versuchsanstalt* (*AVA*). Using their command of scientific German, the two aerodynamicists painstakingly read through the countless documents in the laboratory files that, fortunately, were largely intact. The data they analyzed concerned high-speed wing and airfoil theory, including sweptwing research on wings and complete models having various sweepback angles. Root and Smith immediately realized the importance of the data, and recognized the necessity of getting it to high-speed aircraft designers as soon as possible. They requested that all the Göttingen material be microfilmed. The microfilming of the reports took three weeks by five shifts working night and day.[57]

Root wanted to get the material back to the Bureau of Aeronautics, the NACA, and Douglas as soon as possible, and after making a preliminary survey of the material, NavTechMisEu transmitted the microfilmed reports to the Bureau of Aeronautics. Dr. Clark Millikan, acting director of the Guggenheim Aeronautical Laboratory at Caltech, served as courier, escorted by Abraham Hyatt. Root and Smith then tried to get the sweptwing data back to Douglas before the second D-558 mockup conference. Both men believed it highly desirable to obtain flight-test data on the swept configuration. Smith arrived back at El Segundo in the early part of August. Root remained in Europe for the next several months.[58]

Early in 1945, NACA scientist Robert T. Jones had informed his superiors of the sweptwing research he had made at Langley Laboratory. During the early summer, John Stack requested the Douglas company to incorporate 35° wing sweep on the D-558 configuration, but the Navy decided to proceed with the original straight-wing planform and approach wing sweep cautiously.[59] After several discussions between the Bureau of Aeronautics and the NACA, and after having had a chance to evaluate the microfilmed data transmitted to the company from captured German reports, Douglas agreed to develop a sweptwing research airplane as part of the D-558 program.[60]

At the second mockup conference on the D-558 program, August 14–17, 1945, the Navy and NACA requested initial design studies of a sweptwing D-558.[61] From the start, Douglas, the Navy, and the NACA planned to incorporate rocket propulsion in the plane, since they felt there was little point in testing the sweptwings on a turbojet airplane inasmuch as existing turbojets lacked the thrust capability to propel the plane to sufficiently high Mach numbers where the sweptwings could be fully evaluated. NACA stipulated that the plane should have sufficient rocket fuel for 2 minutes of operation at 4,000-lb thrust, to allow sufficient time for the plane's internal recording instrumentation to stabilize and take accurate measurements. The NACA later modified this requirement to 100 seconds of engine operation at 6,000-lb thrust, or slightly over 2 minutes of operation at 4,500-lb thrust.[62]

Douglas and NACA divided up responsibility for aircraft design between them. The NACA would have complete responsibility for high-speed wind-tunnel testing, while Douglas would have complete responsibility for low-speed tests.[63] The Navy directed Douglas to develop the airplane with the equivalent stalling and low-speed characteristics of a conventional straight-wing airplane. In response, Douglas technicians mounted a sweptwing on a D-558 wind-tunnel model and tested it for low-speed stability and control data. They concluded that the company could build the sweptwing plane with satisfactory low-speed handling characteristics.[64] This was of paramount importance to the D-558-2 design team, for they recognized that the sweptwing, while offering performance increases at high speeds, had undesirable low-speed characteristics, particularly at the stall, that could pose a danger to the pilot. The Navy recognized the need for data on low-speed sweptwing behavior by procuring, early in 1946, two highly modified Bell P-63 Kingcobras that featured sweptwings. Bell, Navy, and NACA pilots flew the two planes, designated L-39's, in extensive low-speed investigations.

Douglas began initial low-speed investigations of the proposed sweptwing version of the D-558 in late October 1945, using the Cooperative Wind Tunnel at Caltech.[65] At the same time, the NACA at Langley Laboratory began testing models of swept D-558 configurations with both swept-aft wings and swept-forward wings. The Douglas design team, after several arrangement studies, found it impossible to fit a turbojet engine and fuel, and a rocket engine and fuel, into a D-558-1 type fuselage. It became clear to the team that an entirely new design was required.[66]

In the original D-558 proposal Douglas made to the Navy, the company included provisions for modifying two of the D-558 aircraft for rocket propulsion, installing rocket boosters and replacing the TG-180 turbojet with a Westinghouse 24C turbojet. The design team now planned the new sweptwing aircraft around a Westinghouse 24C engine for take-off and landing, and a Reaction Motors, Inc. A6000C4 engine for high-speed research, the same four-cylinder liquid oxygen-and-alcohol-fueled rocket engine used in the XS-1. Though the Navy designated the RMI engine the LR-8, there was no difference between it and the Army LR-11, aside from Navy policy to give engines even numbers, and Army policy to give them odd ones.

In designing the D-558-2, the design team wanted to keep its low-speed performance characteristics as near as possible to those of the straight-wing D-558-1. Responsibility for the aerodynamics of the air-

Early Configuration Study for D-558-2

craft lay in the hands of Kermit E. Van Every. After returning to El Segundo, A. M. O. Smith became more involved with other company projects, though he did conduct performance investigations on inlet design and jettisonable nose design for the D-558-2. Likewise, L. Eugene Root also embarked upon other company ventures. Finally, in mid-1946, Douglas Vice-President for Engineering Arthur E. Raymond asked Root to join Project RAND, thus removing Root from the D-558-2 project.[67] In designing the new sweptwing airplane, Van Every and his assistants had to arrive at a satisfactory aerodynamic configuration for both low- and high-speed flight.

In designing the fuselage, Douglas retained the circular cross section planform, but decided to employ side inlets for the Westinghouse 24C turbojet rather than a nose intake. Thus, the nose shape resembled that of the Bell XS-1. As with the D-558-1, Van Every decided to keep the fuselage of straight cylindrical section in the vicinity of the wing-fuselage junction in order to minimize velocity increases in the airflow at that point. Further, because of a lack of specific information, Douglas did not design a wing-fuselage fillet for the D-558.[68] On the wing itself, Van Every substituted a NACA 63 series airfoil section in place of the NACA 65 series used on the D-558. His reason for doing so was to use the superior low-speed characteristics of the 63 series to give the plane good stalling characteristics, while, at the same time, minimizing degradation in high-speed performance.[69] Further, he tapered the section from 63-010 (10 percent thickness-chord ratio) at the wing root to 63-012 (12 percent thickness-chord ratio) at the tip, in order to give the plane the best possible flaps-up stall behavior. Additionally, the design team increased the wing area from 150 sq. ft.—as on the D-558-1—to 175 sq. ft. on the D-558-2, so the sweptwing D-558-2 would have the same stall speed as the D-558-1. Finally, to improve behavior at the stall, the design team incorporated wing fences and automatic leading edge slats, as well as simple flaps.[70]

As a compromise, the D-558-2 design team selected a wing sweep angle of 35° at the 30 percent wing chord line. The 35° choice seemed to offer both good high-speed characteristics and satisfactory low-speed behavior as well. The team retained the same wing span as the D-558-1, 25 feet, which caused a reduction in the aspect ratio from 4.17, as on the D-558-1, to 3.57. On both the Bell XS-1 and the Douglas D-558-1, the respective design teams had incorporated thinner airfoil sections on the horizontal stabilizers in order to give the stabilizer a higher critical Mach number than the wing. On the D-558-2, the design team raised the critical Mach number of the stabilizer by giving it a greater sweepback angle. Thus, the stabilizer retained the same 63-010 airfoil section as the wing, but the sweepback angle of the stabilizer was 40° instead of 35°. As on the XS-1 and D-558-1 the D-558-2 design team placed the horizontal stabilizer high on the vertical fin to keep it out of the wing wake and also made the stabilizer adjustable in flight.[71]

Like the earlier D-558-1, Douglas decided to employ an escape capsule for the pilot of the D-558-2. Unlike the earlier airplane, however, the design team built the D-558-2 Skyrocket to a lower load factor. Instead of an ultimate 18g load factor as on the D-558-1, the team designed the D-558-2 with an ultimate load factor of 12g at 11,250 lbs. and a limit load of 7.3g at 13,500 lbs. The D-558-2, like the D-558-1, was designed for a design Mach number of 1 at sea level.[72]

The Navy Bureau of Aeronautics granted Douglas preliminary authorization to develop a sweptwing version of the D-558 on January 29, 1946, and, by March, the design team had chosen the basic planform of the airplane.[73] It did not differ appreciably from the final configuration of the airplane. On March 18 and 19, 1946, Douglas held a mockup inspection, and visiting NACA and Navy representatives approved the design. Douglas now turned to detail design development. Because of the sweptwing design and structural difficulties in assembling it, the design team did not attempt to locate either the landing gear or the turbojet fuel supply in the wing. This necessitated locating the gear and fuel in the fuselage, and required a considerable increase in fuselage diameter over that of the earlier D-558-1. The team located the Westinghouse 24C turbojet in the fuselage below the wing with 2 tanks immediately above the center section of the wing containing 250 gallons total of gasoline— not kerosene—for the turbojet. The jet exhaust passed out and slightly downwards—about 8°—from a ventral tail pipe. Douglas located the alcohol tank for the rocket engine above the tail pipe in the aft fuselage. It contained 195 gallons of fuel. In front of the wing above the turbojet intake ducts the Douglas team placed the spherical liquid oxygen tank, capable of holding 180 gallons of liquid oxygen.[74]

Ahead of the liquid oxygen tank, Douglas positioned an 11-gallon hydrogen peroxide tank. This tank supplied 90 percent-strength hydrogen peroxide to the turbine pump, for, unlike the XS-1's, the Skyrocket did use a turbine pump to feed the RMI rocket engine. The turbine pump nestled between the alcohol tank and the aft gasoline tank for the turbojet. It obtained its power from the decomposition of the hydrogen peroxide over a catalyst. Two separate centrifugal pumps connected to the turbine shaft fed the alcohol and liquid oxygen to the rocket engine. To ensure that the fuel tanks would have proper inlet pressures for the pumps prior to the operation of the turbine pump, the design team incorporated 3 spherical and 4 cylindrical helium tanks to pressurize the alcohol tank to 30 psi, the liquid oxygen tank to 50 psi, and the peroxide tank to 400 psi. The design team chose helium over nitrogen because calculations showed that the helium would result in a weight saving of 30 lbs. The helium tanks stored the gas at 2,000 psi. The main consideration that dictated the location of the propellant tanks was to avoid any shift in the plane's center of gravity when the engine operated.[75] Ahead of the liquid oxygen and hydrogen peroxide tank was the D-558-2's instrumentation compartment.

The D-558-2 Skyrocket contained the same basic instrumentation package as the D-558-1 Skystreak. It had the same 30-channel Miller oscillograph that Douglas had specially built for the D-558 program. Its strain gauge installation, however, was far more extensive than that of the earlier D-558-1 Skystreak. During the design of the Skystreak, Douglas engineers had succeeded in isolating the fuselage from the wing by using special links equipped with strain gauges.[76] Due to structural differences in the Skyrocket's wing attachment, the design team could not do this, necessitating installation of a large number of strain gauges in the wings and tail surfaces to record wing loads. Douglas distributed 226 channels of 4 strain gauges each—a total of 904 strain gauges—throughout the wing for acquisition of stress information. More than 4 miles of strain-gauge wiring and over 3 miles of pressure tubing ran from wing and tail surface stations to the instrumentation compartment. Like the earlier Skystreak, the Skyrocket also had 400 pressure orifices cut into

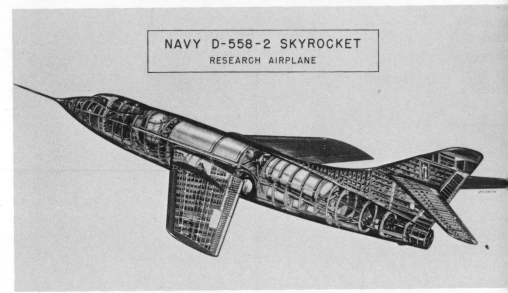

NAVY D-558-2 SKYROCKET
RESEARCH AIRPLANE

Douglas D-558-2 Skyrocket Cutaway Showing Internal Details

the wing and tail connected to the Miller oscillograph for pressure distribution surveys.[77]

By October 1946, at which time the three D-558-1 Skystreaks were nearing completion, Douglas had released over 95 percent of the D-558-2's engineering drawings to the shops, completed about 80 percent of the tooling, and 70 percent of the fabrication. The company had begun assembly of the first two wings for the aircraft.[78] The structure of the Skyrocket followed closely that of the Skystreak. Of semimonocoque design, the fuselage was of heavy-gauge magnesium sheet over heavy aluminum frame construction, with no stringers. The wings and tail surfaces were of more conventional high-strength 75S aluminum alloy rib and stringer construction. As on the Skystreak, the Skyrocket employed tungsten alloy counterweights to balance the ailerons, and the flight controls lacked aerodynamic balance, power boost, or tabs. Also, as in the Skystreak, the Skyrocket featured a control wheel for the pilot.[79]

Douglas and the Navy decided to delete the last three Skystreak airplanes, together with the alternate wings for the airplanes, and the provision for rocket propulsion in the D-558-1 which Douglas had set forth in their April 1945 engineering proposal to the Navy. Accordingly, on January 27, 1947, the Navy issued a revision to the Douglas contract providing for the deletion of three D-558-1 Skystreaks and their replacement by three D-558-2 Skyrockets. The cutting back of the Skystreaks from six to three served to reduce the cost of the project. Slightly over a month later, on March 1, 1947, the Navy issued contract amendment 5A, the first formal authorization to proceed with the Phase Two Skyrocket program.[80] While Douglas constructed the three D-558-2 airplanes, the NACA continued to furnish needed data on airplane performance derived from tests in the Langley 8-foot high-speed tunnel, the Langley spin tunnel, and from firings of telemetry-equipped rocket-propelled models from NACA's Pilotless Aircraft Research Division at Wallops Island, Virginia.

In early November 1947, Douglas completed the first D-558-2 Skyrocket. Like the three D-558-1 Skystreaks, the planned three D-558-2's received a batch of BuAer serials, 37973, 37974, and 37975. Like the first XS-1, the D-558-2 #1, BuAer No. 37973, did not have its RMI engine when completed. Though Douglas had "frozen" design of the rocket installation in July, the company did not consider the installation flightworthy pending a full ground check of the rocket system. Douglas, the Navy, and the NACA did not expect the RMI engines to be ready before August 1948. They decided to conduct initial flight trials on the first two aircraft with just the turbojet engines. Douglas would retain the D-558-2 #3, BuAer No. 37975, until it could complete the aircraft with the LR 8 rocket engine. The NACA was willing to accept the D 558 2 #2, BuAer No. 37974, without its rocket engine, and began stability and control research on the plane. At a later date, when the RMI LR-8 engine became available, the NACA could return the plane to Douglas for installation of the engine.[81]

The Skyrocket impressed most observers by the grace of its lines. From nose to tail, the plane consisted of a series of unbroken lines flowing smoothly together. Though later modified, the cockpit of the D-558-2 did not break the fuselage lines, and was flush to the ogival shape of the fuselage nose. The nose itself ended in a long-pointed instrumented nose boom vaguely reminiscent of a swordfish. Because the plane did not yet have its rocket engine, the Skyrocket had a pointed tail cone. Unlike the crimson Skystreak or the orange XS-1, the D-558-2 featured a glossy white finish overall. Douglas had not chosen the color for its aesthetic appeal. Late in the summer of 1947, Walter C. Williams, head of the NACA Muroc Flight Test Unit at Muroc Dry Lake, had informed Douglas that red did not prove desirable from a visibility or photographic standpoint, and that white would be better. Douglas complied to make the Skyrocket more easily trackable.[82] On December 10, 1947, Douglas trucked the D-558-2 #1, BuAer No. 37973, to Muroc Dry Lake in preparation for its initial contractor flights. The white airplane, with "Skyrocket" emblazoned on its nose, joined the growing stable of research airplanes flying from the unique lake in the Mojave desert.[83]

NOTES

1. Letter, Walter S. Diehl to author, 6 Jan. 1972. Also BuAer Conf. letter Aer-E-23-WSD, Aer-E-24-WHM Serial No. C35304 dated 19 Dec. 1944, cited in letter, Director, Enginering Division to Chief, BuAer, Aer-E-11-EWC, Serial No. C-12002, dated 26 Apr. 1945. Found in D-558 file, Historian, Naval Air Systems Command (hereafter cited as NASC).

2. Ames interview, 26 July 1971.

3. Letter and recording, L. Eugene Root to author, 18 March 1972. Also Parrish, *Who's Who in World Aviation, 1955*, p. 264.

4. L. J. Devlin, "General Summary of Project," Model D-558 Navy-Industry Conference, Douglas El Segundo plant, 10 Nov. 1947, pp. 1–2.

5. Interview of Frank N. Fleming by the author, 25 May 1972. Also "Development History of the Douglas Aircraft Corporation X3 Airplane," n.d. Transmitted to the author from Air Force Museum A1 X-3/his file.

The Douglas-AAF studies led to the issue of contract W33-038-ac-10413 on 30 June 1945 to cover development of a supersonic airplane under Project MX-656. The plane was to be capable of Mach 2.0 at 30,000 feet, and able to take off and land under its own power from a conventional airfield. This resulted in the development of the turbojet X-3, under the direction of project engineer Frank N. Fleming. An excellent design, the X-3 unfortunately failed to achieve its design goals because of inability of the engine manufacturer— Westinghouse—to deliver the planned J-46 powerplants within required size and performance specifications. Lower-rated Westinghouse J-34's had to be substituted in place of the J-46's, resulting in subsonic-level flight performance.

6. Letter and recording, L. Eugene Root to author, 18 March 1972.

7. Parrish, *Who's Who in World Aviation, 1955*, pp. 82, 85, 139. Frank J. Malina, "Origins and First Decade of the Jet Propulsion Laboratory," in Eugene M. Emme, ed., *The History of Rocket Technology: Essays on Research, Development, and Utility*, (Detroit, 1964), pp. 48–50. Also Kármán, *The Wind and Beyond*, pp. 239, 242, 261.

8. Edward H. Heinemann, "The Development of the Navy-Douglas Model D-558 Research Project," Douglas El Segundo plant, 17 Nov. 1947, pp. 1–2.

9. Letter and recording, L. Eugene Root to author, 18 March 1972. Letter, Edward H. Heinemann to author, 10 Feb. 1972. Letter, Leo J. Devlin to author, 12 March 1972. Letter, A.M.O. Smith to author, 31 March 1972.

10. Letter, A.M.O. Smith to author, 31 March 1972.

11. *Ibid.*

12. Devlin, "General Summary of Project," p. 3.

13. *Ibid.* Also Douglas letter B300-JWR-104, 13 April 1945, Rogers to Chief, BuAer. In NASC D-558 file.

14. Devlin, "General Summary of Project," p. 3.

15. Letter, A. M. O. Smith to author, 31 March 1972.

16. Douglas general arrangement three-view blueprint prepared by R. G. Smith, 16 January 1945. Transmitted to author by A. M. O. Smith.

17. Letter, A. M. O. Smith to author, 31 March 1972, and trip notes.

18. NACA Conference letter to Chief, BuAer 9 March 1945, cited in letter, Director, Engineering Division to Chief, BuAer, Aer-E-11-EWC, Serial No. C-12002, dated 26 Apr. 1945. In NASC D-558 file.

19. Douglas letter B300-JWR-104, 13 April 1945, Rogers to Chief, BuAer. In NASC D-558 file.

20. *Ibid.*

21. Letter, Director, Engineering Division to Chief, BuAer, Aer-E-11-EWC, serial No. C-12002, dated 26 Apr. 1945. In NASC D-558 file.

22. *Ibid.*

23. *Ibid.*

24. *Ibid.*

25. *Ibid.*, notation on bottom of final page of letter.

26. *Ibid.*

27. Ames interview, 26 July 1971.

28. A. O. Van Wyen, *D-558 Program Notes,* NASC D-558 file.

29. GALCIT wind tunnel data sheet transmitted to author by A. M. O. Smith.

30. Letter, A. M. O. Smith to author, 31 March 1972. Also letter and recording, L. Eugene Root to author, 18 March 1972.

31. Douglas El Segundo, "Brief Specification for the Model 558 High Speed Test Airplane," 28 March 1945. Copy in D-558 file, Soulé record collection, LaRC.

32. Heinemann, "Development of the Navy-Douglas Model D-558 Research Project," pp. 7–8. Also "Brief Spec. for the Model 558 High Speed Test Airplane."

33. Robert C. Donovan, "Escape Method Developed for Douglas D-558 Skystreak," *Aviation Week,* XLVII, No. 10, (Sept. 8, 1947), 34–37.

34. *Ibid.*

35. Ames interview, 26 July 1971.

36. *Ibid.*, also Devlin, "General Summary of Project," p. 3. It should be noted that the D-558 design had an ultimate load factor of 18g, just like the XS-1. The limit load factor was 9g. Later, on the D-558-2, these figures were lowered to 12g ultimate and 7.3g limit.

37. Ames interview, 26 July 1971.

38. K. E. Van Every, "Aerodynamics of D-558," Model D-558 Navy-Industry Conference, Douglas El Segundo plant, 10 Nov. 1947, pp. 2–6.

39. *Ibid.*, p. 5.

40. Douglas Aircraft Company, *Summary Report U.S. Navy Transonic Research Project Douglas Model D-558,* Report E. S. 15879, 31 Aug. 1951. pp. 61–62, 67. Hereafter cited as *D-558 Summary Report.* Also letter, A. M. O. Smith to author, 31 March 1972.

41. *D-558 Summary Report,* p. 67.

42. GALCIT wind tunnel data sheet transmitted to author by A. M. O. Smith.

43. *D-558 Summary Report,* pp. 64, 65. Also letter, Robert R. Gilruth to author, 27 Jan. 1972.

44. Van Wyen, *D-558 Program Notes,* p. 1.

45. At a later date, January 27, 1947, the Navy revised the contract to

provide for the deletion of three D-558 turbojet aircraft and the substitution of three D-558-2 sweptwing rocket- and jet-powered airplanes.

46. Heinemann, "Development of the Navy-Douglas Model D-558 Research Project," p. 6.

47. *Ibid.*, pp. 6–7.

48. *Ibid.*, pp. 10–12.

49. *Ibid.*, pp. 11–12.

50. *Ibid.*, p. 13.

51. *D-558 Summary Report*, p. 24. Also Walter C. Williams, Memo for Chief of Research, "Visit to Douglas Aircraft Corporation, El Segundo Plant," 29 Oct. 1946.

52. Heinemann, "Development of the Navy-Douglas Model D-558 Research Project," p. 17.

53. *Ibid.*, p. 12. R. C. Donovan, "General Description Model D-558 Airplanes," Model D-558 Navy-Industry Conference, Douglas El Segundo plant, 10 Nov. 1947, p. 6. Also, "How New Douglas Skystreak Will Probe the Transonic," *Aviation*, XLVI, No. 5, (May 1947), 54–56.

54. Capt. L. D. Coates, USN, to Chief, BuAer, "Progress Report for Period Ending 31 Oct. 1946," n.d.

55. Van Every, "Aerodynamics of D-558," pp. 7–9. Also Williams Memo to Chief of Research, 29 Oct. 1946.

56. Muroc Army Air Field Historical Report, 1 Jan. 1947–30 June 1947, pp. 2, 23. In Air Force Archives, Maxwell AFB.

57. Letter and recording, L. Eugene Root to author, 18 March 1972.

58. *Ibid.*, also letter, A. M. O. Smith to author, 31 March 1972.

59. Letter, Walter S. Diehl to author, 6 Jan. 1972.

60. Devlin, "General Summary of Project," pp. 3–4.

61. *D-558 Summary Report*, p. 22. Edward H. Heinemann, "The Navy-Douglas D-558-2 Skyrocket," Douglas El Segundo, n.d., p. 2.

62. Devlin, "General Summary of Project," pp. 4–5.

63. Van Every, "Aerodynamics of D-558," p. 11.

64. *Ibid.*, pp. 10–11.

65. GALCIT wind tunnel data sheet transmitted to author by A. M. O. Smith.

66. Van Every, "Aerodynamics of D-558," p. 11. Also Devlin, "General Summary of Project," p. 5.

67. Letter, A. M. O. Smith to author, 31 March 1972. Letter and recording, L. Eugene Root to author, 18 March 1972.

68. Van Every, "Aerodynamics of D-558," pp. 15, 16.

69. *Ibid.*, p. 12.

70. *Ibid.* Also Heinemann, "The Navy-Douglas D-558-2 Skyrocket," p. 4.

71. Van Every, "Aerodynamics of D-558," pp. 12, 15–16.

72. *D-558 Summary Report*, p. 18. Also Donovan, "General Description Model D-558 Airplanes," p. 7.

73. *D-558 Summary Report*, p. 22. Also, Douglas El Segundo, "Model D-558 Phase II Mockup Conference," 18 March 1946. In D-558 file, NASM.

74. *D-558 Summary Report*, p. 20. Donovan, "General Description Model D-558 Airplanes," pp. 8–9.

75. Donovan, "General Description Model D-558 Airplanes," pp. 8–9.

76. *D-558 Summary Report*, pp. 24–25. Also Heinemann, "The Navy-Douglas Model D-558 Research Project," pp. 12–13.

77. Donovan, "General Description Model D-558 Airplanes," p. 12. Also Heinemann, "The Navy-Douglas Model D-558 Research Project," p. 5.

78. Capt. L. D. Coates to Chief, BuAer.

79. Donovan, "General Description Model D-558 Airplanes," p. 10. Heinemann, "The Development of the Navy-Douglas Model D-558 Research Project," pp. 10–12.

80. *D-558 Summary Report*, p. 22. Van Wyen, *D-558 Program Notes*, pp. 1–2. Devlin, "General Summary of Project," p. 5.

81. John J. Gardner, Memo for Chief of Research, "Visit to Douglas El Segundo Plant to discuss D-558 Phase 2 rocket system," 9 July 1947. Letter, J. W. Crowley (NACA Assoc. Dir. of Aero. Research) to Chief, BuAer, 18 Nov. 1947. Donovan, "General Description Model D-558 Airplanes," p. 9.

82. Letter, Walter C. Williams to Robert Donovan, 25 Aug. 1947. Also Heinemann, "The Development of the Navy-Douglas Model D-558 Research Project," p. 10.

83. Muroc Army Air Field Historical Report, 1 July 1947–31 Dec. 1947, p. 26. In Air Force Archives, Maxwell AFB.

PART

TWO

Through the "Sound Barrier"

IV

THE BELL XS-1

CONTRACTOR PROGRAM

W hen Bell completed the XS-1 #1, serial 46-062, in late December 1945, the company already had plans for its flight test program. The Army had delivered a Boeing B-29A Superfortress, serial 45-21800, for the company to use as a launch aircraft. Company technicians removed the bomb bay doors, and cut out a portion of the lower fuselage in front of the aft pressure bulkhead of the B-29 for clearance of the XS-1's horizontal stabilizer. They added an extendable ladder from the forward right side of the bomb bay for the pilot to use for entering and, if necessary, leaving the rocket plane while it remained shackled to the launch B-29.

The NACA hoped that eventually Bell would obtain a satisfactory turbine pump for the fuel system of the XS-1, so that the XS-1 could be converted from its "temporary" high-pressure fuel system to a turbopump fuel system, which would permit attainment of its original performance estimates, including a possible 1,700 mph top speed. Langley personnel considered the air launching of the XS-1 a "cumbersome" method of operation, and hoped that some method of safe ground launching might emerge.[1] By the fall of 1945, the AAF and NACA had not selected the actual test site for the airplanes. NACA hoped the aircraft could fly from Langley Laboratory, where a large military airfield existed. Before the XS-1 entered its research program, the AAF and NACA desired to investigate two aspects of its operations. First, the air-launch method of operation, and, second, the feasibility of operating the exotic rocket airplane from a conventional flying field. Bell had completed the XS-1 #1 without its rocket engine, and the company, together with the AAF and NACA, felt that preliminary glide trials of the airplane could answer both questions. The Army selected Pinecastle Field, Orlando, Florida, as the site of the XS-1 glide trials.[2] During the trials, the NACA would supervise all details of the flight testing, and analyze all gathered data. Bell would furnish the B-29 launch crew and the XS-1 pilot.

The NACA assembled a small team to participate in the Pinecastle tests. The team consisted of representatives from the Langley Flight Research Division and Instrument Research Division. The director of the group was a young engineer, Walter C. Williams. Williams held a B.S. in aeronautical engineering from Louisiana State University. After graduation in 1939, he joined the Glenn L. Martin company at Baltimore, Maryland, but soon left for NACA's Langley Laboratory where he worked on aircraft stability and control. While at Langley, Williams became interested in the transonic research airplane concept, and had worked in the initial group of John Stack, Milton Davidson, and Harold Turner on research aircraft studies. When the XS-1 progressed to the flight stage, Williams came over from the Flight Research Division to head up the flight-test program on the airplane.[3] Together with Williams was another Langley engineer, Gerald M. Truszynski. Truszynski held a B.S. in electrical engineering from Rutgers University, and, after graduating in 1944, joined the Langley Instrument Research Division working on the design and development of radar and telemetry equipment. Truszynski had charge of the radar tracking equipment used on the Pinecastle tests, which consisted of an SCR-584 antiaircraft gun-laying radar equipped with a camera for more accurate flight-path data.[4] Both Williams and Truszynski later assumed key roles in directing the NACA flight-research program at Muroc Dry Lake.

The Bell XS-1 test team consisted of both a launch plane crew and an XS-1 pilot. The B-29 launch crew consisted of pilots Harold Dow and Joseph Cannon, and flight crewmen Ivan Hauptmann, William Means, and Herman Schneider. The XS-1 pilot was Bell's chief test pilot, Jack Woolams. Commissioned as an Army pilot in 1938, Woolams subsequently served as a P-36 pilot with the 79th Pursuit Squadron. He left the service to return to college, graduated from the University of Chicago, and joined Bell as a test pilot. While with Bell, Woolams participated in the

Bell P-59 program, demonstrating notable airmanship on several occasions. He attained an altitude of 45,765 feet on July 14, 1943, in the second XP-59A, then raised this to 47,600 feet on December 15, 1943. During P-59 dive tests at Niagara Falls, Woolams landed a YP-59A on its belly when air pressure forcibly extended the gear and broke the gear retracting links. During the same series of tests, a P-59 Woolams flew lost its tail in a high-speed dive. The cockpit canopy jammed, and he only escaped after twisting in the cockpit and kicking the canopy loose with his feet. While the Bell design team built the XS-1, Woolams made suggestions on the design, particularly cockpit layout, from a pilot's point of view.[5]

One question bothering Bell engineers was whether the XS-1 would separate cleanly from the B-29 at launch. Unless positive separation forces existed, the XS-1 might snag the B-29, possibly resulting in the loss of both airplanes. Bell decided to make captive flights with the XS-1 shackled in the B-29's bomb bay, and record pressure distributions between the two airplanes. Bell completed the first captive flight of the XS-1 on January 10, 1946. After recording pressure distribution from the XS-1's pressure pickups in the instrumented wing, the company concluded a positive separating force did exist. Cautious about relying solely upon recorded data, however, the company modified one of the bomb bay's bomb releases to eject the XS-1 with a nose-down pitching moment. Further, technicians installed a steel tube forward of the propellant tanks so that it projected from the fuselage for six inches on either side. They then installed wooden guide posts in the B-29, so that if the XS-1 tended to yaw and drift at launch, the steel tube and guide posts would steer it clear of the mother airplane.[6]

On January 19, 1946, the silver and black B-29 rumbled down the runway at Pinecastle Field, lifted into the air, and strained upwards, the orange XS-1 locked firmly in its belly. To see if the XS-1 needed the steel pipe and guideposts to prevent drifting, the Bell launch crew had daubed the tube and guide rails with red paint. On the first flights, Bell planned to launch the rocket plane with the inboard engines of the B-29 shut down and feathered, with the B-29 flaps in the takeoff position, and at a launch speed of 150 mph. Then, gradually, the company would go to high power, flaps in cruise position, and higher launching speeds. The company tracked the launches with cameras mounted on the B-29's wing and stabilizer tips. At 27,000 feet above Florida, the B-29 released Woolams and the XS-1. While the NACA test group monitored the glide flight, Woolams familiarized himself with the plane's handling characteristics. He found the plane very easy to fly, and became so preoccupied with the rocket plane that he almost undershot the landing.[7]

Post-flight inspection showed the XS-1 dropped clean without brushing the guideposts, and no traces of red paint showed from the pipe or guideposts. Subsequent flights proved the guide rails and ejector unnecessary. In all, Bell completed 10 flights on the airplane at Pinecastle, one in January, 8 in February, and one in March. The XS-1 proved extremely responsive to the pilot, and Woolams considered the airplane the best he had ever flown. After several flights to familiarize himself with the general handling characteristics of the plane, Woolams made detailed data-gathering flights on the XS-1's longitudinal and directional stability, and its rate of roll. The XS-1 suffered damage on two glide flights. On the fourth flight, Feb. 11, 1946, the main gear retracted on landing, and the plane damaged its left wing. A week later, on the next flight, Feb. 19, 1946, the nosewheel retracted during the landing runout, damaging the underside of the fuselage nose. But annoying as these accidents were, they did not delay the flight test program. Highly pleased with the results of the glide flights at Pinecastle, Bell flew the XS-1 via its B-29 mother airplane back to Buffalo. The company now began preparations for the powered flight portion of the contractor test program.[8]

Back at Buffalo, changes took place in the XS-1 design and flight test team. When the AAF contracted with Bell for the development of the XS-2 supersonic sweptwing research airplane, XS-1 project engineer Stanley W. Smith left the XS-1 program to assume leadership of the XS-2 program. Bell engineer Richard H. Frost replaced him on the XS-1 effort. Though an engineer, Frost was a test pilot by training and avocation. He had joined Bell as a test pilot in mid-1943, serving in this capacity until a serious accident in February 1945. He had to bail out of a burning P-63 Kingcobra at high altitude, and severe burns on his hands kept him grounded for six months. During that time he developed instrumentation to make radio-controlled dive tests in P-59's, one of Robert Stanley's ideas to acquire dive information without risking the life of the pilot in the attempt. Radio control appeared so promising that the Navy had Frost run a series of remote control tests on the Grumman F7F Tigercat, and the Army had him do the same to a Lockheed P-80 Shooting Star. Then Frost moved up to take Stanley Smith's place on the XS-1 program.[9]

Frost had to get the RMI powerplant installed and checked out, and then get the XS-1 through its contractor powered flight program. While the XS-1 #1 was at Pinecastle, Bell completed fabrication of the 8 percent wing and 6 percent tail originally intended for the airplane. So, when the plane arrived back at the Bell plant, Bell technicians installed the thinner wing and tail on the airplane, after removing the thicker 10 percent wing and 8 percent tail. The 10 percent wing and 8 percent tail went to the XS-1 #2, serial 46-063, then being completed at the Bell plant. The first available RMI XLR-11 engine went into the latter airplane. But at the same time that Bell readied the second XS-1 for powered-flight trials, the company had to replace its chief test pilot.

Together with Alvin M. "Tex" Johnston, another Bell test pilot, Jack

Woolams had secured two wartime P-39 Airacobras and modified them for air racing. They replaced the drab wartime camouflage with a striking yellow-and-black color scheme, and readied the planes for the 1946 Thompson Trophy air race. On Friday, August 30, the Friday before Labor Day, Jack Woolams took Cobra I, one of the racers, out over Lake Ontario for an engine test. Skimming low over the water, something went wrong. The converted fighter plunged into the lake, killing Woolams instantly.

At the time of his death, Woolams had little doubt he would be the first man to fly faster than sound. But he did not consider the possibility particularly sensational. In an article, ironically published after his death, he wrote that the flights

> . . . will be the logical result of a great deal of hard, cooperative work. There will, of course, be some danger, as there must be in flying at new altitudes and speeds.
>
> But we are well prepared. I have complete confidence in the airplane and the men who have worked so long and hard on the project. And I am completely confident that the research we are conducting will more than justify the time and expense when the results are made available to the aeronautical industry.[10]

On Monday, September 2, Woolams' friend Tex Johnston took off from Cleveland Airport with eleven other competitors. For the better part of an hour his powerful Cobra II led a mixed pack of modified fighters around the 30-mile closed course, and when Johnston landed, he had captured the Thompson Trophy at an average speed of 373.9 mph, 90 mph faster than the previous record set by Roscoe Turner in the 1938 Thompson race.[11] After landing, Johnston turned over half of the $19,400 purse to Jack Woolams' widow.[12]

The Tuesday after the accident, Robert Stanley announced that another Bell pilot would replace Woolams on the XS-1 program. This pilot was 23-year-old Chalmers H. "Slick" Goodlin. Despite his youth, Goodlin had considerable background in flying. He soloed in several aircraft—a J-3 Piper Cub, Aeronca C-3, and Waco F-2 among others—before his seventeenth birthday. In 1941, he enlisted in the Royal Canadian Air Force for flight training, won a commission as a Pilot Officer, and served as a flight instructor in Ontario. He transferred to the Royal Air Force's Fighter Command, and served as a Spitfire pilot until he left the RCAF in December 1942 for the U.S. Navy. After carrier qualification, he flew as a Navy test and ferry pilot, then joined Bell in December 1943 as a company test pilot.[13]

While with Bell, Goodlin had had a fair share of close calls. Shortly after joining Bell, Goodlin went aloft in a production P-39 for a production test. The engine caught fire, and Goodlin barely escaped from the smoke- and flame-filled cockpit in time to use his parachute. Besides making some remote control flights in modified YP-59's and a Navy F7F, Goodlin flew as test pilot on the Bell L-39 low-speed sweptwing research airplane and on the Bell XP-83, a Bell prototype long-range jet fighter. During one XP-83 test flight, the plane caught fire in midair, and the right wing began to burn away. Goodlin stayed with the burning jet until the second crewman, a Bell flight-test observer, could bail out. Then Goodlin parachuted from the stricken plane.[14] In sum, Goodlin was an excellent pilot of the "stick and rudder" school whose lack of formal engineering training did not detract in the least from his ability as a research pilot.

In September 1946, NACA designated Walter C. Williams as project engineer for the XS-1. Later that month, NACA detailed a group of 13 engineers, instrument technicians, and technical observers from Langley Laboratory, under the direction of Williams, to Muroc Dry Lake to assist in the XS-1 flight-research program. The small group arrived at the dry lake on September 30, 1946.[15] NACA Hq. considered the group a unit of Langley Laboratory on temporary assignment to Langley. The head, Walter Williams, reported directly to Hartley A. Soulé, Chief of the Stability Research Division at Langley, and the man responsible for establishing the NACA Muroc test group. The NACA personnel arrived at Muroc at a time of greatly increased awareness of the problems of transonic flight, largely because of gloomy predictions by "Sunday supplement" writers, but mostly from the recent death of Geoffrey de Havilland in the D.H. 108.

Though the Pinecastle trials had proven the feasibility of air launching the XS-1 and the good low-speed handling qualities of the little rocket airplane, they also clearly demonstrated the inadequacy of attempting to operate the plane from a conventional airfield. Clearly what was needed was a more suitable secluded location where flight testing could take place without worry of overflying populated areas, and where the rocket plane could have a large emergency landing area to set down upon. Only one location fitted these qualifications: the Army airfield at Muroc Dry Lake.

Almost fittingly, the dry lake was nearly as exotic as the research airplanes themselves. In keeping with its strange environment, the Mojave desert houses many flat dusty plains devoid of ridges, dunes, or brush. These are dry lakes: Cuddeback, Searles, and Koehn, to name a few. Early in the twentieth century, a silver and gold mining firm set up an encampment on one such lake, and, after the company name, dubbed it Rodriguez Dry Lake. It is now known as Rogers Dry Lake, the largest dry lake in the world. A vast expanse of parched clay and silt, the lake is dry for 10 months of the year. When dry, it can support up to 250 psi of pressure on its surface. Roughly shaped like a lopsided figure-8, it has a surface area of 65 square miles. Over the year, winds erode its surface and heat chips and cracks the clay until, by the fall, the lake resembles a huge quilt or puzzle. Then come winter rains. The wind blows the water back and forth across the lakebed, smoothing and filling in the cracks. Then, the rising temperatures of the new year dry off the water and evaporate it, and the lakebed is once more virtually glass-smooth. For these reasons, automobiles and airplanes can move smoothly across its surface, and even the heaviest of aircraft can take off and land without fear of sinking into the lakebed. Rogers Dry Lake is the largest natural landing field in the world.[16]

In 1910, Clifford and Effie Corum, together with Clifford's brother Ralph, settled on a 160-acre plot of land on the edge of Rodriguez Dry Lake. They recruited for other settlers to join them, and soon a tiny community developed along the Santa Fe Railway where it edged across the dry lake. The brothers opened a small general store, dug wells for water, and held Sunday church services in their home. They decided to name the community Corum, but post office authorities objected because California already had a township named Cor*am*, and the similarity in spelling would surely cause confusion. The Corums then suggested Muroc, created by spelling the name backwards, but the Santa Fe Railway objected because of a rail stop named Murdock. Instead, the railroad suggested Dorado, Ophir, Yermo, or Istar. But the Corum brothers persisted, and the little settlement became known as Muroc. The settlers soon applied the name to the dry lake as well.[17]

By the 1930s, Muroc represented little more than a spot on the map. North of the lake ran highway 58 over which, during Depression years, "Okies" streamed, entering California at Needles and then wending their way along through the desert communities of Essex, Ludlow, Barstow, Boron, Mojave, and on into Bakersfield, in their search for a livelihood; this is a path immortalized by John Steinbeck. Around the same time, Muroc gained notoriety as the site of supposedly the largest moonshine distillery in southern California; at night liquor runners and prohibition agents attempted evasion and interception on the clay lakebed.[18]

In early 1933, Col. Henry H. "Hap" Arnold, commanding officer of March Field, Riverside, California, desperately needed a bombing and gunnery range for his bomber and pursuit pilots to hone their deadly skills. The Navy refused the Army Air Corps the use of the Pacific Ocean.[19] Just north of March Field, over the San Diego mountains, lay the Mojave, the most logical choice for such a range, for it was largely unpopulated and desolate to begin with. Arnold decided to scout the Mojave to determine its suitability. Arriving at Muroc one morning at 6 A.M., he liked the looks of the expansive dry lake, an ideal range and landing area. After his return to March Field, proceedings were initiated to gain title to the land. Most of the land already belonged to the government, and it was on these portions that the Air Corps immediately began operations.[20]

In September 1933, a cadre of soldiers from March Field, under the direction of Sgt. Harley Fogelman, established a camp on the eastern shore of the lake and laid out the bombing and gunnery range. Except for an occasional forced landing or some limited private testing of aircraft from the lakebed, Muroc Dry Lake remained relatively tranquil until Pearl Harbor.[21] The war brought a building boom and an influx of 40,000 people.

In 1942, the AAF designated the bombing and gunnery range as Muroc Army Air Base. In November 1943, it became Muroc Army Air Field, complete with barracks, a control tower, and a concrete runway. P-38 fighter pilots flew practice missions from the base, and B-24 and B-25 crews departed for bombing runs over the range. To train bomber crews for antishipping strikes, engineers constructed a 650 ft. replica of a Japanese _Mogami_ class heavy cruiser in the middle of the dry lake, which pilots promptly dubbed the "Muroc Maru." In 1950, when Army demolitions personnel disassembled the "vessel," they found numerous unexploded bombs in its midst.[22]

In 1942, the Materiel Center at Wright Field designated the north end of the dry lake as the Materiel Center Flight Test Site. That fall, the nation's first turbojet, the XP-59A, arrived at Muroc for its initial flight tests, held in great secrecy. In 1944, the AAF redesignated the north end of the lake as the Muroc Flight Test Base. Then, in October 1946, both the crew-training and flight-test activities at Muroc merged into a single test facility at Muroc Army Air Field, under the direction of the Air Materiel Command at Wright Field. Both during and after the war, Muroc witnessed a steady procession of exotic airplanes undergo tests from its lakebed. In July 1946, for example, a captured German Heinkel He 162 from Freeman Field made two flights. Later, two B-17's landed on the lakebed under remote control after completing a pilotless flight from Hawaii to California. It was into this environment of strange and unique airplanes that the XS-1 came.[23]

In preparation for the XS-1, technicians at Muroc erected two huge tanks, one a 15,000 gal. capacity tank for liquid oxygen, the other a 3,300 gal. capacity tank for liquid nitrogen. They dug a loading pit for the XS-1 to roll into before being hoisted into the B-29 above it, and modified a standard Army fuel trailer to function as a mixing tank for alcohol and water for the XS-1's rocket fuel.[24] On October 7, 1946, the XS-1 #2, joined to its B-29 launch airplane, departed from Bell's Niagara Falls plant accompanied by a P-51D chase airplane and a C-47 for personnel transportation. They arrived at Muroc on October 8 and 9.

Getting promptly to work, Richard Frost and the Bell test team readied the XS-1 for a glide flight the next day, October 10.[25]

The first attempt at a flight met with failure. During the climb to launch altitude, Goodlin noticed an increase in cabin pressure and actuated the cabin-pressure dump valve, which failed to function. The emergency pressure relief valve also failed to operate properly and, as a last resort, Goodlin released the cabin door lock. With internal pressure now 9 psi above outside atmospheric pressure, the door shot out, bending the entry ladder from the B-29 and jamming between the ladder and the XS-1. Goodlin could not return to the B-29, and remained in the XS-1 while Harold Dow brought the B-29 in for a safe landing.[26]

After repairing the door and ladder damage, and checking the operation of the dump valves, Bell attempted another glide flight the next day, October 11. This one was completely successful. The Muroc Army Air Field historian reported laconically,

> The B-29 carrying the XS-1 took off at 1413 the 11th of October. The Rocket was released between 1455 and 1456, landing at 1503. The mission was completed successfully.[27]

On October 14, Goodlin completed the XS-1 #2's second glide flight, followed by the third three days later, on October 17. Then, for about the next month, Bell performed routine maintenance on the P-51 chase airplane, installed more efficient filters in the alcohol-water mixing unit, and modified the propellant pressurization system of the XS-1 #2 so that the pilot could regulate it from the cockpit.[28]

On December 2, Bell checked the XS-1's fuel jettison system on a glide flight during which Goodlin vented 1,930 lbs. of alcohol-water ballast. Four days later, the company attempted the first powered flight. It almost ended in disaster. During the climb to altitude, a nitrogen valve froze in the intense cold, preventing nitrogen from entering the liquid oxygen tank. Thus, the rocket engine could not be fired, nor could Goodlin jettison the propellants. The B-29 had to land with the XS-1, heavy with the full fuel load, still shackled in the bomb bay. Then the nose landing gear of the XS-1 inadvertently extended. If the B-29 landed with the XS-1's gear extended, the gear might cause both planes to crash, since, even with the XS-1's gear retracted, the separation between the XS-1's belly and the ground was less than a foot. Company president Lawrence Bell had brought a group of Bell company directors to watch the first powered flight of the rocket plane. Now, the officials worried over the launch crew's predicament. Richard Frost, in the chase P-51D, suggested that Goodlin retract the XS-1's nose gear during the B-29's landing approach. As the bomber swept down towards the Muroc runway, Goodlin raised the nose wheel. It remained up as the B-29 landed. Relieved, Bell said tersely, "Keep trying," and returned to Buffalo.[29]

On Monday, December 9, 1946, Bell again tried to obtain a successful powered flight. After climbing to altitude, all aircraft systems indicated satisfactory operation. A Muroc observer reported later,

> The Rocket was dropped at 1154 from an altitude of 27,000 feet. When the first unit was turned on, a streak of flame came from the tail of the rocket and continued to glow until the unit was shut off. The second unit was fired with results coincidental with those of the first. A FP-80 was following the Rocket to observe its reactions and also to take photographs. When the pilot of the XS-1, Chalmers Goodlin, fired the four units simultaneously, the FP-80 could not maintain a speed consistent with that of the Supersonic.[30]

To Goodlin, the rate of drop away from the B-29 seemed twice as fast with the full fuel load as the glide-flight drops; on this flight the XS-1 grossed 12,012 lbs. Ten seconds after drop he ignited the first chamber, then fired chamber 2. Under 3,000-lb thrust, the XS-1 accelerated rapidly. Goodlin shut off chamber 2 and began a slow climb at 330 mph IAS on chamber one. Sitting in the cockpit, Goodlin could barely hear the rocket's operation. At 35,000 feet he relit chamber 2, and sped to Mach 0.79. He found the handling characteristics of the rocket plane very good. After shutting down both chambers 1 and 2, Goodlin dove to 15,000 feet. During the dive, the XS-1 began a slight snaking motion, caused by lateral shifting of the fuel load. Though Bell had installed transverse fuel tank baffles to prevent longitudinal shifting of the fuel load in flight, the baffles did not prevent fuel from sloshing from side to side. Goodlin did not consider the snaking serious, however, for he could easily control it.[31]

Goodlin pulled out into straight and level flight at 15,000 feet and ignited all 4 chambers. The orange rocket plane shot forward with "Terrific acceleration . . . comparable to the application of water injection power in a conventional fighter from a standing start."[32] After a few seconds of full power, the liquid oxygen line pressure dropped, and Goodlin shut the engine off. Just then a fire-warning light came on in the cockpit of the plane, and Goodlin radioed Richard Frost in a chase P-51 if Frost could see any signs of fire. Frost could not, but the fire-warning light remained on until Goodlin landed on the lakebed. The test team found a small fire occurred in the engine bay of the airplane, burning some wiring but not causing further damage. Replacement of wiring kept the plane grounded for slightly over one week.[33]

Though the XS-1 outdistanced the slower FP-80 Shooting Star photographic plane, the rocket-research aircraft completely outclassed any other conceivable chase plane, particularly the propeller-driven P-51D Mustang of Richard Frost. Frost recommended that he be furnished a P-80 in place of the P-51 for the remainder of the Bell XS-1 program. The P-80 became the standard chase plane on future XS-1 flights. On December 20, Goodlin completed the rocket plane's second powered flight, and on January 8, 1947, attained Mach 0.8 at 35,000 feet. As part of its contractor requirements, Bell had to demonstrate satisfactory stability and control characteristics to Mach 0.8. At this speed, Goodlin reported the plane under "perfect control," with only a "very slight shuddering" indicating compressibility phenomenon. The NACA strain-gauge installation in the plane indicated the compressibility buffet to be of negligible magnitude.[34]

By the end of January 1947, Goodlin had completed 10 contractor flights in the XS-1 #2. In February, he began a series of flights to demonstrate the XS-1's structural strength and to gather buffet-boundary data. He made pullups to 8.7g at Mach numbers from 0.4 to 0.8 without damaging the XS-1's robust structure. At the same time, the RMI XLR-11 engine proved equally satisfactory. Though the RMI company only guaranteed the engine for one hour of service, the engine in the XS-1 #2 continued to function excellently beyond this time limit.[35] On the last day of the month, Bell flew the XS-1 #2 via B-29 back to Buffalo for minor modifications to the propulsion system to improve ventilation of the engine compartment, and also to perform a required 50-hour check on the launch B-29. The company planned to complete the check and modifications of the XS-1 #2 by early May so that it could complete its final contractor test flights.[36]

Early in March 1947, Bell completed the XS-1 #1, serial 46-062.[37] The chief difference between this airplane and the XS-1 #2 lay in the wing configuration. After its glide trials at Pinecastle with the 10 percent-thick wing and 8 percent-thick tail in early 1946, Bell installed the XLR-11 rocket engine in the plane and replaced the wing and tail with the newly fabricated 8 percent-thick wing and 6 percent-thick tail. The XS-1 #1 also had a slightly higher gross weight than the XS-1 #2. Thus, because of the increased weight and thinner wing section, Bell predicted that the XS-1 #1 would have a higher stalling speed than its sister aircraft.

On April 5, 1947, Bell's B-29 arrived back at Muroc, the XS-1 #1 nestling in the bomb bay. After a weather delay, Goodlin made a glide flight in the XS-1 #1 on April 10, noticing little difference in the handling qualities of the plane in comparison with those of the XS-1 #2 with its thicker wing and tail surfaces. The next day, Bell made the airplane's first powered flight. All went well until the landing. Upon touchdown, the XS-1 #1 skipped back above the surface, coasted for about 100 feet, then landed hard. The nosewheel and its locking structure absorbed the landing load, the locking structure sheared, and the nosewheel retracted. The XS-1 skidded to a halt on its main landing gear and nose undersurface. Repairs took two weeks, and to make the best use of the delay, NACA engineers from Walter Williams' little unit completed instrumentation installation in the rocket plane.[38] Late in April, Bell technicians at Muroc completed repairs to the XS-1 #1, and on April 28 and April 30, Goodlin completed the plane's second and third powered flights. After 2 unsuccessful flight attempts he completed the fourth powered flight of the XS-1 #1 on May 5.[39]

Bell completed modifications to the XS-1 #2 at Buffalo on May 7, 1947. That same day, the launch B-29 left Muroc to ferry the XS-1 #2 back to California. It returned 2 days later with the second XS-1. The end of the planned 20 powered flight program was now in sight, and Bell concentrated on final demonstrations of airworthiness before delivery of the airplanes to the AAF Air Materiel Command. By May 21, Goodlin completed 2 buffet-boundary investigations in the XS-1 #1. The next day, Bell test pilot Alvin M. "Tex" Johnston checked out in the XS-1 #2 in the first flight of this airplane since its return to Muroc, and executed an 8g pullout. After a one-week weather delay, Slick Goodlin performed an airspeed calibration flight in the XS-1 #2 on May 29, 1947, bringing the Bell contractor program to a close. Robert Stanley, now Bell's Vice-President for Engineering, offered project engineer Richard Frost the last flight in the XS-1 before Bell turned the planes over to the Air Materiel Command. But Frost declined. He knew the importance of the airplane, and he did not want to risk the program's progress just to say he flew it.[40] During the almost 8-month contractor program on the airplane, Bell met all the requirements. The planes completed a total of 20 powered flights, pulled the requisite 8g loading, and demonstrated satisfactory handling characteristics to Mach 0.8.

Shortly after Bell completed the contractor program, an incident occurred that nearly claimed the Bell XS-1 #2. Ironically, it happened not in the air, but on the ground. On June 5, five C-54's loaded with representatives of the Aviation Writers' Association landed at Muroc to observe a flying show at the field. The display included the latest experimental airplanes, the Army AAF XB-43, XB-45, XB-46, N9M, P-82, and P-84, as well as the Navy XFJ-1 and XF6U. Douglas test pilot Gene May showed off the red D-558-1, Slick Goodlin made a powered flight from the B-29 in the XS-1 #1, and, on the ground, Richard Frost gave a ground demonstration of the XS-1 #2's rocket engine. He fired the first cylinder, then lit off the third, which exploded. Amid the roar of the engine, the explosion went unnoticed until a fire-warning light flashed in the cockpit. Frost, leaning into the cockpit on a ladder, quickly got down and ran along the fuselage to see what was wrong. The paint on the rear fuselage blistered before his eyes in the invisible alcohol flame. Frost's shouts for assistance brought a quick response from the Bell ground crew, who removed access doors so that the Muroc fire department could put out the fire. The fire department doused the flames quickly, but the fire severely damaged the engine bay and aft fuselage of the plane, and Bell had no choice but to ferry it via B-29 back to Buffalo for repairs.[41]

Originally, when Bell had the XS-1 under development, the AAF planned to place a separate contract with the company for research flights after the company completed acceptance tests on the airplane. The NACA would get one airplane for its own flight tests.[42] At a joint AAF Air Materiel Command-NACA conference at NACA Hq. in February 1947, the NACA agreed to furnish fuel, maintenance, and a flight crew for the XS-1 airplanes, and the Army agreed to furnish fuel, spare parts, maintenance, and a flight crew for the launch B-29.[43] In anticipation of the NACA XS-1 program, De Elroy Beeler joined the NACA Muroc unit in January from Langley Laboratory as engineer in charge of the XS-1 loads program. Gerald M. Truszynski rejoined the project as instrumentation engineer in March 1947, and Joseph R. Vensel, a former test pilot, arrived from NACA's Lewis Flight Propulsion Laboratory in April to head up NACA flight operations at Muroc.[44] In June 1947, the AAF decided to let the Air Materiel Command's Flight Test Division at Wright Field play a direct role in the XS-1 flight-research program.

On June 30, 1947, NACA and AAF Air Materiel Command representatives met in conference at Wright Field to discuss the future program of the Bell XS-1. The conference marked the initiation of a two-pronged transonic research program. The representatives decided to let the AMC's Flight Test Division conduct an accelerated test program to investigate transonic flight phenomena to a Mach number of 1.1 using the XS-1 #1. The AMC would seek to attain this speed as rapidly as was consistent with safety, in as few flights as possible. The NACA, on the other hand, would conduct a slower and more detailed research program, making thorough examinations of transonic stability and control and flight loads using the XS-1 #2. Because of the different emphasis in each phase of the flight program, the two XS-1's would have different instrumentation packages. The XS-1 #1, the AAF aircraft, would have detailed instrumentation for speed measurement; measurement of normal, longitudinal, and transverse acceleration; measurement of elevator-stick force; and recording of aileron, elevator, and rudder positions. The NACA XS-1 #2 would have more detailed instrumentation to record all of the quantities measured on the AAF XS-1 #1, plus measurement of angular velocity in roll or pitch; sideslip angle; and aileron, elevator, and rudder forces.[45] Both had a 6-channel telemeter installed to transmit airspeed, control surface position, altitude, and normal acceleration to the ground, so that, as Walter Williams later recalled, "if we lost the airplane, we could at least find out a little about what had happened."[46]

NOTES

1. Letter, H. J. E. Reid (dir., Langley Laboratory) to NACA Hq., 29 Dec. 1945.

2. _Ibid_. The actual decision to use Pinecastle had been made about a month before the Reid letter.

3. Biographical data sheet in NASA Historical Archives. Also Stack interview, 19 May 1971.

4. Biographical data sheet in NASA Historical Archives. Also interview of Gerald M. Truszynski by the author, 21 May 1971.

5. Jack Woolams, "How We Are Preparing to Reach Supersonic Speeds," _Aviation_, XLV, No. 9, (September 1946), 38–39. Also Ronald D. Neal, "The Bell XP-59A Airacomet: The United States' First Jet Aircraft," pp. 171–72.

6. Stanley and Sandstrom, "Development of the XS-1 Airplane," 9 Jan. 1948, p. 15. Also date from information supplied to NASM. Found in X-1 Series #2 File, NASM.

7. Stanley and Sandstrom, "Development of the XS-1 Airplane," 9 Jan. 1948, p. 15. Also Lundgren, _Across the High Frontier_, pp. 64–65. Date from chronology of rocket research aircraft flights prepared by Robert W. Mulac, Langley Research Center. Hereafter cited as Mulac, XS-1 #1 (or#2) chronology. Copy in NASA Historical Archives.

8. _Ibid_.

9. Interview of Richard Frost by the author, 25 May 1972.

10. Woolams, "How We Are Preparing to Reach Supersonic Speeds," p. 39.

11. _The New York Sun_, 3 Sept. 1946.

12. John H. Newland, "Stardust on his Boots," in Gene Gurney, ed., _Test Pilots_ (New York, 1962), p. 124.

13. _Air Trails Pictorial_, XXX, No. 4, (January 1948), 15, 127–28. Frost interview, 25 May 1972.

14. _Ibid_. Also Chalmers Goodlin, "Test Pilot's Bail Out," in Gurney, ed., _Test Pilots_, pp. 71–74.

15. Walter C. Williams, "A Brief History of the High-Speed Flight Station," in NASA Historical Archives. Also Williams biographical data sheet in NASA Historical Archives.

16. Air Force Flight Test Center, ARDC, _Experimental Research Aircraft_, pp. 3–4.

17. John Ball, Jr., _Edwards: Flight Test Center of the U.S.A.F._ (New York, 1962), pp. 12–14.

18. Gladwin Hill, _Dancing Bear: An Inside Look at California Politics_, (New York, 1968), p. 16. Wesley Price, "They Fly Our X-Ships," _The Saturday Evening Post_, CCXXIII, No. 1, (July 1, 1950), pp. 26–27, 105.

19. H. H. Arnold, _Global Mission_, (New York, 1949), p. 136.

20. _Ibid_. Also AFFTC, _Experimental Research Aircraft_, p. 2; and Ball, _Edwards_, pp. 14–15.

21. _Ibid_. (Except Arnold).

22. Ball, _Edwards_, pp. 42–43. _Experimental Research Aircraft_, p. 2.

23. Muroc Army Air Field Historical Report, 1 July 1946–30 September 1946, pp. 1, 2. In Air Force Archives, Maxwell AFB.

24. Stanley and Sandstrom, "Development of the XS-1 Airplane," 9 January 1948, pp. 15–16.

25. Progress report, Project MX-653, Richard Frost to Commanding General, Air Materiel Command, 21 October 1946. Hereafter cited as Frost, *MX-653 report*, and date.

26. *Ibid*. Also Lundgren, *Across the High Frontier*, p. 162.

27. Muroc Army Air Field Historical Report, 1 October 1946–31 December 1946, p. 11. In Air Force Archives, Maxwell AFB.

28. Frost, *MX-653 report*, 21 Oct. 1946.

29. Lundgren, *Across the High Frontier*, p. 163. Also Stanley and Sandstrom, "Development of the XS-1 Airplane," 9 January 1948, p. 16. And Frost, *MX-653 report*, 13 Dec. 1946.

30. Muroc AAF Historical Report, 1 Oct. 1946–31 Dec. 1946, p. 12.

31. Chalmers H. Goodlin, *Pilot's Report, Flight* 5, 9 Dec. 1946.

32. *Ibid*.

33. *Ibid*., also Frost, *MX-653 report*, 13 Dec. 1946.

34. A. J. Marchese, *MX-653 report* (rough draft), 14 Jan. 1947.

35. Frost, *MX-653 report* (rough draft), 28 Jan. 1947. Frost, *MX-653 report*, (rough draft), 10 Feb. 1947.

36. Marchese, *MX-653 report*, 10 March 1947.

37. Marchese, *MX-653 report*, 1 April 1947.

38. Frost, *MX-653 report*, (rough draft), 11 April 1947.

39. Frost, *MX-653 report*, (rough draft), 28 April 1947. Frost, *MX-653 report*, (rough draft), 12 May 1947.

40. Frost, *MX-653 report* (rough draft), 12 May 1947. Frost, *MX-653 report*, 2 June 1947. Lundgren, *Across the High Frontier*, p. 67. Muroc AAF Historical Report, 1 Jan. 1947–30 June 1947, pp. 20–21. Frost interview, 25 May 1972.

41. Frost, *MX-653 report*, 16 June 1947. Also Lundgren, *Across the High Frontier*, pp. 67–68. Also Muroc AAF Historical Report, 1 Jan. 1947–30 June 1947, pp. 31–32.

42. Air Materiel Command, Correspondence Summary of Project MX-653 History, 14 Jan. 1947, p. 2. Transmitted to the author by Ezra Kotcher.

43. Letter, J. W. Crowley (Acting Dir. of Aero. Research) to Brig. Gen. A. R. Crawford, 19 Feb. 1947. In LaRC files.

44. NACA High-Speed Flight Station, "X-Press: 10th Anniversary Supersonic Flight," 14 Oct. 1957, pp. 11, 12.

45. Hartley A. Soulé, Memo for Chief of Research (NACA), "Army proposal for accelerated tests of the XS-1 to a Mach number of 1.1," 21 July 1947. In LaRC files. Also see Charles E. Yeager, "The Operation of the XS-1 Airplane," in *Air Force Supersonic Research Airplane XS-1 Report No. 1*, 9 Jan. 1948, p. 17. And Walter C. Williams, "Instrumentation, Airspeed Calibration, Tests, Results and Conclusions," in *Air Force Supersonic Research Airplane XS-1 Report No. 1*, 9 Jan. 1948, pp. 21–22.

46. Statement of Walter C. Williams at the AIAA History Session, San Francisco, Calif., 28 July 1965, in NASA Historical Archives.

V

THE AIR FORCE AND NACA XS-1

PROGRAM

I n midsummer 1947, the AAF began preparations to fly the XS-1 faster than sound. Overall responsibility for directing the AAF XS-1 program rested upon James H. Voyles, AMC XS-1 project engineer; Paul F. Bikle, chief of the AMC Flight Test Division's Performance Engineering Branch; and Colonel Albert Boyd, chief of the AMC's Flight Test Division. An Army pilot since 1929, Boyd specialized in flight testing military aircraft. On the XS-1 program, he had responsibility for selecting the AMC test crew that would fly the airplane at Muroc. He was highly respected as a pilot by other service test pilots. Most recently, Boyd had flown from Wright Field to Muroc to win the world's air-speed record back for the United States. At Muroc, he flew a modified Lockheed Shooting Star, designated P-80R, over a 3-kilometer course. During 4 low-altitude speed runs, he averaged 623.738 mph, bringing the speed record back to the United States for the first time in 24 years.

In searching for a pilot, Boyd turned to the Fighter Test Section of the AMC's Flight Test Division. One day, Major Kenneth Chilstrom, chief of the Fighter Test Section, called a meeting of the fighter test pilots at Wright Field. He announced the AAF was going to fly the XS-1, and he wanted the names of those pilots interested in flying the rocket airplane. Among the many pilots who expressed an interest was Capt. Charles E. "Chuck" Yeager, a 24-year-old fighter pilot from Hamlin, West Virginia.[1]

Charles Yeager enlisted in the Army in September 1941 and, after a brief stint as a mechanic and crew chief on a Beech AT-11, left for pilot training. He proved an adept pupil, with all the aggressiveness and skill of a born fighter pilot. In March 1943, he won his wings as a Flight Officer and began training as a fighter pilot with the 357th Fighter Squadron based at Tonopah, Nevada. During a practice mission against some B-24's, the supercharger on his P-39 disintegrated, setting the plane on fire. Yeager jumped clear and pulled his ripcord. The opening parachute knocked him unconscious, and when he landed he cracked a vertebra. After recuperating in a hospital, he left for England in January 1944 as a replacement P-51 pilot.

He set an impressive record in the European Theater of Operations. On March 4, 1944, while on a bomber-escort mission he shot down a Messerschmitt Bf 109. The next day, however, three Focke Wulf Fw 190s teamed up to shoot down his Mustang. He parachuted safely to earth, and managed to contact the French underground. Over three weeks later, he slipped across the Spanish border, carrying a wounded fellow escapee to safety. Back in England, the AAF, after twice promoting Yeager to captain, restricted him to noncombat flying for security reasons, to prevent his possible recapture on future flights. The restriction lasted until after D-day. Then he began a meteoric combat record. On October 12, 1944, he shot down five Bf 109s; on November 6 he destroyed a Me 262 jet fighter and damaged two others; on November 27, four Fw 190s fell before his guns. By the time of his return from combat, he had shot down eleven German warplanes, shared in the destruction of another, damaged three more. He held the Distinguished Flying Cross, the Bronze Star, the Silver Star with oak leaf cluster, the Air Medal with six oak leaf clusters, and the Purple Heart.[2]

Back in the United States, Chuck Yeager served briefly as a flight instructor at Perrin Field, but the AAF posted him to Wright Field as a pilot in the Fighter Test Section. He checked out in the jet-propelled P-59, then into the higher performance P-80. Shortly after Maj. Kenneth Chilstrom asked for the names of pilots interested in flying the XS-1, Col. Boyd called Yeager into his office. He filled the young pilot in on the details of the project, and again asked him if he'd be interested in flying the plane. Yeager replied affirmatively. Boyd then asked Yeager who he would recommend for the project, excluding himself. Yeager recommended 1st Lt. Robert A. Hoover and Capt. Jack Ridley.[3]

Like Yeager, Robert Hoover had seen combat in Europe during the war. He joined the AAF upon the outbreak of hostilities as a flight cadet, and received training in twin-engine aircraft, though he preferred flying fighters. After arriving overseas in England, he test-flew aircraft at a repair depot, flying aircraft ranging from fighters to four-engine bombers. He requested combat duty, and the AAF transferred him to the 52nd Fighter Group, flying British-designed Spitfire Mk. V fighters. On his sixtieth mission, a Fw 190 shot his Spitfire down. Not as lucky as Yeager had been, Hoover spent the remainder of the war in *Stalag Luft I*, a Nazi POW camp for captured Allied airmen. After release, Hoover joined the Flight Test Division at Wright Field.[4]

Capt. Jack L. Ridley held a B.S. in mechanical engineering from the University of Oklahoma. During the war he served as engineering liaison officer at the Consolidated Vultee plant in Fort Worth, Texas, on the B-32 and B-36 program. He had completed pilot training in May·1942. In March 1944, he attended the AAF School of Engineering at Wright Field, then received assignment to Caltech, where he earned an M.S. in aeronautical engineering in July 1945. The AAF assigned him to the AMC Flight Test Division at Wright Field, where he underwent test-pilot training in the spring of 1946.[5]

Yeager's choices coincided with those of Col. Boyd. Boyd selected Charles Yeager as project pilot, Robert Hoover as alternate, and Jack Ridley as flight-test project engineer. He notified Lt. Gen. Benjamin W. Chidlaw, deputy commander of the Air Materiel Command, of his decision. Then he sent Yeager, Hoover, and Ridley to Buffalo for familiarization.[6]

At Bell, the three pilots met with the XS-1 design team and observed a test firing of the XS-1 #2's rocket engine. By mid-July, Bell had completed repairs to the aircraft following its near-disastrous fire at Muroc on June 5. Rather than waste time trying to patch the damaged airplane, Bell simply replaced the entire tail assembly of the XS-1 #2 with that of the XS-1 #3, serial 46-064, then awaiting completion. As an additional safety measure, Bell replaced all the aluminum alcohol, oxygen, and nitrogen lines in the engine compartment with lines of stainless steel.[7] The AMC Flight Test Division chief selected Maj. Robert L. Cardenas, an experienced test pilot, as B-29 launch aircraft pilot, and Lt. Edward L. Swindell as B-29 flight engineer. Late in July, Bell technicians attached the XS-1 #2 beneath the B-29 Superfortress for ferrying back to Muroc. The AMC test team then departed from the Bell plant for California. They arrived at the desert test center on July 27, 1947, one day after President Harry Truman signed the Armed Forces Unification Act creating a separate Department of the Air Force.[8]

Bell had closed down the company test facility at Muroc in mid-July, but the AMC borrowed Richard Frost to run a little ground school for the Air Materiel Command test team. Through the remainder of July and into early August, Frost briefed the Air Force crew on the airplane systems and the intricacies of launching it in flight. On Wednesday, August 6, Yeager made his first glide flight in the XS-1 #1. At 5,000 feet, while the B-29 climbed to launch altitude, Yeager clambered down the access ladder into the XS-1's cockpit and wriggled inside. At 18,000 feet, Cardenas dropped the rocket plane as Frost and Robert Hoover watched from 2 chase P-80's; Yeager was on his own. Like Woolams, Goodlin, and Johnston before him, he found the plane's control characteristics highly satisfactory and, as the plane glided towards the lakebed, he made 3 slow rolls. The next day, Yeager completed another glide flight with equal success. On August 8, Yeager dropped away from the B-29 on his final familiarization glide flight, and engaged Hoover's chase P-80 in a mock dogfight all the way down. The AMC test crew now concentrated on preparing for the first Air Force powered flights.[9]

Walter Williams' NACA Muroc Flight Test Unit also moved forward with plans for its own part in the two-pronged AF-NACA transonic research program. In August, the unit's first two research pilots arrived at Muroc, Herbert H. Hoover and Howard C. Lilly. A former Navy pilot, Lilly came to Muroc from NACA's Lewis Flight Propulsion Laboratory at Cleveland. During the 1946 Thompson Trophy Race at Cleveland, Lilly placed seventh in a P-39. Herbert H. Hoover, a NACA pilot since 1940, had been one of the first pilots deliberately to fly through thunderstorms on bad-weather flying research. He already had a reputation as a cool pilot in tight situations. Once, during an instrumentation calibration flight in a NACA SB2C Helldiver, the plane's cockpit canopy hood came loose in flight, smashing Hoover across the forehead and inflicting a deep cut that bled profusely. Though stunned by the blow and blinded by blood flowing into his eyes, Hoover instinctively retained control of the dive bomber, cleared his eyes, and, despite his injuries, brought the plane back to Langley for an emergency landing. On another occasion, while firing a rocket-propelled model from a P-51 in a Mach 0.7 dive, the model disintegrated, showering the Mustang with wreckage. The wreckage punctured the plane's coolant tank, but again Hoover brought the plane in for a successful forced landing. After arriving at Muroc in August, Hoover studied the XS-1 under Richard Frost's careful tutelage, and also kept abreast of the Douglas contractor program then underway on the D-558-1 Skystreak. Howard Lilly had no background in compressibility research, so Hoover fitted a P-51 with a Machmeter and accelerometer, and had Lilly fly it into the region of trim changes and buffeting to familiarize him with the characteristics of compressibility.[10]

Late in August, after checking out the rocket engine of the XS-1 #1 on the ground, Yeager readied himself for the first Air Force powered flight. As with his wartime Mustang fighters, he named the XS-1 #1

"Glamorous Glennis," in honor of his wife, and painted the inscription in red and white letters on the plane's nose. For the first flight, Yeager had strict instructions not to exceed Mach 0.8 in the rocket plane; the flight was for pilot familiarization rather than for acquisition of research data. On August 29, Cardenas lifted the heavy bomber off the runway at Muroc and droned upwards to launch altitude. At 7,000-ft pressure altitude, Yeager entered the XS-1 #1. During the final minutes before drop he pressurized both the fuel and liquid oxygen tanks, checked the fuel jettison system, and turned on the data recording switch that automatically activated the NACA recording instrumentation. Then, as Cardenas finished intoning the countdown, Yeager dropped away from the B-29 in the XS-1 #1, at 255 mph 21,000 feet above the tan desert.

Heavy with fuel, the rocket plane fell more than 500 ft. before Yeager ignited the first rocket chamber. Then, as the plane accelerated, he shut down chamber one and ignited chamber two, then shut down chamber two and ignited chamber three, following this with a slow roll. During the roll, the plane attained zero g, and chamber three shut down due to a drop in lox tank pressure, but he reignited it when the plane regained a nose-down attitude. He then shut off chamber three and fired chamber four, then shut down the engine and nosed into a dive, completely powerless. During the dive he vented some of the propellants to check the XS-1's jettison system, and noted the same snaking oscillation due to fuel sloshing that Goodlin had noticed on his first powered flight.

The full fuel load, combined with a dive entry speed of Mach 0.7, caused the XS-1 to pick up speed rapidly in the dive. Richard Frost, flying a chase FP-80, followed Yeager down and suddenly found he was traveling slightly over .8 Mach, with the P-80 buffeting and shaking from compressibility. At 5,000 feet, Yeager recovered from the dive, fired chamber one and initiated a shallow climb, then fired the remaining chambers in sequence. Climbing steeply in a vain attempt to keep below Mach 0.8, the pilot reached 35,000 ft., began recovery into level flight, and finally dropped the nose and rolled out to a normal attitude at 30,000 ft. after attaining Mach 0.85 during the recovery. Then he shut off the engine, jettisoned his remaining propellants, and glided down to the lakebed.[11]

Chuck Yeager's flight to Mach 0.85 brought a rapid note from Col. Albert Boyd that neither the XS-1 pilot nor airplane was expendable, "so please approach higher speeds progressively and safely to the limit of your best judgment."[12] Yeager and Jack Ridley responded that discussions between the AMC test team, NACA, and Bell project engineer Richard Frost suggested that no trouble would be encountered to Mach 0.85, and that when Yeager attained Mach 0.83 without difficulty, he felt safe in proceeding to Mach 0.85. The reply reiterated that the AMC test team regarded safety as of paramount importance.[13]

With Yeager now fully checked out in the airplane, the Air Force could begin research-flying the XS-1 #1. The Air Force desired to attain supersonic speed as quickly as was safely possible. The NACA favored a more cautious incremental approach to Mach 1. Writing about the program a decade later. Walter Williams stated.

> We were enthusiastic, there is little question. The Air Force group —Yeager, Ridley—were very, very enthusiastic. We were just beginning to know each other, to work together. There had to be a balance between complete enthusiasm and the hard, cold facts. We knew and felt that if this program should fail the whole research airplane program would fail, the whole aeronautical effort would be set back.[14]

The successful flights of the XS-1 during the contractor program had not served to mute the voices of Cassandras who predicted the rocket would explode, or that it would disintegrate from compressibility effects. In the background lurked the image of Geoffrey de Havilland's D.H. 108 coming apart over the Thames less than a year before. Richard Frost was more optimistic; he knew Bell had designed the plane according to the best aerodynamic knowledge available, with thin wings, a bullet fuselage, and a high tail. Beyond that, some educated guesswork went into the design. "If it could be done," he reflected later, "we knew we could do it."[15]

NACA and the Air Force did have some information to go on in predicting the transonic behavior of the XS-1. The Bell acceptance tests of the airplane agreed with low-speed wind-tunnel test results. Wind-tunnel data ended at about Mach 0.85, but predicted satisfactory behavior at those speeds. Wing-flow data ended around Mach 0.93 with inconclusive results. With the test information disappearing at the point where scientists expected critical changes to occur in stability and control characteristics, NACA engineers "developed a very lonely feeling as we began to run out of data."[16]

Yeager completed his second powered flight in the XS-1 #1 on September 4, attaining approximately Mach 0.89. But on the flight the telemeter failed, preventing acquisition of stability and control data, so Yeager repeated it on September 8 successfully, and then followed with a fourth flight to Mach 0.91 on September 10.[17] Now the AMC team decided to probe gingerly around Mach 0.9 to evaluate elevator and stabilizer effectiveness and buffeting.[18] Yeager reached Mach 0.92 on September 12, the fifth powered Air Force flight of the XS-1 #1, but the AMC temporarily suspended flights of the rocket plane after this flight pending installation of a faster stabilizer actuator. Yeager departed for Wright Field for final checks in a pressure suit—at the high altitude the XS-1 would make its speed runs, 50,000 feet and higher. Yeager needed a pressure suit to survive should cockpit pressurization be lost.[19]

While at Wright Field, Yeager and Jack Ridley reported to Col. Albert Boyd on the progress of the flight program. Then both flew back

to Muroc. The NACA Muroc Flight Test Unit, in addition to monitoring
the Air Force flights and performing data reduction and technical advis-
ing, had readied their XS-1 #2, with its 10 percent-thick wing and 8 percent-thick tail, for its acceptance flight. Since neither Herbert Hoover
nor Howard Lilly had yet checked out in the plane, the task fell to Yeager. Yeager made the NACA acceptance flight in the plane on September 25.[20]

In early October, the XS-1 #1 with Yeager returned to the air. By
now, the AMC flights had settled into a standard routine. Richard Frost,
Bell project engineer, flew low chase for the XS-1, and Lt. Robert Hoover
flew high chase, both in Lockheed P-80's. Frost flew formation about
1,000 feet above and behind the B-29, and when Robert Cardenas began
the countdown, Frost would nose over in a dive, pass below the B-29, and
be off Yeager's wing as the XS-1 dropped from the bomb bay. Frost then
would pull into level flight, then into a slight climb as Yeager ignited the
rocket engine. The accelerating rocket plane invariably left Frost's P-80
straggling far behind. Ten miles ahead of the B-29 and at about 48,000
feet, Bob Hoover flew along in his P-80, on high chase. After drop, Yeager
would climb towards Hoover's plane, so that at the climax of the mission,
he would pass Hoover at close range. The broad clear contrail generated
by the engine furnished Frost with a big marker to follow. But after
Yeager passed Hoover and shut off the engine, if it had not already
starved itself of propellants, the contrail ended. Hoover then had to keep
the little rocket plane in sight as it descended powerless to the lakebed, an
extremely difficult job, for the plane was small and hard to see against the
earth. Frost, catching up from the launch, also had to concentrate on
spotting the orange rocket plane. If the chase pilots momentarily shifted
their glance, they would lose sight of the hard-to-follow plane.[21]

After completing an airspeed calibration flight to Mach 0.925 on
October 8, the AMC test crew readied the airplane for another stability
and control investigation on October 10, one more flight in the incremental step-by-cautious-step towards the first supersonic forays. On
October 10, 1947, Cardenas dropped the XS-1 from the launch B-29
above the yellow-brown Mojave. Chuck Yeager fired the 4 chambers of
the rocket engine, nosed the orange XS-1 upwards in a climb to 38,000
feet, then shut down the cylinders one by one. After performing an
accelerated stall, he dropped 2,000 ft., tripped 2 of the rocket cylinder
switches on the cockpit panel, and accelerated in a climb to 40,000 ft.
The rocket plane picked up speed rapidly at the high altitude, and
Yeager reached an indicated Mach number of 0.94. Then, as the last of
the liquid oxygen and water-alcohol fed into the combustion cylinders,
the rocket engine sputtered for lack of fuel, and the young pilot switched
it off. The XS-1 #1 coasted upwards to 45,000 feet before arcing over for
its return to earth. On the long glide downwards, frost formed on the

inside of the canopy, persisting despite Yeager's efforts to scrape it off. Robert Hoover and Richard Frost, riding alongside the powerless plane in their chase P-80's talked the XS-1 pilot down to a "blind" landing on the lakebed.[22]

NACA's reduction of the data recorded by the plane's internal instrumentation, combined with ground radar tracking, surprised the waiting NACA and AMC test teams. It revealed that the XS-1 had flown faster than ever before, perhaps even as fast as the speed of sound. Although the cockpit Machmeter indicated only 0.94, corrections for the readings pushed the true Mach number up to 0.997 at a pressure altitude of 37,000 feet, approximately 658 mph.[23] That morning, high above Muroc, Chuck Yeager had possibly become the first man to exceed the speed of sound.

To Richard Frost, the message was clear: repeat the flight, but at a higher Mach number to ensure a clear-cut case of supersonic flight.[24] Early on the morning of Tuesday, October 14, long before the sun cast its light upon the dry lake, the participants in the continuing drama of the XS-1 #1 rubbed sleep from their eyes and set about making final preparations for the rocket plane's ninth powered flight.

Yeager himself was not in the best of condition that day. Over the intervening weekend, he had taken his wife Glennis to aviatrix Florence "Pancho" Barnes' Fly-Inn, a popular dude ranch and gathering spot for Muroc pilots located southwest of the base. He took out a horse for a night ride in the desert, but on returning to the ranch, failed to see a gate locked across the corral. The horse ran into the gate, bolted, and threw Yeager off. Though he made little of the accident, he was in considerable pain. Realizing the goal of the last few months to be just within reach, and unwilling to risk losing the chance to make the first supersonic flight, Yeager visited a civilian physician in nearby Rosamond, rather than go to the base hospital. The doctor's inspection revealed two broken ribs. Yeager decided to keep quiet about his accident. If the pain prevented him from crawling from the mother B-29 into the cockpit of the XS-1 in flight, he would cancel the mission before the drop.[25]

Muroc came alive with activity at 6 A.M. the morning of the flight. The orange XS-1 #1 lay bare, its insides and plumbing exposed, as ground crewmen readied it and its rocket engine for flight. As Yeager gathered with the rest of the B-29 launch crew and Jack Ridley, the talk centered on the upcoming flight: check out the stabilizer setting for optimum control effectiveness before initiating the high-speed run, be cautious. The test crew already knew of Yeager's weekend accident, though not about the injury, and to relieve tension, Ridley, Frost, Hoover, and Cardenas presented the test pilot with glasses, a rope, and a carrot.[26] After coffee in the service club, Yeager gave the XS-1 a preflight check, then suited up. He conferred with Walter Williams and De E. Beeler of the NACA Muroc Flight Test Unit; the NACA engineers stressed caution, and warned him not to exceed Mach 0.96 unless absolutely certain that he could safely do so. Then Yeager entered the B-29. At 10:02 A.M. the B-29's four Wright R-3350 piston engines began to clatter, and the huge four-bladed propellers slowly revolved, then with increasing speed. From the Muroc control tower, a skeleton structure, came clearance for takeoff. Cardenas began the takeoff roll, the bomber, with its orange parasite, trundling down the concrete runway and finally lifting into the clear blue sky.[27]

As the Superfortress began straining for altitude, a complex series of operations took place on the ground. The Air Force closed Muroc Dry Lake and its environs to nonauthorized aircraft. Richard Frost and Robert Hoover prepared to take off in their chase P-80's. At the NACA facility, now grown to 27 from the original 13, Gerald Truszynski and his instrumentation engineers readied their telemetry reception equipment and the 2 SCR-584 radar sets to track the flight. Others remained close to the flight communications monitors to keep informed on the progress of the mission. The final trial of 3 years of intensive research and development would come within a mere 30 minutes, 8 miles above the desert floor.

At 5,000 ft., Yeager left the relative security of the B-29's bomb bay for the transfer ladder and, with Ridley helping him, he squirmed into the open cockpit hatch of the XS-1. Ridley locked the hatch in place, sealing Yeager into the rocket plane. The B-29 continued its climb. Hoover and Frost joined up for chase. On the ground below, Truszynski's radar tracked the spiraling bomber as it climbed upwards. At the 5-minute warning before launch, Yeager pressurized the fuel and liquid oxygen tanks, and checked the fuel jettison system. Then, with nothing else to do, he waited for the drop. At the 1-minute warning, NACA radar cleared the B-29 to launch the rocket plane, and Jack Ridley asked Yeager, "You all set?" Hunched in the cockpit, tense but ready for flight, the young pilot replied, "Hell, yes, let's get it over with." Then Cardenas voiced the countdown. At 10:26 A.M., at a pressure altitude of 20,000 ft. and an indicated airspeed of 250 mph, the XS-1 #1 dropped free from the dark bomb bay of the B-29, out into the bright sunlight.[28]

As the plane dropped earthwards like a winged bomb, Yeager fired chamber 4, then 2, then shut off 4 and fired 3, then shut off 2 and fired 1. Under the combined thrust of chambers one and 3 the XS-1 began to climb, racing away from Richard Frost in his P-80 and the ponderous B-29. Yeager cut on chambers 2 and 4, and under a full 6,000-lb thrust the rocket plane accelerated for altitude, trailing a cone of fire and streaming shock diamonds in the exhaust. From Mach 0.83 to 0.92, Yeager cautiously tested stabilizer effectiveness. Though the rudder and conventional elevator lost effectiveness, the stabilizer still proved effective, even as speed increased to Mach 0.95. At 35,000 ft., he shut down 2 chambers, continuing the climb on the remaining 2. Yeager began to level off around 40,000 feet, and fired one of the 2 shutdown cylinders.[29] Describing the flight later, Yeager said,

> With the stabilizer setting at 2° the speed was allowed to increase to approximately .98 to .99 Mach number where elevator and rudder effectiveness were regained and the airplane seemed to smooth out to normal flying characteristics. This development lent added confidence and the airplane was allowed to continue to accelerate until an indication of 1.02 on the cockpit Mach meter was obtained. At this indication the meter momentarily stopped and then jumped to 1.06 and this hesitation was assumed to be caused by the effect of shock waves on the static source. At this time the power units were cut and the airplane allowed to decelerate back to the subsonic flight condition. When decelerating through approximately .98 Mach number a single sharp impulse was experienced which can best be described by comparing it to a sharp turbulence bump.[30]

Yeager had attained an airspeed of 700 mph, Mach 1.06, at approximately 43,000 ft. He was the first pilot to exceed the speed of sound. There had been no violent buffeting, no wrenching of the plane. He cut out the XLR-11 engine, though fully 30 percent of the propellants remained. Aside from the Machmeter readings, Yeager did not note anything spectacular about breaching the "sound barrier."

The XS-1 #1 coasted up to 45,000, and Yeager performed a 1g stall in clean configuration. Then the nose of the plane dropped downwards towards Muroc Dry Lake. Before the flight, ground crewmen had bathed the cockpit glass with Drene shampoo to prevent frosting, and Yeager did not encounter any on the trip earthwards. During the glide back, Yeager could hear the ticking of the cockpit clock in the virtually soundless airplane. Frost's and Hoover's P-80's joined up, and 14 minutes after dropping away from the B-29, the tires of the XS-1's landing gear brushed the clay of Muroc Dry Lake. The little plane, travelling at 160 mph, rolled approximately 2½ miles across the lakebed before coming to a stop. Yeager got stiffly out, his ribs paining him, fatigued, having completed the first manned supersonic flight in aviation history.[31]

Though word of Yeager's achievement flashed out to those with a need to know within the NACA, industry, the Air Force, and the Navy, it remained highly classified and officials did not release it immediately to the public. Not everyone at Muroc knew of the feat, and it did not appear in the Muroc semiannual historical report.[32] To the outsider, the XS-1 remained another airplane flying at the lake like the North American XP-86, the Hughes XF-11, the Curtiss XP-87, the Northrop YB-49, and the Douglas D-558-1 Skystreaks.

The Air Force did not rest on its accomplishment, however. Yeager made 4 more flights in the XS-1 before the end of October. On November 6, he dropped away from the B-29, fired up the XLR-11 engine and streaked to Mach 1.35 at 48,600 feet, slightly over 890 mph, and twice as fast as a conventional P-51D Mustang fighter. By early November, the myth of a sound barrier had been laid in its grave. Many questions still remained to be answered about aircraft stability and control and loads in the transonic region, but the barrier syndrome disappeared. The XS-1 had proven that a properly designed airplane, flown by a skilled pilot, could pass from subsonic to supersonic flight without damage.

One week after Charles Yeager became the first pilot to exceed the speed of sound, NACA pilot Herbert Hoover initiated the NACA program on the XS-1 #2 with a familiarization glide flight. Hoover thought the plane had pleasant stall characteristics with adequate warning and mild motions. On landing, the XS-1 #2 touched down hard on its nosewheel, and the landing strut collapsed. Repairs and subsequent maintenance work, along with the annual winter rains, kept the XS-1 grounded until December 16, when Hoover made the first rocket flight ever performed by a NACA pilot, attaining Mach 0.71. He flew again on another checkout flight the next day.[33]

Because of the accelerated flight program on the XS-1 airplane, Secretary of the Air Force Stuart Symington directed that initial data from the program be prepared for presentation to the aircraft industry for use by contractors.[34] On December 22, *Aviation Week* disclosed Yeager's supersonic flight. The Air Force and NACA neither confirmed nor denied the story, and the Justice Department under Attorney General Tom C. Clark began an investigation to see if the government could prosecute the magazine for violation of national security.[35] On January 9, 1948, senior officials of the Air Force, the Navy, the NACA, and private industry met at Wright Field for a conference on the XS-1's research results. Among those who attended were John Stack, Walter Williams, Hartley Soulé, Ira Abbott, and Hugh Dryden of the NACA; Ezra Kotcher, Maj. Gen. Lawrence C. Craigie, Maj. Gen. F. O. Carroll, Col. Albert Boyd, and Dr. Hsue-Shen Tsien of the Air Force; and Lawrence Bell, Robert Stanley, and Richard Frost of Bell, as well as Ridley and Yeager of the Air Force test team. The seminar covered the history of the XS-1 program, the operation of the airplane, its tests, and test results. Speakers pointed out that while the XS-1 generally experienced most of the difficulties predicted previously by engineers, the magnitude of such problems had not been as serious as had been expected.

In speaking of the future program of the XS-1 airplane, Charles L. Hall of the AMC's Aircraft Projects Section, spoke of possibly using the XS-1 for applied research and equipment testing, such as research on aerodynamic heating, weapons systems for supersonic aircraft, and problems of crew safety. He announced that for these and other reasons, the Air Force had already contracted with Bell for four advanced XS-1 aircraft.[36]

As events turned out, however, both XS-1's continued to fly as aerodynamic research vehicles, and neither the Air Force nor NACA made tests of aircraft equipment or systems in the two rocket planes. During the remainder of January 1948, Yeager made three supersonic flights in the XS-1 #1, and NACA completed seven other subsonic flights in the XS-1 #2. In January, Howard Lilly checked out in the NACA XS-1, and by the end of the month, Hoover had worked up to Mach 0.925 in the NACA airplane.[37]

In addition to their special duties, the AMC XS-1 test team participated in test programs on other military aircraft. At the end of September 1947, the first 26 Republic P-84 Thunderjets arrived at Muroc for accelerated service tests. Late in November, while flying one of the planes, Hoover experienced an inflight fire. He jumped from the cockpit, but struck the horizontal stabilizer, breaking both legs. The accident grounded him for 3 months, forcing him out of the XS-1 program. The test team replaced him with Capt. James T. Fitzgerald, Jr.[38] Fitzgerald attempted a checkout flight in the XS-1 #1 on February 24, 1948, but after launch the plane experienced an inflight fire; Fitzgerald jettisoned the remaining propellants and landed on the lakebed.[39]

The NACA program went more smoothly, as Hoover and Lilly concentrated on making the XS-1 #2's first supersonic flight. On March 4, Herbert Hoover attained Mach 0.943 at 40,000 feet. Then, 6 days later, March 10, 1948, Hoover dropped from the B-29 on a stability and loads investigation, fired 3 of the 4 rocket cylinders, and began to climb, leveling out at 42,000 feet. The XS-1 #2 rapidly accelerated to Mach 0.93, and Hoover fired the fourth cylinder. Under full thrust, the rocket research aircraft shot to Mach 1.065, approximately 703 mph. Herbert Hoover had become the first civilian pilot to exceed the speed of sound. After engine burnout he coasted to the dry lake. Despite emergency efforts, Hoover found he could not extend the nose landing gear. He held off the nose as long as possible, and even though the plane skidded to a stop on the underside of the nose, the damage was slight. NACA had the plane back on flight status within 10 days, and later that month Lilly also exceeded Mach 1 in it.[40]

On March 26, 1948, Yeager completed the XS-1 #1's 22nd Air Force flight, attaining the highest speed ever made by an XS-1 airplane. After launching from the B-29 Superfortress at 31,000 ft. and 240 mph, Yeager climbed on 3 cylinders at Mach 0.85 to 50,000 feet, leveled off, and, under full power, began a shallow dive. The XS-1 #1 reached Mach 1.45 at 40,130 ft., as determined later by NACA analysis of radar tracking data and instrumentation readings, an airspeed of approximately

957 mph. After performing two stall checks, he continued down to land on the lakebed.[41]

In April, Lilly continued the NACA stability and control and aerodynamic loads program on the XS-1 #2, but on April 16, the NACA plane came to grief. As the plane touched down, it began a skipping motion, and on the third contact, the nose landing gear collapsed, tripped the landing gear operating mechanism, and caused the left main gear to retract partially. The XS-1 #2 skidded to a halt resting on the nose wheel, right main wheel, left wingtip, and tail cone. The accident kept the plane grounded throughout the summer of 1948.[42] Both XS-1 aircraft had peculiar behavior on landing, sometimes—as in Lilly's case—resulting in nosewheel failure. In part, it stemmed from pilot technique and training. The XS-1 would touch down at about 130 mph, sometimes bouncing back into the air. During the bounce, its speed would drop off to 125 mph or less, and at these low velocities, the elevator lost control effectiveness. Simultaneously, the nose would begin to drop. After the bounce, most pilots would be reluctant to pull the control column all the way back—exactly the corrective action required on the XS-1—for fear of stalling out. But with the XS-1's low elevator effectiveness at this speed—around 125 mph—the plane required almost full up elevator to keep the nose from dropping through. Consequently, most pilots would handle the control column gingerly, and by the time the nose dipped, it was too late. The nosewheel would hit hard and collapse.[43]

During April and May, Capt. James Fitzgerald and Maj. Gustav E. Lundquist performed a series of pressure distribution surveys and stability and control investigations around Mach 1.1 in the XS-1 #1. Air Force officials grounded the airplane in May for installation of strain-gauge instrumentation and engine work. Late in the month, on May 25, Fitzgerald returned the plane to the air on a buffet-boundary investigation. On June 3, 1948, during a low-altitude transonic investigation by Lundquist to Mach 0.95, the left main gear door of the XS-1 #1 opened in flight. Despite the trim problem caused by the opening, Lundquist succeeded in landing on the lakebed. The nosewheel collapsed upon landing, and the B-29 ferried the airplane back to Wright Field—recently redesignated Wright-Patterson Air Force Base—for repairs.[44]

Despite the revelation of the first supersonic flight by *Aviation Week*, the Air Force and NACA waited until June 1948 before confirming the flight. On June 15, 1948, Gen. Hoyt S. Vandenberg, Chief of Staff of the Air Force, and Dr. Hugh L. Dryden, NACA's newly appointed Director of Aeronautical Research, confirmed that the XS-1 had repeatedly exceeded the speed of sound while flown by Air Force pilots Yeager, Fitzgerald, and Lundquist, and by NACA pilots Herbert Hoover and Howard Lilly.[45] Secrecy still prevented disclosure of particular facets of the supersonic flight, and Yeager responded to more inquisitive questioning by replying, "If you had a gold mine, you wouldn't tell the world where it was, would you?" Asked how it felt to fly through the "sound barrier," the young pilot replied, "It was pretty nice, I thought."[46]

At the ceremony, Yeager received another oak leaf cluster to his Distinguished Flying Cross, as well as the Mackay Trophy for 1947, presented annually for the most meritorious flight of the year.[47] With shrewd insight, Hugh Dryden noted,

> The achievement of Captain Charles E. Yeager as the first man to attain sustained horizontal supersonic flight in a piloted aircraft brings to public attention the power of a new tool, the research airplane, in obtaining the basic aeronautical knowledge essential to the design of military aircraft of outstanding performance. . . .
>
> It is not easy for us so close to the event to appraise correctly the significance of the dawn of the supersonic age. There is danger on the one hand of seeming to minimize the accomplishments of a pioneer who ventured where none had traveled before and on the other hand there is danger of arousing undue expectations on the part of the public as to the performance to be expected of tactical military aircraft. The XS-1 is a small research airplane, flown at high speed at high altitude where the air loads on the structure are small. Between it and tactically useful military aircraft of larger size flying at lower altitude where the air loads are much greater there remains much research and development on many difficult problems.[48]

Some doubt still remained in the public mind about the origins of the XS-1. Shortly after completion, many sources stated it drew on German wartime technology, and some suggested it used an American modification of the German Walter HWK 109-509 rocket engine. An editorial written after the Air Force-NACA disclosure stated bluntly, "Moreover, since the XS-1 is admittedly merely an improved copy of a German wartime fighter, it is not impossible that the Germans also knew a thing or two about supersonic flight." This brought a swift and sharp denial from the Air Force and NACA.[49]

Repairs to the NACA S-1 #2 occupied the better part of the summer, and modifications to the plane kept it grounded into the fall. By September 1948, the Muroc Flight Test Unit had prepared a test program for approximately 50 flights. The plane would fly to investigate aerodynamic loads and stability characteristics over a range from Mach 0.6 to Mach 1.2 at an altitude of approximately 40,000 feet. Early in October the Muroc engineers painted the plane white overall to facilitate tracking. In November, it returned to flying status. In October 1948, NACA sent another research pilot to Muroc to replace Howard Lilly, who had died the previous May in the crash of the D-558-1 #2: Langley research pilot Robert A. Champine. A former Navy fighter-bomber pilot,

Champine had joined the Langley research-pilot staff in December 1947, and had flown the Bell L-39 low-speed sweptwing research airplane. After Lilly's death, Herbert Hoover remained on at Muroc to train a replacement. Hoover made a check flight in the XS-1 #2—now designated simply X-1 #2—on November 1. After a second check of the plane on November 15, Hoover turned it over to Champine, who made his first flight in the aircraft on November 23. Over the next 2 weeks, Champine completed a further 3 flights for pilot familiarization. NACA technicians installed handling qualities instrumentation in the airplane for further research work.[50]

At 12:30 P.M. on December 17, 1948, John Stack, Charles Yeager, and Lawrence Bell gathered in the office of President Harry Truman at the White House to receive the Robert J. Collier Trophy award for 1947, an award given annually for "the greatest achievement in aviation in America, the value of which has been demonstrated by actual use during the preceding year." The citation to the award read:

> To John Stack, Research Scientist, NACA, for pioneering research to determine the physical laws affecting supersonic flight, and for his conception of transonic research airplanes; to Lawrence D. Bell, President, Bell Aircraft Corporation, for the design and construction of the special research airplane X-1; and to Captain Charles E. Yeager, U.S. Air Force, who, with that airplane, on October 14, 1947, first achieved human flight faster than sound.[51]

Along with the citation, the description of the project aptly summarized the impact of the orange rocket airplane upon aviation:

> This is an epochal achievement in the history of world aviation—the greatest since the first successful flight of the original Wright Brothers' airplane, forty-five years ago. It was not the achievement of any single individual or organization, but was the result of a sound aeronautical research and development policy involving fine teamwork and cooperation between research scientists, industry, and the military—a factor essential to keeping America first in the air. Without this teamwork the achievement would have been impossible.[52]

Shortly after the award ceremony, the Air Force called Richard Frost back from Bell to arrange a ground-rocket takeoff in the X-1 #1. Though Bell had designed the aircraft with a conventional retractable landing gear, the Air Force and NACA air-launched the airplane for safety and added performance reasons. However, interest in rocket takeoffs from the ground lingered on. At the annual 1948 Wright Brother's dinner, Lawrence Bell broached the subject unofficially to Yeager and Gen. Hoyt Vandenberg. Both men expressed a willingness to perform a ground-launched takeoff in the X-1 #1. Accordingly, Bell engineer Richard Frost prepared a list of recommendations for the Air Force to follow in planning the flight attempt.[53]

To overcome any danger to the landing gear, Frost recommended that new tires, tubes, and brake biscuits be installed, and that the Air Force fill the propellant tank to no more than ¾ capacity, in order to limit the takeoff weight to 10,000 lbs. He suggested further that the takeoff be made as early as possible in the day before the sun heated the runway, and that Yeager avoid braking so as not to put undue strain on the nosewheel. To minimize shifting of the center of gravity, Frost recommended that the Air Force conduct a thorough weight and balance analysis prior to the flight, and make the flight as soon as possible after the analysis so that liquid oxygen boil-off would not materially affect the center of gravity's location. Frost left the choice of stabilizer settings up to Yeager, and recommended that the pilot could reduce normal accelerations of less than 1g—which might result in engine shutdown if they interfered with the fuel flow—if he made an early takeoff when atmospheric turbulence was at a minimum, and also made a spiral climb, which would ensure that normal accelerations did not fall below 1g. Frost also advised that Yeager retract the landing gear before the airplane exceeded 250 mph, that he keep climbing speed below Mach 0.85 in order to retain control effectiveness, and that the pilot fire the rocket engine with brakes locked so as to ascertain proper engine ignition before the plane began its takeoff roll.[54]

On January 5, 1949, Yeager strapped himself into the X-1 #1, completed his preflight check, fired cylinders two and four, then ignited cylinders one and three, and released the brakes. The X-1 lunged forward and darted into the air, spiraling upwards. One hundred seconds after engine ignition, Yeager attained 23,000 ft. As the powerless X-1 began its glide earthwards, Yeager jettisoned the plane's remaining liquid oxygen and alcohol. The rocket plane touched down on the lakebed and rolled to a stop in a cloud of dust as a chase F-86 Sabre winged overhead.[55]

Following the unique ground takeoff—a feat never attempted again with a rocket-propelled research aircraft in the United States—the X-1 #1 remained on the ground because of winter rains that flooded the lakebed. Flight operations resumed in March 1949, and Jack Ridley, recently returned from a stint as pilot and project officer on the XB-47 at Moses Lake, Washington, checked out in the airplane. Though he noticed no difficulties, postflight inspection revealed that a loose engine wire had caused a small engine fire.[56] Capt. James T. Fitzgerald, Jr., who entered the X-1 program as Yeager's alternate following Robert Hoover's P-84 accident, had by now himself been killed. Early in September 1948, Fitzgerald was severely injured in a TF-80 crash at Van Nuys,

California. He had died of his injuries 11 days later.[57] On March 21, 1949, Air Force Maj. Frank K. Everest, Jr., completed a check-out flight in the X-1 #1, making a 3-cylinder rocket flight to Mach 1.22 at 40,000 ft.[58]

Like Yeager, Everest also hailed from West Virginia. He had joined the Civilian Pilot Training Program at West Virginia University in 1940 and, after receiving a private pilot's license in February 1941, had applied for Army flight training. He received his commission and wings as a fighter pilot on July 3, 1942, and arrived in the Middle East as a P-40 pilot in early 1943 attached to the 314th Fighter Squadron. He saw extensive combat against German Bf 109s, Fw 190s and Ju 52s, and flew support missions during the Italian campaign. He transferred back to the United States in 1944 as a P-40 instructor in Venice, Florida, and used the opportunity to check out in the A-20, A-24, A-25, C-78, P-47, and P-51. Everest soon requested a return to combat flying, and transferred to Chihkiang, China, as a replacement P-40 pilot. The AAF soon assigned him as acting squadron commander of the Mustang-equipped 29th Fighter Squadron. Japanese flak shot down his P-51 in May 1945 while on an antishipping mission over the Yangtze River, and he spent the remainder of the war as a POW at Nanking and Fengtai until release in August 1945. After arrival back in the U.S., Everest joined the test pilot staff at Wright Field, beginning test pilot training in May 1946. He checked out in the P-59 and P-80, and later flew a variety of acceptance tests on the P-80, P-84, and F-86 Sabre. In January 1949, he became assistant chief of the Fighter Test Section at Wright Field.[59]

Early in January 1949, Col. Albert Boyd called Everest into his office at Wright Field for a discussion on the Air Force X-1 #1 program. Boyd stated that the Air Force no longer planned any more high-speed record runs in the aircraft, but that the service was planning high altitude investigations to determine the behavior characteristics of manned high-speed aircraft at altitudes above 50,000 ft. Further, such flights could lead to breaking the world's altitude record of 72,395 ft. set by the Army Air Corps-National Geographic Society balloon *Explorer II* on November 11, 1935, piloted by Capts. Orvil A. Anderson and A. W. Stevens.[60] Boyd then asked if Everest would be interested in making the altitude flights. Everest replied affirmatively and, after being fitted for a high-altitude pressure suit, drove west to Muroc in March.[61]

During Everest's second flight in the X-1 #1, on March 25, the airplane suffered a rocket fire and automatic engine shutdown. Despite the disappointing flight, the Air Force X-1 test team and Bell agreed to attempt a maximum altitude investigation on Everest's next flight. But on this flight, April 19, 1949, Everest could only get 2 of the 4 cylinders firing, and he had to turn back at around 60,000 ft.[62] He was wearing

The saga begins at Pinecastle, Florida . . .

Early in 1946, NACA sends a small test team to Pinecastle to participate in the XS-1 #1's initial glide tests. The team includes (left to right): Gerald Truszynski, unidentified C-45 crew chief, Walter C. Williams, Norm Hayes, Robert Baker.

During the night the XS-1 #1 is shackled in the B-29's bomb bay, where it awaits a morning glide flight.

As with any new airplane, there are difficulties. On February 19, 1946, the nosewheel collapses as Bell test pilot Jack Woolams lands. The XS-1 #1 skids to a halt, damaging the nosewheel door.

. . . then shifts to Muroc Dry Lake, California.

In the fall of 1946, Bell goes to Muroc Dry Lake with the XS-1 #2 for the plane's initial powered flight. On December 9, 1946, the B-29 climbs to launch altitude with the orange XS-1 #2 swathed in frost.

As a chase Lockheed P-80 Shooting Star tries vainly to keep up, . . .

. . . Bell test pilot Chalmers "Slick" Goodlin ignites the XS-1 #2's rocket engine and streaks to Mach 0.79 high above the Mojave.

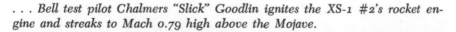

In 1947 the Air Force and

NACA team up to exceed Mach 1.

The Air Force selects a young test pilot at Wright Field to fly the Bell rocket plane. He is Capt. Charles E. Yeager, a World War II fighter ace.

Six key members of the NACA and Air Force decide when the XS-1 #1 should attempt to exceed the speed of sound. They are (left to right): Joseph Vensel, Gerald Truszynski, Capt. Charles E. Yeager, Walter C. Williams, Capt. Jack Ridley, and De E. Beeler.

There are some pessimistic predictions that Yeager will meet the same fate at British test pilot Geoffrey de Havilland, who died at or near Mach 1 when his D.H. 108 Swallow disintegrated from compressibility over the Thames estuary. (This is the D.H. 108 #3, a sister to the D.H. 108 #2 in which de Havilland died.)

But on October 14, 1947, Capt. Yeager reaches Mach 1.06 at 43,000 ft. in the Bell XS-1 #1, the first manned supersonic flight.

Inside the rocket plane, the oscillograph film records irrefutable proof of Yeager's pioneering sonic journey. It shows the jump caused as the bow shock wave passes over the static pressure ports as the plane noses through the speed of sound.

150   155   160

3

5 H

On December 17, 1948, President Harry Truman, at the White House, presents the Robert J. Collier Trophy for 1947 to (left to right): John Stack, Capt. Charles Yeager, and Lawrence Bell.

Beginning in 1948 and continuing until 1951, NACA flies an extensive stability and control research program to supersonic speeds, using the Bell XS-1 #2.

The D-558 series join the X-1's in the skies above Muroc.

In April 1947, Douglas sends the scarlet D-558-1 #1 Skystreak to the dry lake. Eugene F. "Gene" May begins flying it from the Muroc North Base.

The Navy seeks to break the world airspeed record, so, on August 17, 1947, Comdr. Turner Caldwell sweeps low over a measured course at Muroc in the D-558-1 #1 at an average speed of 640.7 mph.

After the loss of Howard Lilly in the NACA D-558-1 #2, NACA flies the D-558-1 #3 in an extensive flight-research program. Here it is seen with tip tanks and a special instrumented nose boom prior to takeoff from the dry lake in 1950.

In November 1947, Douglas completes the D-558-2 #1 Skyrocket, minus its rocket engine. On Feb. 4, 1948, it makes its first flight at Muroc Dry Lake.

In 1950, Douglas modifies the D-558-2 #2 and D-558-2 #3 for air launching from a Navy P2B-1S (Air Force B-29). Here the D-558-2 #2 is carried aloft to launch altitude.

After the launch, the Skyrockets are chased by another sweptwing airplane, the North American F-86A Sabre.

Beginning in 1951, the X-1's and D-558-2 #2 start approaching Mach 2 —twice the speed of sound.

Flying the all-rocket D-558-2 #2 . . .

. . . *(left to right): Douglas test pilot William Bridgeman reaches Mach 1.88 and 79,494-ft. altitude; Lt. Col. Marion Carl, USMC, attains 83,235-ft.; finally, on November 20, 1953, NACA research pilot A. Scott Crossfield becomes the first man to fly at twice the speed of sound. The Skyrockets continue to fly until 1957.*

On December 12, 1953, Maj. Charles Yeager reaches Mach 2.44 in the Bell X-1A, then nearly loses his life as the X-1A tumbles wildly out of control. After a 50,000-ft. drop, he manages to recover and land on the lakebed. Eight months later, Maj. Arthur Murray cautiously takes the plane to 90,000 ft. Then the Air Force turns it over to NACA . . .

. . . who modify it for a high altitude, high Mach research program. After one check flight, the plane suffers a low-order inflight explosion prior to launch on August 8, 1955. The NACA B-29 launch crew jettison it into the desert where it explodes and burns. NACA retains two X-1's, including the X-1E.

The X-1E is actually the extensively rebuilt X-1 #2. It has a new thin wing, a stepped canopy, and a low-pressure fuel system. It flies through 1958, bringing the X-1 saga to a close after 12 years of research flying.

an early-model pressure helmet with a fixed visor that could not be opened and, as the airplane glided earthwards, he felt a pressure in his eardrums. Because of the design of the helmet, he could not lift the visor, hold his nose, and blow, nor could he remove the helmet, for the cockpit contained only nitrogen from the pressurized system, and no oxygen. Inevitably, one eardrum ruptured, but fortunately the damage was slight and, after letting the rupture heal, Everest resumed research flights in the rocket plane.[63] Serious engine difficulties returned to plague Everest on his next flight, May 2, 1949. After launching from the B-29, he attempted to ignite all 4 chambers, but only chambers 2, 3, and 4 fired. As he pulled the X-1 into a climb, the plane shuddered from an internal explosion, and the XLR-11 engine shut down. At the same time, Everest lost rudder control. As the X-1 dropped down, chase pilot Richard Frost came alongside in his chase F-80 and observed that the number one chamber had exploded, jamming the rudder. Everest retained sufficient control to land the X-1 #1 on the lakebed, and the Air Force ferried it to Wright Field for repairs.[64]

Ground inspection of the aircraft revealed that the exhaust of the other chambers had ignited vapor streaming from chamber one, which had not fired. The fire moved inside the cylinder, ignited the heavy concentration of liquid oxygen and alcohol inside, with a resulting excess chamber pressure that blew the number one chamber out of the airplane.[65] The Air Force did not like the apparently continuing problem of engine fires in the X-1 series, and hired back Richard Frost from Bell, together with Bell engineer William Smith, to investigate the cause of the recurring fires. Smith and Frost traced the engine trouble to the spark plugs used in the engine. They found the regular plugs had gaskets made of asbestos covered with a thin sheet of copper. These could not withstand the high internal pressure of the cylinder, and would blow out. Smith solved the problem by installing solid gaskets made of copper rather than the copper-covered asbestos.[66]

In May, the NACA X-1 #2 returned to the air in its stability and control program, recording spanwise pressure distribution and aircraft behavior following pilot-induced motions and pull-ups.[67] While the NACA program remained the most productive in terms of transonic data, the Air Force program continued to be the most spectacular. The X-1 #1 returned to Muroc from Wright-Patterson Air Force Base in mid-June, 1949. The Air Force still planned to continue the high-altitude research program, and hoped eventually to reach 80,000 ft. during the course of a further 4 flights. Aside from simply exceeding the altitude record of *Explorer II* the Air Force wanted to investigate flight at high lift coefficients.[68] Over the remainder of June and July, Air Force and NACA technicians readied the X-1 #1 for flight, reinstalling research instrumentation removed for engine repairs. After a ground run to ensure proper rocket operation, Everest went aloft on July 25, 1949, for his fifth X-1 flight, this third attempt to attain high altitude.[69] Everest only attained 66,846 ft., but it was higher than the rocket airplane had ever flown before.[70] On August 8, 1949, Everest launched from the B-29 on his fourth altitude attempt.

The X-1 #1 separated cleanly from the B-29 and Everest fired 3 of the 4 rocket cylinders, then pulled into a steep climb. The rapidly accelerating X-1, growing lighter as it burned off its heavy load of propellants, quickly outdistanced Charles Yeager's chase F-80. Everest used the stabilizer trim for control, and around 45,000 ft., nosed over into level flight prior to going supersonic. The little rocket plane quickly accelerated from Mach 0.9 to over Mach 1, and Everest again used the stabilizer trim to reenter a climb. He turned off the Machmeter, which could not register accurately at high altitudes, and as the X-1 climbed, the altimeter reading lagged by at least 5,000 ft. For the final portion of the climb, Everest attempted to light the X-1's fourth rocket cylinder, but the ignition failed. The X-1 continued climbing, still under only 75 percent power. The controls grew sluggish at the increasing altitude, and finally, around 65,000 ft., the 3 chambers exhausted the propellants and shut off from fuel starvation. The abrupt deceleration hurled Everest forward in his shoulder harness. Still coasting powerless into the deep purple sky above it, the X-1 continued upwards in an arc for a few more thousand feet, until it attained the apex of its climb at 71,902 ft. Then, momentum spent, it slowly began its drop back to earth.[71]

As the X-1 #1 coasted downwards, Everest performed several stall checks during abrupt pull-ups down to Mach 1.1 from 60,000 to 30,000 ft. At 30,000 ft., Yeager's chase F-80 picked up the orange rocket airplane and the two airplanes descended to the lake.[72] Later that month, on August 25, 1949, Everest again went aloft in the X-1 for another attempt to reach extreme altitudes. This flight resulted in another X-1 "first," but a strictly inadvertent one.

As Jack Ridley closed the entrance hatch to the X-1 #1, Everest noticed a tiny crack in the Plexiglas canopy. The crack measured only about an inch long, and appeared confined to the inner shell of the canopy. After a smooth drop and light-off, Everest began his climb, leveling off to go supersonic, and resuming his climb. As he passed through 65,000 ft. altitude, a loud sighing sound filled the cockpit and Everest's T-1 partial pressure suit inflated automatically. Everest realized at once that he had lost cockpit pressurization, and, glancing up, he saw that the tiny one-inch crack had extended to 6 inches and broken through to the atmosphere. Recognizing the danger he was in—for should the suit fail, he would die in seconds—Everest shut off the XLR-11 engine, and nosed over in a dive. F-80 pilots Yeager and Capt. Arthur "Kit" Murray saw the vapor trail abruptly break off, and Yeager asked Everest if anything was wrong. The pressure of the suit severely constricted the body and made normal speech impossible. Everest could only reply to Yeager's anxious questions with a succession of grunts that further alarmed those listening in on the conversation. When the X-1 reached 30,000 ft., Everest eased out of his supersonic dive, and at 20,000 ft. he opened the dump valve to depressurize the suit, reported the canopy failure, and assured those listening that he was all right. After jettisoning the remaining propellants, he brought the X-1 in for a landing on the lakebed. Everest and the X-1 had made the first operational emergency use of a pilot's pressure suit to save both the pilot and aircraft.[73]

The cracked canopy forced the Air Force to suspend the X-1 #1's altitude flights until Bell could deliver a new canopy to Muroc. While waiting for the new canopy, the Air Materiel Command decided to cancel further high-altitude investigations with the rocket airplane, since flight experience indicated that the aircraft would probably not exceed Everest's August 8 record height by more than a few thousand feet, and such an incremental increase would not warrant the preparation and added costs of further high-altitude investigations.[74] Everest's X-1 record height of 71,902 ft. remained a record for the two original X-1's with their high-pressure fuel systems.

By late 1949, the X-1 #1 was approaching the end of its service life. The Air Force had already contracted for the more advanced X-1A, X-1B, and X-1D airplanes, as well as the X-2 and X-3 proposed Mach 2 aircraft. Though a true supersonic fighter still lay in the future, one airplane, the North American F-86, could safely exceed the speed of sound during slight dives. Under a contract between the Air Materiel Command's Aircraft Laboratory and the Cornell Aeronautical Laboratory, the Cornell Aero Lab would get both the X-1 #1 and the new X-1A, and instrument the two aircraft for autopilot studies and structural loads measurements. However, in mid-November 1949, the AMC's Aircraft Laboratory decided to relinquish ownership of the X-1 #1, and deliver it to the NACA. Since the NACA could not use the aircraft without a major overhaul, this decision virtually terminated the research program on the X-1 #1 airplane. Forecasting ahead, Hartley A. Soulé, NACA's Research Airplane Projects Leader, wrote that "it is probable that the No. 1 airplane will be sent to the Smithsonian Institution."[75]

On September 7, 1949, Col. Albert Boyd assumed command of Muroc Air Force Base, replacing Col. Signa A. Gilkey who had commanded the desert base during the pioneering flights of Yeager two years previously. Boyd himself had flown the X-1 #1 earlier in the year. Now, when the X-1 #1 returned to flying status in October, it served primarily as a checkout aircraft. Lt. Col. Patrick D. Fleming, former chief of the AMC's Fighter Test Section, checked out in the plane on

October 6, attaining Mach 1.2. Three weeks later, Maj. Richard L. Johnson, then chief of the AMC's Fighter Test Section and holder of the world's air-speed record—670.981 mph, set in a F-86A on Sept. 15, 1948 at Muroc—also flew the X-1 #1.[76]

On Dec. 8, 1949, Headquarters, United States Air Force redesignated Muroc AFB as Edwards AFB, in honor of Capt. Glen W. Edwards, killed in the crash of the Northrop YB-49 #2 Flying Wing on June 5, 1948, at Muroc. Early in the new year, the X-1 #1 resumed flying, and completed its final 4 research flights. The final flight, number 59, came on May 12, 1950. Charles Yeager dropped away from a launch Boeing B-50 Superfortress—a modified and more powerful development of the B-29—for camera footage for use in the RKO movie *Jet Pilot*. The flight came off without difficulties and Yeager brought the rocket plane down on the lakebed for the last time.[77]

The X-1 #1 remained at Edwards until August 1950. While awaiting shipment to the Smithsonian, NACA technicians removed its instrumented horizontal stabilizer for use on the Bell X-1 #3, the turbopump-equipped "Queenie." On August 19, 1950, B-29 Superfortress 45-21800 lifted from the concrete runway at Edwards AFB with the X-1 #1 secured in its bomb bay, piloted by Jack Ridley and Chuck Yeager. The bomber winged its way east to AMC headquarters at Wright-Patterson AFB, where Air Force technicians repainted the X-1. Then Yeager and Ridley ferried the X-1 via B-29 to the Air Force Association convention at Logan International Airport, Boston, Massachusetts.[78] On August 26, at Logan airport, Air Force Chief of Staff Gen. Hoyt Vandenberg presented the Bell X-1 #1 to Dr. Alexander Wetmore, Secretary of the Smithsonian Institution. The X-1, he stated, "marked the end of the first great period of the air age, and the beginning of the second. In a few moments the subsonic period became history and the supersonic period was born."[79] After Ridley and Yeager ferried the X-1 to Washington, the Air Force delivered it to Paul E. Garber, Head Curator, National Air Museum, on August 28. Visitors could look at it, and then at the 1903 Wright biplane—which itself had only been delivered to the air museum less than two years before—and ponder on the progress of aviation in the intervening years between the two airplanes.

While the Air Force X-1 #1 embarked upon its new career as a Washington tourist attraction, the NACA X-1 #2 still fired up its engine in the sky above the lakebed in California on transonic research. In September 1949, John H. Griffith had joined the NACA Muroc unit as a research pilot. In the fall of 1949, NACA Hq. changed the name of the Muroc establishment to the NACA High-Speed Flight Research Station, a more accurate title reflecting both the growth of the unit and its expanded mission, which now included flight testing and assisting in tests on a number of research aircraft besides the original X-1's. The very precise methodical NACA operation of the X-1 #2 for highly specific missions did not preclude, however, eventful flights.

During one preparation to launch, NACA pilot Robert Champine experienced a radio failure. He wrote "Secure the Drop," on a flight card, and passed it into the bomb bay of the B-29. None of the B-29 crewmen were Navy trained, so they failed to realize that Champine was canceling the drop. Suddenly, Champine realized that he was about to be launched. He managed to get everything in working order before the launch crew dropped him, innocently unaware of his predicament.[80]

In the NACA flight planning, the pilot participated actively at every step. Langley Laboratory established the generalities of the aircraft program, through Hartley A. Soulé, Research Airplane Projects Leader for the NACA. At Edwards, NACA engineers planned the order and detail of every flight down to every minute. NACA found that the various research aircraft—particularly the rocket-propelled ones—were very difficult to keep on flying status. The research pilots kept their skills sharp by practice flying and flying chase for other projects in conventional aircraft, such as P-51's and F-80's. After completing a research flight, NACA engineers at Muroc analyzed the records from the internal instrumentation, radar tracking, and telemetry gear. They then prepared the material for publication in the form of NACA Research Memorandums, circulating copies of the drafts to other NACA installations for comment and review. After publication, these documents became part of the general storehouse of aeronautical knowledge available to those with a need to know.

Despite their highly experimental nature, both the X-1 and D-558 airplanes had good flying qualities and pilots liked them. The pilots, however, were under no illusions as to their possible escape in the event of trouble. If you jumped from the X-1, you would almost certainly hit the sharp leading edge of the wing. If you jettisoned the nose of the D-558, you might not have time to use your parachute if you were at low altitude. Robert Champine unexpectedly discovered one day the effectiveness of the horizontal stabilizer over the elevator at transonic speeds. At transonic speeds, the rudder, elevator, and ailerons of the X-1 #2 became ineffective. On one flight, Champine inadvertently moved the stabilizer and found control good. This led to a NACA program to investigate stabilizer pull-ups, pioneering work in the development of the all-moving tail.[81]

NACA grounded the X-1 #2 from the fall of 1949 through the spring of 1950 for installation of additional recording instrumentation to measure wing loads and pressure distribution. In May, the X-1 returned to the air. Because of its 10 percent wing and 8 percent tail, the X-1 #2 was not as fast as the thinner-winged X-1 #1. On May 26, NACA pilot John Griffith attained the fastest speed set in the X-1 #2, Mach 1.20. The nose landing gear collapsed on landing, and repairs plus subsequent instrumentation changes—including changing the instrumentation over from d.c. to 400-cycle a.c.—grounded the plane until August 1950.[82]

By mid-October 1950, NACA had completed nine successful pressure-distribution surveys to determine aerodynamic characteristics at specific wing locations. Then NACA decided to discontinue the program while making an investigation of the airplane's lateral and longitudinal stability and control. But then technicians discovered that the alcohol tank had severely rusted on the inside, and NACA grounded the plane for a complete overhaul and installation of a new alcohol tank.[83] NACA took advantage of the grounding to install new instrumentation in the airplane, and completed the overhaul by mid-March. On April 6, 1951, Charles Yeager flew the aircraft as part of a NACA cooperative agreement with the Air Force for the film *Jet Pilot*. The plane suffered a small flash fire in the engine bay from a slow-closing alcohol valve, but an automatic fire extinguisher quenched it before the blaze caused any serious damage or posed a serious threat to the safety of the pilot and plane.[84]

On April 20, 1951, another NACA pilot checked out in the airplane. This was A. Scott Crossfield. Crossfield, a native Californian, received his private license under the Civilian Pilot Training Program in 1941, and studied three semesters as an engineering student at the University of Washington by the time the Japanese struck Pearl Harbor. In February 1942, fed up with inactivity, he resigned from an AAF cadet program and joined the Navy as a flight student, graduating as a pilot in December 1942. He served as a flight instructor in advanced bombing and gunnery at Kingsville NAS, transitioned into SBD dive bombers, and wound up the war as a Hellcat pilot with Air Group 37 on board the carrier *Langley* (CVL 27), preparing for the invasion of the Japanese home islands. He returned to the University of Washington in 1946, received his B.S. in aeronautical engineering in June 1949, his M.S. in June 1950, and joined the NACA as a research pilot at Muroc in that same month.[85]

Technicians normally adjusted the stabilizer setting on the X-1 on the ground before its flights. On this one it had been set one degree greater than normally. Crossfield and the X-1 #2 dropped away from the launch B-29. While chase pilots Frank Everest and Jack Ridley watched in amazement, the X-1 pitched up, stalled, and rolled over on its back. Crossfield recovered nicely, rolling the little rocket plane back to level flight, adjusted the stabilizer, and ignited all 4 rocket tubes. He began to climb rapidly, the X-1 reaching Mach 0.9 and 41,000 feet before the engine exhausted the fuel. On his return, ice formed on the inside of the canopy because the dehumidifying equipment installed was too weak to rid the cockpit of all the moisture that built up (especially on humid days) and then froze at the high altitude. Using his right sock Crossfield was able to clear the windshield enough so that he could see out; with Jack Ridley flying chase close on his wing, Crossfield brought the X-1 in for a safe landing.[86]

Following three more check flights, NACA grounded the X-1 #2 for installation of a new rocket engine to replace its current one, which had malfunctioned on flight 45, May 15, 1951. At the same time, both launch aircraft, a B-29 and a B-50, were out of operation for maintenance work. The X-1 #2 did not make another flight until July. In July the plane began a wing-loads and aileron-effectiveness program that continued for the next six flights, until NACA changed the program to measure fuselage loads in flight.[87] Late in August, Joseph A. Walker checked out in the plane. Walker, destined to be another Edwards legend, held a B.A. in physics from Washington and Jefferson College. In 1942 he had entered the AAF, flying P-38's on reconnaissance missions over the Black Sea, Austria, and Southern France. He joined the Lewis Flight Propulsion Laboratory in 1945 as a physicist, and transferred to the High-Speed Flight Research Station at Edwards in 1951.[88]

Early in September, on the 9th, Scott Crossfield completed the plane's fifty-third flight, the first of the fuselage-loads and pressure-distribution surveys. But NACA suspended the program temporarily to make way for a special program to investigate whether wing-mounted vortex generators could reduce buffet severity in the transonic region. Walker attempted a buffet investigation with wing-vortex generators on October 23, but the rocket engine cut out and he had to finish it as a glide flight. Bad weather, together with unavailability of a launch airplane, kept the X-1 #2 grounded into November. On November 15, engineers detected the presence of battery acid in the midsection of the airplane and NACA grounded the craft for further inspection. To complete the picture, an investigation by the Bell Aircraft Corporation shortly afterward revealed that the nitrogen pressurization spheres in the X-1 #2 were reaching the point where, from a safety standpoint, they were likely to fail from fatigue. Now the X-1 #2 was grounded for good.[89]

Had conditions at Edwards at that time been other than they were the NACA would have speedily retired the airplane. But circumstances forced NACA to take another look at the worn-out X-1 #2. In August 1951, the X-1D exploded in flight before launch and had to be jettisoned over the Mojave. Less than a month before NACA grounded the X-1 #2, the X-1 #3—the ill-fated "Queenie"—blew up on the ground. Both aircraft were sorely needed, and as NACA engineers surveyed the tired but trim X-1 #2 they concluded that, like the

Phoenix of old, a new high performance airplane just might be developed from the remains of an ancestor aircraft. But that is another story, the story of the X-1E.

NOTES

1. Lundgren, *Across the High Frontier*, p. 38.

2. *Ibid.*, pp. 92–144. Also Parrish, *Who's Who in World Aviation*, 1955, p. 342.

3. Lundgren, *Across the High Frontier*, pp. 39–48, 150–51.

4. Don Downie, "Aerobatics 'Sell' Aviation," *Air Progress*, XV, No. 5 (October-November, 1963), 14–15, 89–93.

5. Biographical data sheet in Edwards AFB Historical Report, Vol. 2, 1 January 1954—30 June 1954. In Air Force Systems Command Archives.

6. Lundgren, *Across the High Frontier*, pp. 48–55.

7. Frost, *MX-653 report*, 16 June 1947; and *MX-653 report*, 15 July 1947.

8. Frost, *MX-653 report*, 1 Aug. 1947. Also Muroc Army Air Field Historical Report, 1 July 1947–31 December 1947, p. 23. In Air Force Archives, Maxwell AFB.

9. Mulac, XS-1 #1 flight chronology. Also Lundgren, *Across the High Frontier*, pp. 172–81.

10. Two letters, Herbert H. Hoover to Melvin Gough, 22 Aug. 1947 and 17 Sept. 1947. Both in LaRC files. Also see Gray, *Frontiers of Flight*, pp. 162–63. Shortal, *History of Wallops Station: Origins and Activities Through 1949*, p. 104. Also Lilly biographical file, NASA Historical Archives.

11. Charles E. Yeager, Pilot's Report No. 1 Powered Flight. In LaRC files. Also Frost interview, 25 May 1972, and Lundgren, *Across the High Frontier*, pp. 194–204.

12. Lundgren, *Across the High Frontier*, pp. 207–208. Also letter, Herbert H. Hoover to Melvin Gough, 17 Sept. 1947. In LaRC files.

13. Lundgren, *Across the High Frontier*, pp. 209–11.

14. NACA HSFS, "X-Press: 10th Anniversary Supersonic Flight," p. 3.

15. Frost interview, 25 May 1972.

16. Walter C. Williams statement at AIAA History Session, 28 July 1965. Also NACA HSFS, "X-Press: 10th Anniversary Supersonic Flight," p. 3.

17. Walter C. Williams, Memo for Chief of Research (NACA), "XS-1 Progress Report for the period Aug. 15–Sept. 12, 1947," 12 Sept. 1947. In LaRC files.

18. NACA HSFS, "X-Press: 10th Anniversary Supersonic Flight," p. 3.

19. Letter, Herbert Hoover to Melvin Gough, 17 Sept. 1947.

20. Mulac, XS-1 #2 flight chronology. Also NASA-Edwards release, 14 January 1959, of NACA/NASA rocket aircraft flights, p. 4.

21. Frost interview, 25 May 1972.

22. Mulac, XS-1 #1 flight chronology. Also Lundgren, *Across the High Frontier*, pp. 222–24.

23. NACA HSFS, "X-Press: 10th Anniversary Supersonic Flight," p. 3. Lundgren, *Across the High Frontier*, p. 224. Exact performance on flight obtained from James A. Martin, "The Record Setting Research Airplanes," *Aerospace Engineering*, XXI, No. 12, (December 1962), 49–54.

24. Frost interview, 25 May 1972.

25. Lundgren, *Across the High Frontier*, pp. 226–29.

26. *Ibid.*, pp. 230–32.

27. *Ibid.*, pp. 232–36.

28. *Ibid.*, pp. 236–40. Also "Man in a Hurry," *Time*, LIII, No. 16 (April 18, 1949), 64–66, 69–71.

29. Lundgren, *Across the High Frontier*, pp. 240–42.

30. Yeager, "The Operation of the XS-1 Airplane," 9 Jan. 1948, p. 19.

31. Lundgren, *Across the High Frontier*, pp. 242–43. See also account by Yeager in *Aviation Week*, XLVIII, No. 25 (June 21, 1948), 13–14. Also "Man in a Hurry," *Time*, p. 65.

32. Muroc AAF Historical Report, 1 July 1947–31 Dec. 1947.

33. H. M. Drake and H. R. Goodman, Memo for Chief of Research (NACA), 9 Dec. 1947, Progress report for XS-1 #2 airplane, 18 Oct. to 5 Dec. 1947. Hereafter cited as *XS-1 #2 PR*, followed by date. Also Hoover pilot reports, 21 Oct. 1947 and 16 Dec. 1947.

34. *Air Force Supersonic Research Airplane XS-1 Report No. 1*, 9 Jan. 1948, "foreword."

35. Robert McLarren, "Bell XS-1 Makes Supersonic Flight," *Aviation Week;* XLVII, No. 25 (Dec. 22, 1947), 9–10. Justice Department attorneys concluded that the magazine had not violated any federal laws, and thus could not be prosecuted for disclosing the supersonic flight. Clark announced his decison on May 27, 1948.

36. Charles L. Hall, "Future Program," *Air Force Supersonic Research Airplane XS-1 Report No. 1*, 9 Jan. 1948.

37. Mulac, XS-1 #2 flight chronology. Hoover pilot report 27 Jan. 1948.

38. Letter, Robert Hoover to author, 2 Nov. 1971. Letter, Brig. Gen. Charles E. Yeager to author, 12 Oct. 1971. See also Downie, "Aerobatics 'Sell' Aviation."

39. Mulac, XS-1 #1 flight chronology.

40. *XS-1 # 2 PR*, 12 March 1948. *XS-1 #2 PR*, 29 March 1948. *XS-1 2 PR*, 13 April 1948. See also "Flying for the Future," *Flying Safety* (September 1951), 16–17. In January 1950, President Truman awarded Hoover the Air Medal for "meritorious achievement while participating in aerial flight on 10 March 1948 . . . in piloting an experimental aircraft faster than the speed of sound, thereby providing valuable scientific data for research in the supersonic field."

41. Yeager, Pilot's report, flight 22, 3/26/48. See also Martin, "The Record-Setting Research Airplanes," p. 51.

42. *XS-1 #2 PR*, 27 April 1948.

43. Interview of A. Scott Crossfield by the author, 2 Feb. 1971.

44. Flight records for flight 35, 6/3/48. Mulac, XS-1 #2 flight chronology. Also Muroc Army Air Base Historical Report, 1 Jan. 1948–30 June 1948, p. 21. In Air Force Archives, Maxwell AFB.

45. *New York Times*, 16 June 1948.

46. *Ibid.*

47. "Capt. Yeager's Story," *Aviation Week*, p. 13.

48. Statement by Dr. Hugh L. Dryden, 15 June 1948.

49. "Supersonic" (editorial) *Washington Post*, June 15, 1948. The story had apparently first appeared in the *New York Herald Tribune*. See Robert McLarren, "Symington Confirms XS-1 Story," *Aviation Week*, XLVIII, No. 25 (June 21, 1948), 13–14.

50. *XS-1 #2 PR's* for 21 June 1948, 2 July 1948, 19 July 1948, 2 Aug. 1948, 13 Aug. 1948, 1 Sept. 1948, 13 Sept. 1948, 27 Sept. 1948, 12 Oct. 1948, 26 Oct. 1948, 5 Nov. 1948, 22 Nov. 1948, 6 Jan. 1949. Mulac, XS-1 #2 flight chronology. Interview of Robert A. Champine by the author, 11 Nov. 1971.

51. National Aeronautic Association news release, 17 Dec. 1948. "Highest Aviation Award Made for Supersonic Flight."

52. NAA release, 17 Dec. 1948.

53. Lundgren, *Across the High Frontier*, pp. 252–55. Frost interview, 25 May 1972.

54. *Ibid.*, pp. 255–59.

55. *Ibid.*, pp. 260–61. Also, Mulac X-1 #1 flight chronology.

56. Flight records for flight 40, 3/11/49. Also, Mulac X-1 #1 flight chronology.

57. Muroc AFB Historical Report, 1 July 1948–31 Dec. 1948, p. 8. In Air Force Archives, Maxwell AFB.

58. Flight records for flight 42, 3/21/49. Also, Mulac X-1 #1 flight chronology.

59. Frank K. Everest, *The Fastest Man Alive* (New York, 1959).

60. *Ibid.*, pp. 78–79. Balloon data from Emme, *Aeronautics and Astronautics*, p. 162.

61. Everest, *The Fastest Man Alive*, p. 81.

62. *Ibid.*, p. 82.

63. *Ibid.*, pp. 83–84.

64. *Ibid.* Also *X-1 #1 PR*, 9 May 1949.

65. Everest, *The Fastest Man Alive*, pp. 83–84.

66. Frost interview, 25 May 1972.

67. *X-1 #2 PR's*, 9 May 1949, 24 May 1949, 7 June 1949.

68. *X-1 #1 PR*, 21 June 1949.

69. *X-1 #1 PR*, 15 July 1949. Also Everest, *The Fastest Man Alive*, p. 85.

70. Everest, *The Fastest Man Alive*, p. 85. Martin, "Record Setting Research Airplanes," p. 52, Table 3.

71. *Ibid.*, Everest pp. 89–91, Martin, p. 52.

72. Everest, *The Fastest Man Alive*, pp. 91–92.

73. *Ibid.*, pp. 96–97. Depressurization occurred around 69,000 ft.

74. *Ibid.*, p. 97. Edwards AFB Historical Report, 1 July 1949–31 Dec. 1949, pp. 60, 62. In Air Force Archives, Maxwell AFB.

75. Hartley A. Soulé, Memo for Chief of Research (NACA Langley), "Research airplane projects—Visit to Wright Patterson Air Force Base on November 17, 1949," 29 Nov. 1949.

76. Mulac, X-1 #1 flight chronology. Flight records for flights 51 and 52. Also Edwards AFB Historical Report, 1 July 1949–31 Dec. 1949, p. 1.

77. Mulac, X-1 #1 flight chronology. Edwards AFB Historical Report, 1 Jan. 1950–30 June 1950, pp. 102, 106. In Air Force Archives, Maxwell AFB.

78. Edwards AFB Historical Report, 1 July 1950–31 Dec. 1950, pp. 124–25. In Air Force Archives, Maxwell AFB.

79. Remarks by Gen. Hoyt S. Vandenburg, 26 Aug. 1950.

80. Champine interview, November 11, 1971.

81. *Ibid.*

82. *X-1 #2 PR*, 4 May 1950, 10 May 1950, 24 May 1950, 8 June 1950, 19 June 1950, 8 July 1950, 18 July 1950, 2 Aug. 1950, 17 Aug. 1950. Griffith pilot report 26 May 1950.

83. *X-1 #2 PR*, 11 Oct. 1950. *X-1 #2 PR*, 9 Nov. 1950.

84. *X-1 #2 PR*, 10 April 1951.

85. See A. Scott Crossfield, *Always Another Dawn: The Story of a Rocket Test Pilot* (Cleveland 1960).

86. *Ibid.*, pp. 125–34.

87. Mulac, X-1 #2 flight chronology. *X-1 #2 PR*, 15 Aug. 1951.

88. Walker biographical file, NASA Historical Archives.

89. *X-1 #2 PR's*, 7 Nov. 1951, 21 Nov. 1951, 4 Dec. 1951. Mulac, X-1 #2 flight chronology. Walker pilot report, 24 Oct. 1951.

VI

THE D-558-1 SKYSTREAK
FLIGHT PROGRAM

As late as October 1946, considerable doubt existed as to whether Douglas would flight test the D-558-1 at Muroc Dry Lake or at the naval station at Inyokern. Douglas still had not selected a project pilot. While Inyokern did not have the facilities and suitable qualities that the Muroc site possessed for flight testing, it did have better living conditions in contrast to the "roughing it" atmosphere at Muroc.[1] NACA did not intend to take an active role in the contractor flight-test program on the Skystreak, and so informed Douglas of this early in 1947 while the Douglas company readied the aircraft for flight. The NACA, however, did assure Douglas that it would cooperate in whatever way it could to provide technical consultation or even instrument supply, if requested by the Navy or Douglas. Otherwise, NACA would simply look on as an interested observer.[2]

Early in April 1947, Douglas sent a test team to Muroc, together with the first D-558-1. Headed by Alden B. Carder, the team included company test pilot Eugene F. "Gene" May, recently designated as project pilot, and members of the company's Experimental Flight Test Division. May had long experience in testing Douglas company aircraft, the A-26, AD-1, and B-18 among others. He flew the Douglas XC-53, an experimental DC-3, in a bad-weather flying program aimed at evaluating heated wings for deicing purposes. His closest call came during the war, while testing a modified A-26. Instructed to perform a terminal velocity dive in the bomber, May nosed over to pick up speed, then found that the plane tended to tuck under. Unable to pull the nose up, May, in desperation, pushed the engine throttles forward to full power. The gambit worked, and the A-26, far above its maximum speed limitations, pulled out low above the ground.[3]

On April 15, Gene May took the scarlet D-558-1 #1 aloft for its initial flight.[4] Immediately after lifting off the lakebed, the plane experienced a partial power loss and May landed the Skystreak straight ahead. As he braked to a halt, the left brake completely disintegrated, necessitating judicious use of full left rudder to hold on course. May terminated another flight attempt on April 21 under similar circumstances, and the Skystreak did not return to the air until the end of May. Landing gear trouble plagued the next six flights, the gear failing to lock up or retract, but, by early July, Douglas technicians had remedied the problem. Following the twelfth contractor flight, July 12, 1947, the Douglas test team felt confident that the aircraft had satisfactory general handling qualities. Accordingly, the company removed the clear canopy used on early low-speed flights, and replaced it with a hooded high-speed cockpit enclosure with flat "V" glass panels. After an airspeed-calibration flight, the company team embarked on serious performance investigations to high Mach numbers beginning with the fourteenth flight on July 17, 1947. By the twentieth flight, August 5, 1947, May had attained Mach 0.85.[5]

In August 1947, the second D-558-1, BuAer No. 37971, joined the Douglas test program. Though destined for NACA service, Douglas completed the airplane without installation of the special NACA research instrumentation. NACA planned installation of this instrumentation after Douglas satisfactorily demonstrated the airplane to the NACA Muroc Flight Test Unit. Gene May performed the first contractor flights on this aircraft on August 15. The next day it flew no less than four times, twice by Navy Comdr. Turner F. Caldwell, Jr., and twice by Marine Maj. Marion E. Carl. Both of these pilots flew the D-558-1 #2 in preparation for an assault on the world's airspeed record.[6]

Nearly a year before, on September 7, 1946, RAF Group Captain E. M. Donaldson had set a world airspeed record of 615.778 mph. During practice to exceed this record, Geoffrey de Havilland had died. The record stood well into 1947 and, in March, Navy officials discussed the possibility of setting a new world airspeed record using the D-558-1 with

Douglas personnel.[7] Douglas and Navy representatives concluded that the D-558-1 program should not be delayed to make a record flight, but felt that the attempt would permit good calibration of instrumentation during the speed trials and demonstrate the ability of skilled pilots to fly at high Mach numbers close to the ground while retaining complete control of the airplane.[8] The Navy decided to continue with the attempt after Col. Albert Boyd, flying the P-80R, set a new world's airspeed record of 623.738 mph on June 19, 1947. BuAer detailed Comdr. Caldwell and Maj. Carl to make the flights.

Comdr. Turner Caldwell was the Navy D-558 project officer. Maj. Marion Carl, a Marine test pilot, had scored 18 victories over Japanese aircraft while stationed in the Pacific during the war. Since 1945, Carl had served at the Patuxent River Naval Air Station, Maryland. While at Patuxent, he flew the early jet aircraft, the American Bell P-59 and Lockheed P-80, and even a captured German Messerschmitt Me 262; in addition, he became the Marines' first helicopter-rated pilot. To set a world airspeed record, Carl and Caldwell had to fly the Skystreak below 75 meters altitude and make speed runs along a 3-kilometer—1.864 miles—measured course. After practicing in the D-558-1 #2 on August 16 and 17, Caldwell took the D-558-1 #1, BuAer No. 37970, aloft on August 20, 1947, to exceed Boyd's record. Carl also flew, with the D-558-1 #2, but that day only Caldwell broke the record, averaging 640.663 mph in four passes over the measured course.[9] Elated, BuAer sent a message of appreciation to the NACA, stating in part, "A great measure of the credit for the success of the D-558 airplane speed record flight is due to the NACA. The highly important introductory research and investigation program leading to recommendations on airplane configuration problems was essential in the development of this airplane."[10]

Five days later, flying the second D-558-1, Carl made another attempt, this time to exceed Caldwell's record. He had noticed that the Skystreak's TG-180 engine indicated 100 percent rpm on the ground, but once aloft, would fall down to 98 percent. He convinced Douglas technicians to increase rpm on the ground to 102 percent so that rpm in the air would be a full 100 percent. On August 25, during an 18-minute flight, Carl averaged 650.796 mph during 4 passes, exceeding Caldwell's record by a healthy 10 miles per hour.[11]

Three days after Carl's record-breaking flight, Capt. Frederick M. Trapnell, USN, completed 2 brief evaluation flights in the D-558-1 #1, attaining Mach 0.86 at 7,000 ft. (approximately 615 mph) on the second flight. Aside from finding lateral control "undesirably coarse" due to the small control wheel, Trapnell felt the aircraft had exceptionally fine flying characteristics and concluded that, "The model D-558 gives the impression of being an outstandingly excellent job of design and engineer-

ing, and a very sound airplane for research purposes . . ."[12] Following
the record flights, the D-558-1 #1, BuAer No. 37970, returned to its
contractor program. The D-558-1 #2, BuAer No. 37971, completed a
further 18 evaluation flights before being turned over to the NACA for
flight research on October 23, 1947.[13]

On November 4, 1947, the Bureau of Aeronautics sent a letter to
Douglas and NACA concerning delegation of responsibility during the
program. As set forth, Douglas would continue to fly a contractor program in the D-558-1 #1 for performance investigations. NACA would
get the second and third aircraft, and perform routine flight maintenance
and inspection on the aircraft. Douglas would perform major maintenance
items and modifications, and expenses would be covered for such work
by the Bureau of Aeronautics. In addition, the Navy would assume
financial responsibility for engine overhaul and replacement expenses.
NACA would procure fuel and oil for the aircraft from the Air Force.[14]
This established the pattern of future D-558 administration. The Navy
provided administration and appropriations, the NACA coordinated and
conducted the research program as well as supplying consultation and
research support, and Douglas assumed responsibility for the design and
construction of the aircraft, as well as demonstrating their satisfactory
handling qualities.[15]

After receiving the D-558-1 #2 from Douglas, the NACA-Muroc
instrumentation section, headed by Gerald M. Truszynski, began installation of research instrumentation, installing a similar instrumentation
package to that being installed in the Bell XS-1 at the same time. This
installation included a 12-channel oscillograph for strain gauges; a 60-
capsule manometer for recording pressure distribution; wheel force and
pedal force transmitters; aileron-, elevator-, and rudder-control position
recorders; a 3-component recording accelerometer; a 4-channel telemeter
and switch to transmit airspeed, altitude, normal acceleration, and elevator and aileron positions; an airspeed-altitude recorder; a sideslip-angle
transmitter; and a gunsight camera to photograph the instrument readings on the pilot's control panel. A 1/10-second timer synchronized the
instrumentation. By late November 1947, NACA technicians completed
installation except for the rudder-control position recorder and the tele-
metering equipment. With the aircraft essentially ready for flight, the
Muroc Flight Test Unit scheduled a familiarization flight for November 25.[16]

NACA research pilot Howard C. Lilly completed the craft's first
NACA flight on November 25 and made another the next day. Instrumentation malfunctions occurred on both flights and Lilly terminated the
second one shortly after takeoff because the landing gear would not lock
up. Otherwise, Lilly reported that the Skystreak handled satisfactorily.[17]

NACA cancelled further flight plans when winter rains flooded the lake, and engine modifications to comply with engine-maintenance technical orders kept the Skystreak grounded into the new year.[18]

During other Skystreak flights, Douglas and the NACA discovered that the scarlet aircraft had extremely poor visual characteristics from a tracking or photographic standpoint, being exceedingly difficult to pick out against the dark blue Muroc sky. Accordingly, Walter C. Williams, the chief of the Muroc Flight Test Unit, requested that Douglas paint the aircraft white or yellow.[19] Over the winter of 1947–48, NACA took advantage of time spent on the ground by painting the fuselage of the D-558-1 #2 white to facilitate optical tracking.[20] Following final instrumentation checks, Lilly returned the Skystreak to the air on February 16, for an airspeed calibration flight, but failure of a ground radio receiver prevented the calibration from taking place.[21]

With the pilot-familiarization flights drawing to a close, the NACA Muroc unit readied the aircraft for its actual flight-research program. On February 17, 1948, William H. Barlow, NACA engineer on the D-558-1 program, outlined the proposed flight-research plans for the aircraft. The initial program planned covered stability and control and aerodynamic loads measurements. Two flights for airspeed calibration at high-altitude (30,000 ft.) and low altitude (during flybys) would be made. NACA planned 13 flights to evaluate static directional stability (through slowly increasing sideslips), dynamic directional stability (through abrupt rudder kicks), and lateral control (through abrupt rudder-fixed aileron rolls) over a Mach number range from 0.4 to 0.85 and at both 10,000 and 30,000 ft. altitude. A further 16 flights would measure longitudinal stability and aircraft loads in both straight and accelerated flight during straight and level-speed runs to maximum speed at 30,000 and 10,000 ft. (to determine static longitudinal control characteristics and wing and tail loads in straight flight), turns from 1 to 4g in ½g increments from Mach 0.4 to 0.85 (to obtain stick-force-per-g data, elevator position variation with normal acceleration, and wing and tail loads in accelerated flight), and abrupt pull-ups from Mach 0.4 to 0.85 at 30,000 ft. (to acquire variation of the coefficient of lift with the rate of pull-up, available control, buffet boundary, buffet loads data, elevator hinge moments, and dynamic stability characteristics). Once this 31-flight program had been completed, NACA engineers would formulate further research programs.[22]

Engine and instrument checks, combined with a wet lake, kept the Skystreak grounded until March.[23] When Lilly did resume flights in the red-and-white aircraft, landing gear difficulties marred the next four flights. The landing gear doors would not lock. Eventually, technicians traced the trouble to a door latch that closed before the landing gear came up. After increasing the clearance between the latch and the door's engaging roller, the landing gear difficulties disappeared.[24] On April 8, 1948, Lilly completed two flights for airspeed calibration, repeating the first because of radar beacon failure. He completed a tower flyby calibration on April 12 and, during the rest of the month, flew the Skystreak on its first pure research flights. By the end of April the Skystreak had completed five directional stability investigations. On April 29, he had attained Mach 0.88 (approximately 580 mph).[25]

On May 3, 1948, Lilly took off for the D-558-1 #2's eighteenth NACA flight. The landing gear would not retract and he brought it back down. After minor maintenance work and an inspection, a ground service crew towed the Skystreak to the west end of the paved east-west runway. Lilly began his takeoff roll and the Skystreak broke ground after about 5,000 ft. of run. The landing gear came up normally, and the research plane continued to accelerate in level flight at about 100–150 ft. altitude, its J-35 engine shrieking loudly. Approximately 2.2 miles east of the start of takeoff, traveling about 250 mph, witnesses saw the Skystreak shed a large piece of external fuselage skin, followed by a gout of smoke mixed with flames. The plane held steady for a few seconds, and then slipped into a left yaw and roll. It struck the ground almost inverted and broke up. The wing, containing the fuel supply, burst into flames.[26] Howard C. Lilly had become the first NACA research pilot killed in the line of duty.

Howard Clifton Lilly's flying career spanned a scant 7 years. He had joined the Civilian Air Pilot Training Program in 1941 and had continued flight training as a naval aviator after joining the Navy in July of that year. He received an honorable discharge from the Navy in September 1942 in order to join the NACA's Langley Memorial Aeronautical Laboratory as a research pilot, later transferring to NACA's Lewis Flight Propulsion Laboratory in Cleveland. He transferred to Muroc in August 1947, trained under Herbert Hoover, and, while flying the Bell XS-1, had become the third man to fly faster than sound.[27] A highly experienced Skystreak pilot, he had flown the previous 18 flights in the D-558-1 #2, and had made one flight in the D-558-1 #3 aircraft as well. All indications—particularly the inflight fire—pointed to mechanical failure of the aircraft itself. But, like Lilly, the Skystreak, with but minor exception, had an excellent record. Before NACA received the D-558-1 #2, Douglas and Navy pilots had made a total of 27 flights in the aircraft. Taken as a whole, the 3 D-558-1 aircraft had successfully completed 127 flights without serious incident, a highly satisfactory record of operations.[28]

NACA formed an accident board to investigate the crash, chaired by Melvin N. Gough. NACA cordoned off the area of the crash and the flight path from runway to crash site. Searchers carefully located bits of wreckage and mapped their location on a grid. About 0.2 miles short of where searchers had found the big section of white fuselage skin, other searchers located bits and pieces of the compressor case, blade fragments, paint chips, and small pieces of fuselage skin. No evidence of burning or fire damage existed, and the findings indicated that the turbojet compressor blades and case had torn out of the fuselage. Close examination of the aircraft wreckage revealed that the disintegrating compressor had sheared the right rudder cable and up elevator cable, impairing both longitudinal and directional control. The crash itself had broken the remaining control cables. Evidence, then, indicated an engine failure in which the compressor section had disintegrated, severing vital control lines and making a crash inevitable.[29]

A memorandum to the D-558 accident board, written slightly over a week after the accident, expressed concern over the lack of protection around control lines and criticized the small size of the Skystreak's canopy, since a pilot could not wear a protective helmet. The writer also criticized the unproven jettisonable-nose method of escape and suggested that when the D-558 aerodynamic research program ended, NACA could equip one of the two remaining aircraft with an autopilot and telemetry equipment and deliberately jettison the nose in flight to measure cockpit motions.[30] In the official accident report released later, the D-558 accident board agreed with most of the suggestions made in this anonymous memorandum. The board exonerated all personnel involved in any way in the ill-fated flight, and placed the blame for the accident on the disintegration of the compressor section of the TG-180 (J-35-C-3) engine. The compressor had severed the main fuel lines, elevator, and rudder cables, causing an inflight fire and subsequent loss of control.[31] The board recommended that all control lines, fuel lines, pumps, and electrical circuits be protected, and that the control cables be shielded, armored, or duplicated. Additionally, the board recommended that the cockpit canopy be redesigned to permit greater visibility and the pilot's wearing of a crash helmet, and that only the latest-type engines complying with the latest known changes in design be used in research aircraft. In particular, the board recommended that the engine access for inspection should be improved in the remaining two D-558 airplanes.[32] NACA quickly pointed out that the value of the Skystreak to high-speed flight research remained unaltered by the accident and the incorporation of these recommended changes.

Essentially the loss of the D-558-1 #2 meant that the D-558-1 #3, BuAer No. 37972, had to assume the research program of the destroyed airplane. In September 1948, NACA returned the D-558-1 #3 to the Douglas plant for modifications recommended by the accident board. The company had already completed modifications to the D-558-1 #1, and this aircraft continued flying in the Douglas contractor program.[33] Originally, Douglas had delivered the D-558-1 #3 Skystreak on November 4,

1947. By the time of Lilly's accident, it had completed four flights.[34] After the aircraft arrived back at the Douglas plant, Douglas technicians added duplicate control cables and ¼-inch stainless steel armor over the emergency fuel pump and fuel lines. Douglas replaced the Skystreak's standard high-pressure fuel hoses with wire-wound fuel hoses following tests in which .22 caliber rifle bullets, simulating disintegrating engine fragments, easily pierced the standard hose. In addition to making safety modifications, Douglas also painted the airplane white.[35]

Early in November 1948, Douglas sent the D-558-1 #3 back to the Muroc facility. Before initiation of the flight-research program on this aircraft, NACA engineers already knew that the aircraft experienced more severe longitudinal and lateral trim changes than those experienced with the XS-1 in the same speed range.[36] Douglas had to complete a satisfactory demonstration flight in the aircraft before NACA would accept it. On January 3, 1949, Gene May made the demonstration flight, which included a 6.8g pullout, constant maximum sideslips left and right at 580 mph, and a high-speed low-level pass at 605 mph IAS.[37] Postflight inspection by a NACA safety representative revealed a badly mangled brass safety wire that had evidently passed through the engine. Rather than pull the engine for inspection, Douglas installed a new engine so as not to delay delivery.[38] On January 22, 1949, the NACA took charge of the D-558-1 #3.[39]

NACA gave the aircraft the call sign "NACA 142," and spent until April readying it for flight. During April, Douglas concluded their performance investigation using the D-558-1 #1, BuAer No. 37970, and delivered this aircraft to NACA on April 21, 1949, for spares support. In total, the D-558-1 #1 had completed 101 flights. During its demonstration program, hopes that the Skystreak series might generate a tactical aircraft had been quashed; though it attained Mach 1 in a dive, its behavior characteristics at this speed deteriorated to such an extent that it could not possibly be used for tactical military flying.[40]

By mid-April the #3 Skystreak entered flight status. Following Lilly's death, NACA research pilot Robert A. Champine, a former Navy fighter-bomber pilot attached to NACA's Langley Laboratory, replaced Lilly at Muroc and on April 22, 1949, he performed the D-558-1 #3's first NACA flight since modification. Instrument malfunctions marred both this flight and a second on April 28, but Champine did get some indication of the aircraft's behavior characteristics at transonic speeds. During a dive to Mach 0.87 on the second flight, wheel force for trim rose from 5 lbs, push at Mach 0.82 to 30 lbs, push at 0.87 Mach. Throughout the dive, the plane exhibited increasing tail heaviness, and initiated a lateral oscillation with very low damping.[41]

NACA again grounded the aircraft for maintenance work, for the turbojet engine had to be removed and replaced. Replacement of the

engine on the Skystreak series involved removal of flight instrumentation; this work kept the Skystreak grounded until August 1949. Then the
plane resumed flying, embarking on a comprehensive handling-qualities
investigation program flown by Champine and John H. Griffith, a newly
arrived NACA pilot. On these flights, instrumentation recorded data
during aileron rolls, sideslips, and abrupt rudder kicks around Mach
0.9.[42] The Skystreak quickly exhausted its fuel supply on these flights,
and NACA decided to employ tip tanks to increase endurance. Additionally, during September and October 1949, NACA instrumentation engineers installed manometers to record pressure distribution from the
orifices in the right wing.

The Skystreak resumed flying on October 31, beginning an uninter-
rupted series of pressure-distribution research flights that continued over
the next seven months.[43] On the last of these flights, NACA flight 22,
June 13, 1950, Griffith attained approximately Mach 0.99, about the
Skystreak's limiting Mach number. In mid-June 1950, NACA engineers
removed the #3 Skystreak's horizontal stabilizer and replaced it with the
instrumented stabilizer from the D-558-1 #1 then in "dead" storage at
the NACA facility. The D-558-1 #1's stabilizer would enable engineers to
measure tail loads. At the same time, NACA technicians converted the
electrical instrumentation system from d.c. to 400-cycle a.c., and installed
a special picture manometer obtained from Langley Laboratory.[44]

Transonic pressure-distribution measurements indicated that a shock
wave first formed at the 45 percent chord position of the upper wing
surface at about Mach 0.76. As the Mach number increased, this shock
moved aft, together with the center of pressure. At about Mach 0.82, a
shock wave would form on the lower wing surface. As the Mach number
increased further, the lower shock moved aft while the upper shock
remained stationary, thus causing a forward shift in the location of the
center of pressure. With a further increase in Mach number, the two
shock waves and the center of pressure would again move aft. This behavior corresponded to that experienced on the NACA XS-1, which also had
a 10 percent wing section.[45]

At transonic speeds the Skystreak became laterally unstable and
presented the pilot with considerable difficulty in maintaining wings-
level control. Wing dropping appeared; for example, the right wing would
drop suddenly and, as the pilot attempted to bring it up, the D-558-1
would roll rapidly left. If the pilot applied corrective aileron, the plane
would roll rapidly right. Usually, the Skystreak displayed a marked
tendency to roll right beginning at about Mach 0.84. As Mach numbers
increased, a trim change caused by a loss in elevator effectiveness appeared. NACA engineers were uncertain whether changes in pressure
distribution or actual physical distortion of the stabilizer and elevators
caused the loss in elevator effectiveness and the resulting trim changes.

This uncertainty led to the decision to install the stabilizer from the D-558-1 #1 on the NACA D-558-1 #3 aircraft.[46]

One interesting experiment NACA engineers undertook on the Skystreak—and also on the XS-1—was the installation of wing-mounted vortex generators. It appeared that the vortex generators might help stabilize the positions of the shock waves on the wing, thus possibly reducing or eliminating the undesirable changes in lateral and longitudinal stability that appeared. Before the conclusion of the pressure-distribution research program, engineers fitted the Skystreak with the vortex generators, and John Griffith completed five vortex-generator research flights. Test results indicated that the vortex generators had little effect on wingpressure distribution until the aircraft reached Mach 0.85. Between Mach 0.85 and Mach 0.89, the generators caused the shock wave to displace more to the rear, improving pressure recovery near the wing trailing edge. Further, the generators prevented flow separation and delayed the onset of wing dropping by 0.5 Mach number.[47]

Now fitted with the new stabilizer and a high-speed picture manometer to record wing-pressure distribution over one spanwise station, NACA engineers readied the aircraft for a thorough investigation of the Skystreak's buffet boundary. To investigate the wing as a potential source of buffet, technicians installed a downwash vane for airflow analysis. NACA planned to record additional longitudinal-stability and trim data, and the strain gauges in the tail would measure the bending and twisting of the horizontal stabilizer and the twist of the elevators.[48] In mid-October 1950, technicians completed final instrumentation and maintenance checks and the Skystreak again entered flight status.[49]

John Griffith completed an instrument- and operation-check flight in the aircraft on October 26. One of the modifications to the aircraft had been the addition of a nose boom. During the check flight the boom performed satisfactorily, and NACA engineers mounted an airspeed head having an angle-of-attack vane onto the boom for future flights.[50] The Skystreak returned to the air on November 29, 1950, on a pilot-familiarization flight for NACA research pilot A. Scott Crossfield, a former Navy flight instructor, fighter pilot, and graduate engineer. The first complete buffet, tail loads, and longitudinal-stability investigation flight came on December 12, 1950. During that month, NACA engineers added an investigation of dynamic longitudinal stability to the longitudinal-stability program because the manometer had additional capabilities.[51] The Skystreak flew this entire longitudinal-stability program over the next year, through the fall of 1951.[52]

Early in the program, elevator twists up to 2° occurred during pullups at Mach numbers around 0.80.[53] Additional data indicated undesirable elevator vibration. NACA engineers removed the elevators and X-rayed them for fatigue cracks, but no flaws appeared.[54] Further investigation revealed that the vibrations increased in amplitude in direct relation to an increase in Mach number and occurred at all high-lift conditions over the entire Mach number range, even in a stall.[55] NACA engineers contacted the Douglas Aircraft Company since Douglas had encountered similar difficulties during the contractor program on the D-558-1 #1. Subsequent discussions with Douglas representatives brought out that during a dive to Mach 0.94, the D-558-1 #1 encountered vibrations so severe that Douglas placed a never-exceed limit of Mach 0.92 on the airplane. The company attempted to lessen the vibrations by shifting the location of the outboard elevator balance weights, but had not effectively evaluated the change, concluding the contractor program without making additional flights. Douglas engineers conceded that the change had been more of a shot in the dark than a seriously considered fix.[56]

The vibration did not readily show on the elevator force and position indicator, and appeared unaffected by the elevator damper. High-Speed Flight Research Station engineers concluded that the vibration probably assumed undesirable proportions before showing up on the force trace.[57] Douglas engineers calculated that the vibrations during the NACA flights caused stresses of approximately 70 percent of the maximum design stress, and that such stresses could eventually lead to fatigue failure. To be safe, NACA engineers decided to replace the elevators currently on the D-558-1 #3—these elevators had originally been on the D-558-1 #1 aircraft on over 100 flights, including the dive to Mach 0.94—with the D-558-1 #3's original elevators, which had only been used for 22 NACA flights.[58] NACA did not complete replacement of the elevators until late April 1951. The first flight following replacement came on May 2, 1951.[59]

In September 1951, technicians removed the high-speed picture manometer from the airplane[60] and, in October, the Skystreak began a lateral-stability investigation program in conjunction with the buffet and tail-loads program.[61] Following Flight 56 (Nov. 9, 1951), NACA grounded the airplane for extensive maintenance work due to severe fuel leaks and engine ignition problems until January 1952.[62] Winter rains kept the lakebed closed, precluding any research flights, and HSFRS engineers decided to add strain gauges for vertical-tail-loads measurements.[63] Design and installation of the strain-gauge instrumentation—which involved cutting two access doors in the base of the vertical fin—began immediately. Additionally, NACA technicians installed instrumentation for measuring rudder hinge-moments and transverse acceleration at the tail in preparation for the anticipated vertical-tail-loads program.[64]

But when the D-558-1 #3 resumed flying in June 1952, it embarked on a lateral-stability and aileron-control-effectiveness investigation. NACA filed Skystreak flight data from the horizontal-tail-loads and tail-buffeting program because of a shortage of engineers. NACA needed all available engineers for the D-558-2 Skyrocket, Bell X-5, and, later, the Douglas X-3 programs.[65] NACA felt the lateral-stability and control program to be more important than the vertical tail-loads investigation, and, consequently, postponed the vertical-tail-loads program indefinitely.[66]

During the lateral-control program, Scott Crossfield and NACA research pilot Stanley P. Butchart flew the jet aircraft in abrupt aileron rolls to obtain aileron effectiveness data over a Mach number range from 0.4 to the limiting Mach number at 10,000 ft., 25,000 ft., and 35,000 ft. altitudes.[67] As indicated earlier, in other NACA and Douglas flights, lateral stability decreased rapidly above Mach 0.85. Throughout the summer of 1952, the 2 pilots confirmed that aileron effectiveness sharply dropped at velocities above Mach 0.88 by making aileron rolls at speeds approaching Mach 0.9. Concurrently with the lateral-stability program, the High Speed Flight Research Station continued the dynamic-longitudinal-stability investigation.[68]

NACA-Edwards engineers concluded the lateral-stability program on the Skystreak with flight 63, August 12, 1952. During a post-flight inspection, maintenance personnel noticed a looseness in the horizontal stabilizer mountings. Further inspection revealed that the assembly required extensive repairs.[69] During necessary repair work, NACA technicians discovered that the strain gauges installed for the vertical-tail-loads program likewise needed extensive repair work. However, project engineers decided that the vertical-tail-loads program would not return data valuable enough to justify the man-hours needed to repair the gauges, and abandoned the planned vertical-tail-loads program.[70] Despite this, the Skystreak still had an active program ahead of it. The dynamic-stability program had yet to be concluded, and then the aircraft would be used briefly as a pilot trainer for research pilots. After repairs to the horizontal stabilizer had been completed, the D-558-1 #3 resumed flying in January 1953.[71]

During the dynamic-stability program, NACA planned to record aircraft response after elevator and rudder pulses over a Mach range to 0.90 at 25,000 ft. and 35,000 ft. altitudes. Though NACA had acquired some dynamic-stability data during the lateral-stability program, roughly two-thirds of the elevator pulse data remained to be gathered, as well as almost all of the rudder pulse data. Project engineers planned to record the data from these flights on IBM cards and send it to Langley Laboratory for computation on IBM machines.[72]

Stanley Butchart completed the first flight in the dynamic-stability program on January 29, 1953, and made four more flights by mid-February. This rounded out the flight portion of the dynamic-stability investigation, though NACA engineers believed that one or two additional flights might be necessary to provide fill-in data.[73] On March 27, 1953, NACA research pilot John B. "Jack" McKay checked out in the Skystreak and on April 1 and 2 he completed two additional flights to provide additional dynamic-stability data. These last two flights marked the end of the aircraft's planned NACA program, and NACA relegated it to a pilot-training vehicle.[74]

The Skystreak had not ended its research days, however, for NACA decided to conduct a brief investigation of the effects of tip tanks upon the plane's buffet characteristics.[75] During May and June, McKay completed an additional six flights. Data acquired from the tip tank/buffet program indicated that the tanks had no appreciable effect upon aircraft buffet up to a Mach number of 0.85. McKay completed his last flight in the aircraft on June 3, 1953, and one week later, on June 10, 1953, A. Scott Crossfield took the plane up for its final flight, NACA flight 78.[76] In July 1953, after four-and-a-half years of active research flying, NACA retired the D-558-1 #3 Skystreak and removed its research instrumentation. NACA placed the Skystreak in dead storage in late 1953, like the D-558-1 #1, and in 1954 returned the aircraft to the Navy at Alameda Naval Air Station.[77]

Developed essentially as a turbojet-powered backup for the Bell XS-1, the 3 D-558-1 Skystreak aircraft completed a total of 225 flights. Unlike some of the other research aircraft, they had not required extensive changes in configuration as a result of flight testing. Douglas had installed a high-speed canopy and extended the aircraft's tail cone to improve engine cooling and prevent erosion of the skin around the tail pipe, but these changes did not require extensive reworking of the aircraft.[78] The only other modifications had involved protection of the control systems of the 2 remaining aircraft following the loss of the D-558-1 #2. The loss of the second Skystreak produced an increased awareness of the hazards of research flying in NACA and industry personnel, and the changes made to the Skystreak were duplicated on other research aircraft as well, notably the Northrop X-4 and the Bell X-5.

Generally speaking, pilots liked the flying qualities of the D-558-1 aircraft, though they found the cockpit very cramped—the pilot could not turn his head, and crash helmets had to be covered with chamois skin to prevent windshield scarring. The Skystreak had satisfactory flying characteristics until reaching about Mach 0.85, when aileron and elevator effectiveness decreased appreciably.[79] In the low-speed spectrum, the Skystreak had good control characteristics as it approached the stall condition, but it encountered abrupt roll-off at the stall. Pilots therefore always executed the landing approach at about 210 mph, landing at 143 mph, well above the stall. Despite the high landing speed, pilots found the landing characteristics satisfactory.[80]

Like the X-1 and the D-558-2, the Skystreak in the 1948–50 time period provided virtually the only means of acquiring data on transonic flight conditions pending the development of improved ground-research techniques such as the slotted throat wind tunnel. Its construction enabled NACA and the industry to combine into one aircraft all the important and current developments of the aeronautical state of the art and then determine from flight testing whether or not the elements fitted together to produce a workable design. It freed the Bell X-1 rocket-research aircraft to explore supersonic flight conditions during its short rocket flights.

Carrying 634 lbs. of research instrumentation and flown by highly trained scientist-pilots, the D-558-1 represented an ideal first-generation simple transonic research airplane. Its value can be judged on the wide basis of research areas it explored: handling qualities, pressure distribution, buffeting, tail loads, static and dynamic longitudinal and lateral stability and control. Initiated as a research airplane, it ended its days as a pilot-familiarization aircraft. Perhaps not as spectacular as the rocket-research aircraft, the D-558 Phase One Skystreak nevertheless constituted a necessary step on the road to supersonic flight.

NOTES

1. Williams memo, 29 Oct. 1946. Later, perhaps because of the availability of NACA personnel and better locale, Douglas agreed to conduct the contractor tests at Muroc.

2. Edwin P. Hartman, Memo for the Director of Aeronautical Research (NACA), "Douglas flight tests of 558 at Mojave," 14 Feb. 1947.

3. *Ibid.* Also, Gene May and Guy Halferty, "My Biggest Thrill," *Flying*, LII, No. 6 (June 1953), 12–14, 51–54.

4. Letter, Bureau of Aeronautics to Bureau of Aeronautics representative, Douglas Aircraft Company (Naval Speedletter Aer-DE-237) 14 April 1947, in NASC D-558 file. Also Mulac, D-558-1 flight chronology.

5. Mulac, D-558-1 flight chronology. Also May and Halferty, "My Biggest Thrill," p. 52.

6. *Ibid.*

7. Paul E. Purser, Memo for Chief of Research (NACA), "Douglas D-558 Phase 2 airplane—Discussion with Douglas representatives concerning tests of rocket-powered models," 1 April 1947.

8. Heinemann, "Development of the Navy-Douglas Model D-558 Research Project," p. 18.

9. D-558 Summary Report, p. 38.

10. Naval Communications Message from BuAero AC-2 to NACA, received by NACA 22 Aug. 1947. (This message was sent following Caldwell's flight, but before Carl's.)

11. *Ibid.* The figure of 650.796 is taken from Emme, *Aeronautics and*

Astronautics, p. 158. For Carl's explanation of flight, see William Askins, "The Ultimate Fighter Pilot," *Air Progress*, Vol. XXVII, No. 3 (Sept. 1970), 46–49, 76–77. Both Carl and Caldwell later flew the D-558-2 Skyrocket, Carl setting an altitude record in the all-rocket aircraft.

12. Capt. Frederick M. Trapnell, Memorandum to Bureau of Aeronautics (Piloted Aircraft Division), D-558, Evaluation flight on·3 Sept. 1947.

13. William H. Barlow, Memo for Chief of Research (NACA), "Progress report on D-558-1-#2 airplane test program to Dec. 8, 1947," 8 Dec. 1947. Hereafter NACA D-558-1 #2 Progress Reports are cited as follows: *D-558-1 #2 PR* followed by date. With the initiation of the NACA D-558-1 #3 program, the individual airplane number (i.e., #3) will be dropped since this was the only Skystreak that NACA operated following the May 1948 accident to the D-558-1 #2.

14. Letter, Chief BuAer to NACA Headquarters and BuAer Rep., Douglas Aircraft Corporation, 4 Nov. 1947 (letter Aer-AC-25).

15. Heinemann, "Development of Navy-Douglas Model D-558 Research Project," p. 1.

16. *D-558-1 #2 PR*, 8 Dec. 1947.

17. Mulac, D-558-1 flight chronology. Also, *D-558-1 #2 PR*, 8 Dec. 1947.

18. *Ibid.* Also, *D-558-1 #2 PR*, 18 Jan. 1948.

19. Letter, Walter C. Williams to Robert C. Donovan, 25 Aug., 1947.

20. *D-558-1 #2 PR*, 2 Feb. 1948.

21. *D-558-1 #2 PR*, 13 Feb. 1948; also, *D-558-1 #2 PR*, 2 Mar. 1948. See also D-558-1 flight chronology.

22. William H. Barlow, Memo for Chief of Research (NACA), "Research Program for D-558 Phase I No. 2 Airplane," 17 Feb. 1948.

23. *D-558-1 #2 PR*, 29 Mar. 1948.

24. *D-558-1 #2 PR*, 13 April 1948. Also, Mulac, D-558-1 flight chronology.

25. *Ibid.* Also, *D-558-1 #2 PR*, n.d.; and *D-558-1 #2 PR*, 12 May 1948.

26. M. N. Gough, A. Young, and H. A. Goett, *Aircraft Accident Investigation Report Douglas D-558-1 Airplane, BuNo 37971, Muroc Air Force Base, Muroc, California, May 3, 1948*, p 2. Hereafter cited as *Skystreak Accident Report*.

27. Biographical data on Howard C. Lilly from the Lilly Biographical File, NASA Historical Division.

28. *Skystreak Accident Report*, pp. 2, 3.

29. *Ibid.*, p. 3.

30. Author unknown, Memo for D-558 Accident Board, "Comments on Operation of Research Airplanes," 11 May 1948, pp. 1–2. The author also recommended the air launching of all research aircraft because of the proven feasibility of the XS-1 operations, and because it would provide altitude for the pilot to escape or take corrective action in case of difficulty. The Accident Board agreed that more consideration should be given to the potential of air launching for all research aircraft in their official report.

31. *Skystreak Acident Report*, pp. 10–11.

32. *Ibid.*, pp. 12–13.

33. *D-558-1 #3 PR*, 27 Sept. 1948. At this time, the D-558-1 #1 (BuNo.

37970) was flown in a series of high-speed dives to obtain stability and control characteristics up to the maximum practicable Mach number. Beyond Mach 0.85, the control characteristics of the Skystreak deteriorated badly and the plane experienced marked lateral instability and a decrease in longitudinal stability above Mach 0.9. Surprisingly, however, the D-558-1 #1 did attain Mach 1 during a 35° dive made on September 29, 1948. Apparently, this was the only time that the Skystreak ever reached Mach 1. See *D-558 Summary Report* pp. 22, 28, 50–51.

34. *D-558-1 #3 PR*, 18 Jan. 1948.

35. *D-558-1 PR*, 27 Sept. 1948. An interesting example of the close weight-and-balance tolerances of research aircraft came to light during the painting of the aircraft: "When the aircraft was sprayed with the white undercoat, as mentioned in my preceding report, the control surfaces were painted. I had seen a schedule of work, issued by the office of the chief engineer for this division, which called for a white paint coat on the entire ship, except the control surfaces. I called this to the attention of the aircraft project engineer and investigation proved that the shop order was in conflict with the original order. Further investigation showed that the reason for not painting the surfaces involved a problem of weight and balance. With the original red color the surfaces were just within the allowable margins and the addition of the white undercoat threw them over the limits. The solution was to remove the white, rubbing down into the red just slightly and then fog a light mist coat of red on the units." From letter, R. B. Cox (Douglas Aircraft Company) to Walter C. Williams, 11 Oct. 1948. This explains why the NACA Skystreak flew its entire research program with red ailerons, elevators, and rudder.

36. *D-558-1 PR*, 27 Oct. 1948. Also, *D-558-1 PR*, 5 Nov. 1948.

37. Letter, Eugene F. May to Walter C. Williams, 4 Jan. 1949.

38. *D-558-1 PR*, 11 Jan. 1949.

39. *D-558 Summary Report*, p. 22.

40. *Ibid.*, pp. 22, 50–51. NACA placed the D-558-1 #1 in dead storage. In 1955, NACA presented it to the California Polytechnic Institute for instructional purposes. In 1965, the institute presented it to the Naval Aviation Museum, Pensacola, Florida, where it is today, repainted in red.

41. *D-558-1 PR*, 28 April 1949; *D-558-1 PR*, 6 May 1949; *D-558-1 PR*, 24 May 1949.

42. *D-558-1 PR*, 24 May 1949; *D-558-1 PR*, 7 June 1949; *D-558-1 PR*, 20 June 1949; *D-558-1 PR*, 5 July 1949; *D-558-1 PR*, 15 July 1949; *D-558-1 PR*, 2 Aug. 1949; *D-558-1 PR*, 15 Aug. 1949; *D-558-1 PR*, 30 Aug. 1949; *D-558-1 PR*, 14 Sept. 1949; *D-558-1 PR*, 23 Sept. 1949; *D-558-1 PR*, 7 Oct. 1949. Also, Mulac D-558-1 flight chronology.

43. *D-558-1 PR*, 24 Oct. 1949; *D-558-1 PR*, 4 Nov. 1949; *D-558-1 PR*, 21 Nov. 1949; *D-558-1 PR*, 16 Dec. 1949; *D-558-1 PR*, 30 Dec. 1949; *D-558-1 PR*, 16 Jan. 1950; *D-558-1 PR*, 31 Jan. 1950; *D-558-1 PR*, 28 Mar. 1950; *D-558-1 PR*, 18 Apr. 1950; *D-558-1 PR*, 4 May 1950; *D-558-1 PR*, 10 May 1950; *D-558-1 PR*, 24 May 1950; *D-558-1 PR*, 8 June 1950. Also, Mulac D-558-1 flight chronology.

44. *D-558-1 PR*, 8 July 1950; *D-558-1 PR*, 19 July 1950; *D-558-1 PR*, 2 Aug. 1950; *D-558-1 PR*, 17 Aug. 1950; *D-558-1 PR*, 29 Aug. 1950; *D-558-1*

PR, 11 Sept. 1950; *D-558-1 PR*, 4 Oct. 1950; *D-558-1 PR*, 11 Oct. 1950; *D-558-1 PR*, 30 Oct. 1950.

45. "DRB" (most likely Donald R. Bellman), *Status of Research with the D-558-1 Airplane* (NACA-Muroc, 14 Sept. 1950), pp. 2–3.

46. *Ibid.*, pp. 1–2.

47. *Ibid.*, pp. 3–4.

48. *Ibid.*, pp. 4–5.

49. *D-558-1 PR*, 30 Oct. 1950.

50. *D-558-1 PR*, 8 Nov. 1950; *D-558-1 PR*, 24 Nov. 1950.

51. *D-558-1 PR*, 5 Dec. 1950; *D-558-1 PR*, 12 Jan. 1951.

52. For Skystreak 1951 program see *D-558-1 PRs* from 29 Dec. 1950 to 7 Sept. 1951 (total 18).

53. *D-558-1 PR*, 19 Feb. 1951.

54. *D-558-1 PR*, 16 Mar. 1951.

55. *D-558-1 PR*, 30 Mar. 1951.

56. *Ibid.*

57. *Ibid.*

58. *Ibid.*

59. *D-558-1 PR*, 11 Apr. 1951; *D-558-1 PR*, 14 May 1951.

60. *D-558-1 PR*, 13 Sept. 1951.

61. *D-558-1 PR*, 6 Nov. 1951. Also, Mulac D-558-1 flight chronology.

62. *D-558-1 PR*, 21 Nov. 1951; *D-558-1 PR*, 4 Dec. 1951; *D-558-1 PR*, 18 Dec. 1951; *D-558-1 PR*, 7 Jan. 1952; *D-558-1 PR*, 21 Jan. 1952; *D-558-1 PR*, 11 Feb. 1952.

63. *D-558-1 PR*, 11 Feb. 1952.

64. *D-558-1 PR*; PRs from Jan. 26–June 27, 1952 (total 11).

65. *D-558-1 PR*; PRs from June 14–Dec. 31, 1952 (total 9).

66. *D-558-1 PR*, 12 July 1952.

67. *D-558-1 PR*, 23 July 1952.

68. *D-558-1 PR*, 30 July 1952; *D-558-1 PR*, 14 Aug. 1952; *D-558-1 PR*, 26 Aug. 1952.

69. *D-558-1 PR*, 26 Aug. 1952.

70. *D-558-1 PR*, 20 Nov. 1952.

71. *D-558-1 PR*, 11 Dec. 1952.

72. *D-558-1 PR*, 11 Dec. 1952; *D-558-1 PR*, 6 Jan. 1953; *D-558-1 PR*, 6 Feb. 1953.

73. *D-558-1 PR*, 6 Feb. 1953; *D-558-1 PR*, 12 Mar. 1953; Mulac, D-558-1 flight chronology.

74. *D-558-1 PR*, 9 Apr. 1953; *D-558-1 PR*, 11 May 1953; Mulac, D-558-1 flight chronology.

75. *D-558-1 PR*, 11 May 1953.

76. *D-558-1 PR*, 10 June 1953; *D-558-1 PR*, 14 July 1953; Mulac, D-558-1 flight chronology.

77. *D-558-1 PR*, 6 Aug. 1953; also Mulac, D-558-1 flight chronology. Today this airplane is at the Marine Corps Museum, Quantico, Virginia.

78. *D-558 Summary Report*, p. 15.

79. NACA Research Memorandum RM L52A08, *Handling Qualities of*

High-Speed Airplanes, by W. C. Williams and A. S. Crossfield, 28 Jan. 1952. Data pertaining to the D-558-1 is on pp. 1, 2, 6, 9, 10, 17.

80. NACA Research Memorandum RM H54K24, *Results of Measurements Made During the Approach and Landing of Seven High-Speed Research Airplanes*, by Wendell H. Stillwell, 4 Feb. 1955, pp. 6–7.

PART

THREE

Through Mach 2

VII

NUDGING TOWARD TWICE
THE SPEED OF SOUND

W hen the D-558-2 #1 Skyrocket arrived at Muroc Dry Lake in early December 1947, the XS-1 #1 had already shattered the myth of the sound barrier. But much still remained for aerodynamicists to learn about transonic and supersonic flight conditions, as evidenced by the detailed programs the NACA conducted on the XS-1 #2 and the second and third D-558-1's. Interestingly, as the XS-1 #1 began its initial transonic research flights towards the first supersonic flight in the fall of 1947, a new aircraft arrived at Muroc that could exceed the speed of sound in a slight dive. This was the prototype North American XP-86 Sabre, serial 45-59597. The Sabre was the first American combat airplane to incorporate a sweptwing for alleviation of compressibility difficulties. North American trucked it to Muroc on September 10, 1947, and North American test pilot George Welch, a World War II fighter ace, made the first flight of the airplane on October 1.[1] In December 1947, the Air Force began evaluation of the XP-86. On April 26, 1948, George Welch began a shallow dive in the Sabre, and dove through Mach 1. The XP-86 became the third American airplane to exceed the speed of sound, following the XS-1 #1 and XS-1 #2.[2]

The Skyrocket filled the need for a research airplane to provide data from full-scale flight testing on the behavior of sweptwing aircraft in transonic research. North American's bold gamble in developing the F-86 furnished the Air Force with an operational fighter having performance superior to any other American fighter airplane. The NACA later acquired the fifth production F-86A, instrumented it for flight research, and shipped it to NACA's Ames Aeronautical Laboratory where NACA research pilots George Cooper and Rudolph Van Dyke flew it in an extensive program involving dives to supersonic speeds.[3] Curiously, then, the F-86 and the Skyrocket complemented one another in sweptwing research.

This is not to say that the capabilities of the two were equal, for the F-86 was simply a fighter airplane with its armament removed and instrumentation installed, while the D-558-2 series were research airplanes from the first, specially built to carry a minimum of 500 lbs. of research instrumentation, though, when developed, they could carry between 800 and 1,100 lbs. of research instrumentation. From the start of its research program, the Skyrocket became the leading flight-research tool for acquiring transonic aerodynamic data on the behavior of sweptwings. It began its research program in February 1948.

The Douglas company had selected its chief pilot, John F. Martin, as project pilot on the D-558-2. Martin had joined Douglas in 1940 after flying as a pilot for United Air Lines. Since then he had flown the initial prototype and engineering tests on a variety of Douglas aircraft, including the A-20 Havoc, A-26 Invader, and the C-54, the military version of the civil DC-4.[4] The story, allegedly true, of how Martin became project pilot illustrates how the company's own test pilots viewed the Skyrocket project. At the time the Skyrocket neared completion, the "sound barrier" still loomed as a dangerous unknown in the minds of most pilots. Yeager's epochal flight lay in the future. When it came time to select a project pilot for the airplane, Douglas El Segundo sent notice to the flight test office at Santa Monica for the company test pilots to submit bids for the flight program. The pilots did not desire to fly the somewhat imposing plane and, after talking among themselves, decided to submit exceptionally high bids that almost certainly would not be accepted. Martin was the only pilot not in on the plot, for he was away delivering an airplane. Unaware of the conspiracy in Santa Monica, he submitted a reasonable bid. The company accepted his bid and designated him as Skyrocket project pilot.[5]

The white Skyrocket waited out at Muroc through January 1948 for a turbojet engine from Westinghouse, and Douglas technicians completed the engine installation and added research instrumentation. By the beginning of February, the plane was ready for flight. On February 4, Martin lifted the first Skyrocket off the lakebed at Muroc. The plane had a sluggish performance on just its turbojet engine, and Douglas decided to improve takeoff performance by installing JATO solid-fuel booster equipment. The early flights of the D-558-2 #1 Skyrocket revealed a "Dutch-roll"-type oscillation, and that the plane had poor visibility for the pilot. Douglas remedied the two problems by increasing the height of the vertical fin by roughly 1½ ft., raising it to an even 13 feet, and installing a raised cockpit similar to the D-558-1 Skystreak.[6] After making 15 flights in the sweptwing airplane, Martin turned it over to company test pilot Gene May.

As with the D-558-1 #1 Skystreak, Douglas retained the D-558-2 #1 Skyrocket for a contractor evaluation program. Over the spring and summer of 1948, Douglas engineers at Muroc readied the D-558-2 #2, BuAer No. 37974, for flight. Like the D-558-2 #1, this airplane lacked its RMI LR-8 rocket engine, but the NACA agreed to accept the airplane and utilize it with the provision that when the rocket engine became available, the NACA could return the Skyrocket to Douglas for installation of the rocket. On November 2 and 7, Gene May completed two demonstration flights in the airplane, and on December 1, 1948, Douglas turned it over to the NACA for initiation of its flight-research program.[7]

Equipped only with its Westinghouse 24C-turbojet—more widely known as the J-34-WE-40—the Skyrocket was limited to about Mach 0.9. NACA planned to use the jet-powered plane for general stability and control and air-loads research to a Mach number of about 0.85. Engine difficulties kept the D-558-2 #2 Skyrocket grounded until May 1949, but NACA engineers took advantage of the time spent on the ground to calibrate and install all instrumentation.[8] On May 24, 1949, NACA research pilot Robert A. Champine completed the plane's first NACA flight. Following this familiarization flight, NACA embarked on the plane's research program beginning with the D-558-2 #2's second flight on June 1, 1949.[9]

By early August, the NACA D-558-2 #2 had completed a total of six flights. Champine had reached Mach 0.87 in a dive in the airplane, the fastest NACA flight yet in the airplane. During the plane's seventh NACA flight, on August 8, 1949, Champine banked into a 4g turn at Mach 0.6. Suddenly and without warning, the nose of the plane pitched upwards violently, attaining a positive acceleration of 6g. Shaken, Champine applied full down elevator, and the Skyrocket responded rapidly. Not taking any chances, however, the NACA pilot landed immediately.[10]

Though model tests had indicated that sweptwing airplanes might experience longitudinal instability resulting in a "pitch-up" phenomenon, the D-558-2 #2's seventh NACA flight provided aerodynamicists with the first indications of the severity and seriousness of the problem. The remainder of the plane's program, prior to installation of the RMI engine, concentrated on this pitch-up problem. In September 1949, John Griffith checked out in the airplane, and for the remainder of the year Champine and Griffith flew the plane. On November 1, 1949, Griffiith entered a 4g turn at Mach 0.6 as Champine had done nearly 3 months previously. As on the earlier flight, the plane became longitudinally unstable and pitched up. Griffith attempted to fly beyond the point of instability and, as the plane's angle of attack increased, the Skyrocket commenced rolling and yawing, then spasmodically snap-rolled. Griffith recovered from the snap roll and, after ascertaining that the plane and engine functioned normally, he continued the flight. During a stall approach with the flaps and landing gear extended and the wing slats closed, at 14,000 ft., the Skyrocket remained stable down to 130 mph, but then pitched up. Again Griffith attempted to fly beyond the point of instability and the bucking plane rolled into a spin. During the spin, Griffith found the plane would not recover with flaps and gear extended. After he retracted the gear and flaps and initiated spin recovery, the plane returned to normal flight at 7,000 ft.[11]

NACA continued the longitudinal-stability-investigation program on the D-558-2 #2 until January 1950, when the High-Speed Flight Station returned the plane to Douglas for installation of its RMI rocket engine —and conversion to air-launch configuration. The decision to modify the Skyrocket for air launching, like the X-1, came about as a result of discussions between Douglas, the Navy, and NACA. As early as the fall of 1948, NACA had considered the possibility of modifying the D-558-2 airplanes for air launching. The X-1 had proven the feasibility of air launching, and it offered increased performance and a greater margin of safety. But in 1948, neither NACA, Douglas, nor the Navy knew the operational characteristics of the Skyrocket with both jet and rocket propulsion. The first flight of the airplane with its rocket engine was still in the future. At a conference on October 21, 1948, Navy, NACA, and Douglas representatives decided to postpone a decision on modifying the D-558-2 aircraft for air launching until Douglas accumulated rocket experience.[12]

The first Skyrocket completed with rocket propulsion was the D-558-2 #3, BuAer No. 37975. The rocket engine increased the plane's speed over 100 knots as compared to the jet-only Skyrockets, raising the maximum level-flight Mach number from approximately 0.82 at 20,000 ft. to 0.99 at the same altitude. It could attain approximately Mach 1.08 at 40,000 ft. in level flight with both turbojet and rocket propulsion. On January 8, 1949, Gene May completed the plane's first flight, making its first rocket flight over a month later, on February 25, 1949. On June 24,

1949, the D-558-2 #3 exceeded the speed of sound for the first time, the first Skyrocket to do so. As the plane went supersonic, May noted, "the flight got glassy smooth, placid, quite the smoothest flying I had ever known."[13]

As soon as the Skyrocket began flying with its rocket engine, the potential advantages of air launching became obvious. The takeoff operations were extremely hazardous. Heavily loaded with rocket fuel and jet fuel, the Skyrocket pilot began his takeoff roll using the jet engine, then added thrust from two of the four chambers on the rocket engine, and then, just before lift off, fired four JATO bottles to kick the plane into the air. The takeoff run consumed three miles and imposed severe strain on the landing gear. Douglas recognized that if the landing gear should collapse, the plane would certainly be lost—along with the pilot. Additionally, the use of rocket fuel on takeoff decreased the maximum attainable Mach number and altitude. NACA concluded that if it operated the D-558-2 #2 with both jet and rocket power using standard ground takeoffs, the plane could attain approximately Mach 0.95 in level flight. Yet, on its jet engine alone, the plane could attain Mach 0.9, and the NACA did not think the 0.05 increase in performance warranted the risk of flying the jet- and rocket-powered plane on research missions.[14]

Douglas recognized the safety and performance advantages accruing from air launching and studied modifying one Skyrocket by removing its turbojet engine and replacing the engine with increased rocket fuel for the rocket engine. Thus modified, and with air launching from a Boeing B-29, Douglas estimated that the plane could attain airspeeds between Mach 1.46 and 1.6. NACA believed this modification highly desirable, for results from the sweptwing airplane could then be directly compared over the same speed range covered by the straight-wing X-1. Further, the supersonic behavior of the D-558-2's NACA 63 series airfoil section could be compared with the supersonic behavior of the unconventional biconvex airfoil then designed for the projected Bell X-2 sweptwing supersonic research airplane.[15]

Hugh L. Dryden, the NACA's Director of Research, firmly supported the Douglas plan, and proposed that Douglas modify the D-558-2 #2 to all-rocket air-launch configuration when NACA returned this plane to Douglas for installation of its RMI engine. The company could modify one of the two remaining Skyrockets to air-launch configuration as well, and would conduct a small demonstration program on the airplanes before turning them over to the NACA for flight research. Dryden conveyed his recommendations to the Navy in a strongly worded letter on September 1, 1949. Nearly three months later, on November 25, 1949, the Bureau of Aeronautics added Amendment 19 to the Douglas D-558 contract, providing for modification of the D-558-2 #2, BuAer No. 37974, and

D-558-2 #3, BuAer No. 37975, to air-launch configuration. Additionally, the company would modify a Boeing B-29 Superfortress to act as a launch airplane.[16]

After receiving the two Skyrockets back at El Segundo, Douglas disassembled the two planes for modification. The modifications to the D-558-2 #3 were not extensive, for the airplane retained both its turbojet and rocket power plants. The company simply installed retractable mounts for the launch hooks. This airplane returned to Edwards Air Force Base for its contractor demonstration flights in September 1950. The modifications to the D-558-2 #2, the proposed all rocket airplane, were more extensive. The company, after receiving the plane in January 1950, removed its Westinghouse J-34-WE-40 turbojet and its gasoline-storage tanks. In its place technicians installed a liquid oxygen tank and an alcohol-water tank. The plane thus had 2 tanks each for the liquid oxygen and alcohol-water propellants, a total capacity of 345 gallons of liquid oxygen and 378 gallons of alcohol-water. The company replaced the air intakes with smooth, flush fuselage panels, removed the jet exhaust outlet, and installed a Reaction Motors LR-8-RM-2 6,000-lb-thrust rocket engine together with its turbopump for fuel supply. Douglas completed modifications to the airplane by August 1950, then installed special NACA recording instrumentation in the Skyrocket. The D-558-2 #2 all-rocket airplane returned to Edwards on November 8, 1950, by which time the modified D-558-2 #3 had completed 4 successful air-launch flights.[17]

To launch the two Skyrockets, Douglas acquired a Boeing B-29A Superfortress from the Air Force. The Navy redesignated the bomber as a P2B-1S, BuAer No. 84029, but to Douglas and NACA launch crews, the plane was known more informally as "Fertile Myrtle." The company designated El Segundo test pilot George Jansen as launch pilot. Jansen had volunteered for the position. A former crop duster, Jansen served during the war as a B-24 bomber pilot with the 44th Bomb Group, the "Eight Balls." During the first Ploesti raid, a daring low-level penetration by B-24s deep into Rumania on August 1, 1943, in an attempt to deprive the Third Reich of its oil, Jansen put his low-level tactics to good use, enabling his bombardier to destroy a vital boiler house serving the Creditul Minier refinery five miles south of Ploesti.[18] After the war he joined Douglas as a test pilot, and flew many of the initial performance investigations on the AD and A2D attack airplanes.

Likewise, the Douglas pilot for the Skyrocket drop flights also had a background of multiengine flying. William B. Bridgeman had trained as a Navy pilot, and flew PBY's from Pearl Harbor and Australia for the first 18 months of the war. Frustrated by a lack of action, he developed stomach ulcers, but after 3 months treatment he requested assignment to a combat squadron. The Navy sent him to Bombing Squadron 109, flying

Consolidated-Vultee PB4Y-1 Liberators, the Navy equivalent to the B-24. Commanded by the flamboyant Capt. Norman "Buzz" Miller, VB-109 entered the war in December 1943 and quickly gained fame as "Miller's Reluctant Raiders." The squadron made antishipping strikes all over the Central Pacific, sinking over 180,000 tons of Japanese shipping. By the end of the war, Bridgeman was a Lieutenant Commander, holder of two Distinguished Flying Crosses, four Air Medals, and a Purple Heart. For a short while, he remained in the Navy after the war as a ferry pilot, then spent a year each with Hawaiian Airlines and Southwest Airlines. He joined Douglas El Segundo in 1948 and flew acceptance tests on AD Skyraider attack bombers and F3D Skyknight night fighters. In 1949, Bridgeman joined the Skyrocket program, making a series of contractor investigations in the D-558-2 #1, BuAer No. 37973.[19]

Early in September, Douglas performed several captive flights of the D-558-2 #3, the jet and rocket airplane, to check out the fuel-jettison system and ability of the turbojet to start at altitude. Then, on September 8, 1950, Bill Bridgeman completed the first Skyrocket drop flight. Jansen launched the D-558-2 #3 at 24,850 ft. and 225 mph. Though the Skyrocket flight plan called for a series of level flight speed runs and coordinated turns, Bridgeman just flew down to a landing on the lakebed, for the airspeed system malfunctioned due to frozen moisture in the lines.[20] Bridgeman completed 3 more jet-only flights by early October. On November 17, he made the first air-launched rocket flight, exceeding Mach 1 in a shallow dive with both the turbojet and one cylinder of the rocket engine firing. Douglas scheduled one more flight before turning the plane over to the NACA. On November 27, 1950, Bridgeman dropped away from the P2B-1S at 30,000 ft., ignited 2 of the rocket cylinders, and began to climb on both turbojet and rocket power. He began a push-over into level flight at 40,000 ft., and fired all 4 cylinders, but negative g forces starved the rocket engine and shut it down. With the Skyrocket moving at approximately Mach 0.92, Bridgeman noted a buffeting not associated with normal Skyrocket transonic behavior and he realized that the J-34 had compressor stall. He pulled the jet throttle to idle, but the engine flamed out. Soon a thin fog formed between the windshield panels, preventing Bridgeman from seeing out. The chase pilot, Maj. Charles Yeager, realized the seriousness of Bridgeman's predicament and began talking him down for a "blind" landing on the lakebed. At about 24,000 ft., Bridgeman succeeded in relighting the J-34 and, as cockpit pressurization returned, the cockpit glass cleared. Bridgeman completed a normal landing.[21] Douglas delivered the D-558-2 #3 to NACA on December 15, 1950.[22]

In late December 1950, Douglas attempted to air launch the D-558-2 #2, BuAer No. 37974, on three separate occasions. Each time, after the P2B-1S had labored to altitude, Douglas scrubbed the attempt, first because of radio failure in the Skyrocket, and then because of deteriorating weather conditions.[22] On January 26, 1951, Douglas made another flight attempt. After entering the Skyrocket's cockpit and priming the rocket system, Bridgeman noticed the fuel pressure dropping off slowly. He had less than a minute to go before the planned launch, but reluctantly decided to abort the mission. He radioed George Jansen, flying the P2B-1S, "No drop. This is an abort." Then he began shutting down the various aircraft systems, preparatory for the long trip back to Edwards.[23]

To his horror, Bridgeman heard Jansen intoning the 10-second countdown. He shouted, "Don't drop me, George!" but Jansen was holding his thumb on the microphone transmission key, and could not hear Bridgeman's protestations unless he took his thumb off the key. Frantically Bridgeman prepared the plane for flight once again; in a snap judgment he decided to attempt an engine light, for, with the falling pressure, if he attempted jettison only one propellant tank might empty and the plane would then go completely out of control. Finally, Jansen launched the white rocket plane, and it fell away from the Superfortress like a large bomb as Bridgeman readied it for flight. The Skyrocket pilot tripped the first rocket switch, glad to feel the push of acceleration as it fired. He ignited the remaining cylinders in rapid sequence, and began a shallow climb. Still upset, he radioed, "George, I *told* you not to drop me." Chase pilot Frank Everest, below Bridgeman in an F-86, responded with a laugh, replying, "You got keen friends, Bridgeman. . . ."[24] Using stabilizer trim, Bridgeman nosed over into level flight at 40,000 ft., and accelerated rapidly through Mach 1. He noted that the plane tended to nose up between Mach 0.9 and 1.0 and that the plane required a large increase in down elevator for trim.[25]

Bridgeman found that elevator effectiveness decreased markedly above Mach 1 and that the plane began a "Dutch roll" oscillation. While in a shallow dive, the D-558-2 #2 attained Mach 1.28 at 38,890 ft. Then the rocket cut out from fuel starvation. Everest's F-86 joined up with the now powerless Skyrocket and both airplanes descended to the lakebed; there Bridgeman completed an uneventful landing. The realization that the mistaken launch of Bridgeman could have had more serious consequences dampened the satisfaction of a successful rocket flight. As a result, Douglas installed an electrical hookup from the research plane to the P2B-1S to indicate through a green light whether or not the Skyrocket was ready for flight. Additionally, Douglas shortened the prelaunch countdown sequence. Douglas then turned to completing the remaining contractor flights in the D-558-2 #2 airplane.[26]

During February and March 1951, Douglas made 4 more attempts to launch the D-558-2 #2, but had to abort each attempt before drop. On one attempt, Bridgeman could not jettison the Skyrocket's propellants,

and P2B-1S, with the D-558-2 #2 locked in the bomb bay, had to land
on the lakebed with the rocket plane carrying a full load of fuel and
oxidizer. On April 5, Bridgeman completed another drop flight in the
all-rocket aircraft. As the Skyrocket accelerated beyond Mach 1, it
developed a rolling motion. This lateral oscillation became wilder at
higher Mach numbers and Bridgeman shut off the engine because of the
severity of the motion. The plane reached a peak Mach number of 1.36
at about 45,600 ft.[27]

Douglas now decided to revise the Skyrocket's flight plans to permit
the plane to approach its maximum airspeed. This involved Bridgeman
climbing to around 50,000 ft., then leveling off for a maximum speed
run.[28] On May 18, Jansen dropped Bridgeman at 34,000 ft. and the
Skyrocket pilot climbed to around 55,000 ft. and leveled off. During the
speed run, the Skyrocket attained Mach 1.72 at 62,000 ft., approximately
1,130 mph, making it the fastest airplane in the world.[29] Ostensibly the
last flight before Douglas turned the D-558-2 #2 over to the NACA, it
actually was the first of a series of maximum speed attempts by the
Douglas company, for the company received permission from the Navy's
Bureau of Aeronautics to make additional maximum speed flights.[30] On
June 11, 1951, Bill Bridgeman pushed the Mach number up to 1.79 at
64,000 ft., approximately 1,180 mph.[31]

On these two record flights, the lateral oscillation—the rolling motion
—did prove completely controllable. Lulled into a feeling the trouble
might not persist, Douglas aimed for even higher speeds. Normally,
following the climb, Bridgeman pushed over into level flight with about
a .6 to .8g load factor. The Douglas test team felt that if he pushed over
more rapidly, with a smaller load factor of about .25g, the Skyrocket
would have increased acceleration. They did not know, however, that at
this low load factor of about .25g, the Skyrocket's lateral oscillation,
previously controllable, would become wild. On June 23, 1951, Bill
Bridgeman dropped away from the P2B-1S, ignited the 4 cylinders of
the LR-8 rocket engine, and began his climb. Near 60,000 ft., he started
his .25g pushover. As the Mach number increased beyond 1.5, the
Skyrocket started to roll violently, throwing Bridgeman from side to side
in the cockpit. The wings dipped as much as 75°, and the Skyrocket's
roll rate approached 90° per second. The pilot attempted to control the
roll with his ailerons, but the gyrations worsened. In a matter of seconds
the ride became so violent that Bridgeman felt it necessary to shut down
the engine, though about 50 seconds of rocket time remained. But the
loss of power had no appreciable effect upon the oscillation and, for a
time, the rolling motions became even wilder.[32] The rolling motions
prevented Bridgeman from turning around for the lakebed landing, and
the Skyrocket, now in a high-speed dive, was getting further and further
away from the lake. In desperation, the pilot hauled back on the control

wheel, making a 4g pullout. The Skyrocket began to climb, and the uncontrollable gyrations disappeared as the speed fell off. Once again under control, the Skyrocket responded smoothly to Bridgeman's control movements. He initiated a turn back to the lakebed, joining the F-86 chase plane on the journey back.[33]

NACA postflight evaluation of the data indicated that the D-558-2 #2 had attained Mach 1.85, approximately 1,220 mph, during its frenzied flight through the upper atmosphere. Douglas decided to go back to a pushover load factor of about .8g in an attempt to control the Skyrocket's wild supersonic motions.[34] During the remainder of June and into early July, the company added a liquid oxygen top-off system in the P2B-1S to replace liquid oxygen that boiled away during the Skyrocket's climb to launch altitude.[35] The next Skyrocket flight came on August 7, 1951. On this flight Bridgeman pushed over at .8g, then decreased the load factor to .6g. At the lower figure, the Skyrocket became left wing heavy and corrective aileron brought no response, so Bridgeman increased the load factor to .8g, whereupon lateral stability returned; so Bridgeman went back to a .6g loading and held the Skyrocket at this loading until the rocket engine starved itself of fuel. On this flight, the Skyrocket attained Mach 1.88 at 67,000 ft., approximately 1,260 mph.[36]

Douglas decided not to attempt flights faster than this, but, instead, to explore the all-rocket D-558-2 #2's altitude capabilities. The day after Bridgeman's Mach 1.88 flight, the Skyrocket test team held a meeting to plan a maximum altitude attempt. Charles Pettingall, chief aerodynamicist of the Douglas testing division, plotted the flight path Bridgeman should follow. On August 15, 1951, George Jansen dropped the D-558-2 #2 from the P2B-1S. Bridgeman ignited all 4 cylinders of the LR-8 engine in sequence, and began the climb. During the climb, the rocket plane attained Mach 1.35. At an altitude of approximately 63,000 ft., the Skyrocket slowly rolled left. After using full opposite aileron, Bridgeman noted that the plane returned to wings-level flight. The Skyrocket continued upwards. Finally, the LR-8 engine exhausted the last of its propellants, and the supersonic climb slowed. Momentum forced the plane still higher and finally the plane peaked at the top of its parabolic flight and started falling earthwards. NACA radar indicated the plane reached a maximum altitude of 79,494 ft. From his vantage point higher than any man had previously flown, Bridgeman compared the earth to "a vast relief map with papier-mâché mountains and mirrored lakes and seas."[37] The Skyrocket was now not only the world's fastest aircraft, but the world's highest as well. Later, in recognition of the talents that joined together to make the Skyrocket the record-breaker that it was, the Institute of Aeronautical Sciences presented Edward Heinemann with the 1951 Sylvanus Albert Reed award and William Bridgeman with the

1953 Octave Chanute award. Douglas now prepared the D-558-2 #2 for delivery to the NACA High-Speed Flight Station.

Using the all rocket D-558-2 #2, Douglas had come close to exceeding Mach 2, twice the speed of sound, less than four years after Yeager and the XS-1 #1 first demolished the sound-barrier syndrome. But now, as the fall of 1951 approached, attention shifted to two new airplanes on the Edwards scene: the X-1-3 and the X-1D. These two rocket-research airplanes represented the first of the advanced X-1's, turbopump-equipped airplanes having almost double the performance capabilities of the original XS-1 aircraft. It appeared that the honor of being first through twice the speed of sound would fall to one of the two planes within the next few short weeks.

The X-1-3, serial 46-064, actually represented the fulfillment of the original XS-1 conception. Bell completed the first two XS-1 airplanes with high-pressure fuel systems because the company could not obtain a satisfactory turbopump to feed the propellants to the Reaction Motors rocket engine. The company planned to complete the third XS-1, the airplane later designated X-1-3, when a suitable turbopump became available for installation. Early in 1947, the Air Materiel Command requested that Bell discontinue all work on the airplane because of a lack of funds to cover the work.[38] In early 1948, the Air Force obtained the necessary funds to continue development, and Bell estimated the plane could be ready for flight at Muroc by the fall of that year. However, Bell did not get the engine for the airplane, and the AMC once again suspended development because of lack of funds.[39] Late in 1949, to fulfill a research contract with the Cornell Aeronautical Laboratory, the AMC authorized continuing development of the X-1-3.[40] In April 1951, the X-1-3, serial 46-064, arrived at Edwards Air Force Base for its initial contractor test flights.[41]

Externally, there were no differences between the X-1-3 and its two earlier sisters, the original XS-1s. But internally the X-1-3 differed markedly from the other airplanes. The X-1-3 used a steam-driven turbopump to suck propellants from the tanks into the engine. Hydrogen peroxide passed over a manganese dioxide catalyst, creating superheated steam that drove the pump turbine. The turbopump obviated the need for nitrogen pressurization for fuel feed, together with the thick spherical liquid oxygen and alcohol tanks. Thus, the X-1-3's fuel tanks matched the external contours of the fuselage. It could carry 126 gallons of liquid oxygen and 205 gallons of alcohol more than the earlier XS-1s. Translated into performance, this meant the X-1-3 had a powered endurance of 4.1 minutes. Bell estimated the plane's maximum performance as Mach 2.44, 1,612 mph, at 70,000 ft.[42]

The X-1D had a different lineage. In mid-November 1947, one month after Yeager's Mach 1 flight in the XS-1 #1, the Air Force authorized Bell to begin development of a series of advanced X-1 airplanes. The Air Force issued Bell a contract to develop four of the aircraft on April 2, 1948, under project MX-984. Though similar in structure and performance characteristics, the planes would receive different alphabetical suffixes, i.e., X-1A, X-1B, X-1C, and X-1D. The letters differed to indicate emphasis in each airplane's flight program. The X-1C, for example, was to be a supersonic armament-test airplane. However, the availability of the F-86 for transonic weapons testing caused the Air Force to drop procurement of the X-1C. Bell continued development of the other three airplanes, the X-1A, X-1B, and X-1D.

The three airplanes retained the same wing and tail planform as the X-1 #1, but had a completely different fuselage configuration. They not only incorporated a low-pressure turbopump fuel system, but were longer than the original two XS-1 planes, and had a stepped semibubble canopy. Bell engineer Richard Frost found that Bell would have to limit the length of the airplanes so that the nose would not prevent the nose landing gear of a B-29 from retracting and so the tail could clear the aft pressure bulkhead located behind the B-29's bomb-bay section. Within these restrictions, Bell could stretch the advanced X-1s slightly over 4½ feet. Rather than incorporate the side entrance hatch utilized in the earlier XS-1s, Frost decided to use a stepped canopy that the pilot could enter from above. Frost was under no illusions—and neither were the Air Force and NACA XS-1 pilots—as to what might happen should an emergency arise and the XS-1 pilot bail out directly in front of the wing's sharp leading edge. Further, the stepped canopy enabled the pilot to enter the rocket plane from the mother ship without exposing himself to the slipstream and, if he had to, he could jump back into the bomber's bomb bay quickly, without having to wriggle out of a side hatch and then up a ladder into the launch plane.[43] Unlike the XS-1s, the advanced X-1s would incorporate a fighter-type control stick rather than the wheel on the earlier planes.

Additionally, the advanced X-1s featured simplified construction over the earlier XS-1s. Routine maintenance had sometimes proven difficult on the XS-1s because of their type of construction, and Bell designed the advanced X-1s so that test personnel could perform maintenance and inspection work more easily, using maintenance separations and panels.[44] As completed, the advanced X-1s could carry 500 gallons of liquid oxygen and 570 gallons of alcohol, giving the plane a powered endurance of 4.65 minutes, and a maximum Mach number of 2.47—1,635 mph—at 70,000 ft.[45] The first advanced X-1 that the Bell company completed was the Bell X-1D, serial 48-1386. It arrived at Edwards Air Force Base in July 1951.[46]

On July 20, 1951, B-29A 45-21800—the standard launch plane for

X-1 flights—lifted off the Edwards runway with the X-1-3 in the bomb bay. At 30,000 ft., 10 miles southeast of the lakebed, base commander Brig. Gen. Albert Boyd, piloting the B-29, launched the X-1-3 on its first glide flight. As the rocket plane settled toward the lakebed landing site, Bell test pilot Joseph A. Cannon found the control forces to be extremely light, with aileron control especially sensitive. While Lt. Col. Frank "Pete" Everest, flying photo chase in a Lockheed T-33, looked on, Cannon made 2 stall checks, one in clean configuration, the other with flaps and landing gear extended.[47] Upon landing on the lakebed, the nose wheel collapsed and Bell spent the rest of the summer repairing the damage.[48]

Four days later, the X-1D went aloft locked in the bomb bay of its launch airplane, a Boeing EB-50A Superfortress, serial 47-006A. After dropping from the B-50, Bell chief test pilot Jean "Skip" Ziegler flew a brief nine-minute glide flight to check out the X-1D's low-speed handling qualities. As on the X-1-3, the X-1D broke its nose landing gear on touchdown. After Bell completed repairs, the company turned the airplane over to the Air Force so that the Air Force could attempt to exceed the speed and altitude marks of Mach 1.88 and 79,494 ft. set by the Douglas D-558-2 #2 Skyrocket in early August 1951.[49]

One week after Bill Bridgeman attained 79,494 ft. in the Skyrocket, the Air Force attempted the X-1D's first powered flight, an effort, as Everest recalled later, to "see what it could do wide open."[50] On August 22, 1951, the EB-50A climbed for altitude, piloted by Maj. Wilbur Sellers—who would die less than 24 hours later in the crash of an F-94B—and Maj. Jack Ridley. Flying chase were Brig. Gen. Albert Boyd in an F-86 and Lt. Col. Gust Askounis, chief of the Experimental Flight Test Section at Edwards, in a T-33.

At 7,000 ft., Frank Everest entered the cockpit of the X-1D from the bomb bay of the B-50. Though the X-1D did not use nitrogen gas to feed propellants into its rocket engine, it did use nitrogen stored at 4,800 psi to pressurize fuel tank regulators, flap actuators, and extension of the landing gear. Upon checking the instrument panel, Everest noted that nitrogen source pressure had dropped from 4,800 psi to 1,500 psi. Disappointed, he climbed back into the B-50 and discussed the problem with Jack Ridley and Bell engineer Wendell Moore. They decided to abort the flight and Everest reentered the X-1D to jettison the propellants prior to returning to Edwards. He began pressurizing the liquid oxygen tank, then stopped to see if the tank gauge was stuck. Satisfied that it was not, he reopened the pressurization valve to bring the liquid oxygen tank pressure up to 46 psi, the required jettisoning pressure. As he did so, an explosion shook the X-1D's innards, nearly knocking the pilot down.[51]

Listeners in the Edwards tower, monitoring the flight, heard chase pilot Gust Askounis radio Everest, "Hey Pete! Drop her, drop her, she's on fire!" In the B-50, Everest turned to see flames pouring from the top of the X-1D into the B-50's bomb bay. He jumped from the burning rocket plane into the bomber, knocking down Jack Ridley, who was about to pull the emergency drop handle to release the X-1D. Everest's knocking down Ridley possibly saved the lives of all aboard the bomber, for the shackles holding the X-1D still contained their removable locking pins and, if Ridley had pulled the drop handle, the X-1D would have jammed in place. As it was, Ridley pulled the usual drop handle in the cockpit and the X-1D fell clear of the launch plane, still burning. It fell about two miles west of the south end of the lakebed, one mile south of a trailer court, and exploded. In response to anxious queries by Askounis and Boyd, Sellers reported that Everest was safe, and the B-50 and its two chase planes slipped down to land on the concrete runway.[52]

Air Force and Bell personnel gathered together on an accident board investigation, a difficult task in light of the explosion when the stricken plane hit the desert. After studying what wreckage existed, the accident board concluded that X-1D had a leak in its fuel system that caused a mixture of alcohol and air to form. The board believed that an electrical spark from the rocket plane's radio transmitter or external power supply plug ignited the explosive mixture.[53]

One research airplane remained that could possibly break Mach 2. This was the X-1-3. On November 9, 1951, the X-1-3 went aloft tucked under the EB-50A—the same launch plane used for the ill-fated X-1D—for a captive test of the rocket plane's jettison system. The X-1-3 carried a full load of alcohol and liquid oxygen. Early in the flight, test pilot Joseph Cannon jettisoned distilled water, simulating hydrogen peroxide, but loss of nitrogen source-pressure forced the test crew to cancel the jettison test of the liquid oxygen and alcohol. Still carrying a full load of propellants, the EB-50A returned to Edwards. The launch plane taxied over to the propellant loading area to take on nitrogen gas to jettison the propellants still in the X-1-3's tanks. After acquiring source pressure, the test crew had a tractor tow the EB-50A, with the X-1-3 still attached, to the east end of the concrete ramp. The ground crew cleared the area behind the B-50. As a precaution, fire trucks stood by for the jettisoning procedure. The test crew gave Cannon an all-clear signal, and the pilot, sitting inside the X-1-3, began tank pressurization.[54]

When the liquid oxygen tank pressure reached 42 psi, Cannon heard a muffled explosion from deep within the rocket plane. At once he suspected the worst, and began to exit rapidly from the X-1-3 while the plane emitted a deep hissing sound and liquid oxygen vapor swathed it like fog. As Cannon left the cockpit, a violent secondary explosion knocked him to his hands and knees; he tried to get up, but succeeding blasts pinned him to the ground. Bell personnel, William H. Means,

X-1-3 project foreman, and Walter Myers, were near the X-1-3's cockpit when the first explosion occurred, and they saw Cannon attempting to crawl away from the burning plane. Means and Myers pulled Cannon to safety, carried him to a Bell pick-up truck, and drove him to the base hospital. Though badly burned, he recovered from his injuries.[55] But the explosions and subsequent fire destroyed both the rocket-research airplane and its B-50 launch airplane, the same B-50 the X-1D had almost claimed nearly three months previously.

The X-1-3 accident investigation board officially attributed the explosion to a failure in the high-pressure nitrogen system. The nitrogen storage system, known as a tube bundle assembly, utilized 410 stainless steel, a type of steel having an extremely low impact rating at low temperatures. Steel manufacturers did not recommend use of this type steel at low temperatures. The nitrogen tubes were next to the supercold liquid oxygen tank. The accident board theorized that the cold liquid oxygen lowered the temperature of the surrounding structure, so that when Cannon pressurized the system, the nitrogen tubing shattered. Pieces of the tubing, for example, were located as much as 250 feet from the wreckage.[56] Following the X-1-3 accident, NACA operations head Joseph R. Vensel and NACA research pilot Scott Crossfield conducted tests dropping a 1 lb. weight through 2 inches onto a bottle of chilled nitrogen. The bottle exploded like a bomb.[57]

Thus it was that the year 1951, which had held bright promise of seeing the first Mach 2 flight, passed into history leaving behind shattered hopes and the wreckage of three airplanes. Mach 2 remained an elusive goal for the next two years.

NOTES

1. Muroc AAF Historical Report, 1 July–31 Dec. 1947, p. 24. Also Ray Wagner, *The North American Sabre* (New York, 1963), p. 16.

2. Wagner, *The North American Sabre*, pp. 17–18.

3. Hartman, *Adventures in Research*, pp. 166–67.

4. Parrish, *Who's Who in World Aviation*, 1955, p. 201.

5. William Bridgeman and Jacqueline Hazard, *The Lonely Sky* (New York, 1955), pp. 63–64.

6. *D-558 Summary Report*, p. 17.

7. *D-558 Summary Report*, p. 22. Mulac, D-558-2 #2 flight chronology. *D-558-2 #2 PR*, 11 Jan. 1949.

8. *D-558-2 #2 PRs*, 11 Jan. 1949; 26 April 1949; 6 May 1949; 20 May 1949.

9. *D-558-2 #2 PR*, 3 June 1949. Mulac, D-558-2 #2 flight chronology.

10. *D-558-2 #2 PR*, 15 Aug. 1949. Champine interview, 11 Nov. 1971. Mulac, D-558-2 #2 flight chronology.

11. *D-558-2 #2 PR*, 14 Nov. 1949. Mulac, D-558-2 #2 flight chronology.

12. Letter, Hugh L. Dryden to Chief, BuAer, 1 Sept. 1949. In NASC D-558 file.

13. *D-558 Summary Report*, p. 23. Also Mulac, D-558-2 #3 flight chronology. Also May and Halferty, "My Biggest Thrill," p. 53.

14. Dryden letter to Chief, BuAer, 1 Sept. 1949.

15. *Ibid.*

16. *Ibid.* Also Van Wyen, *D-558 Program Notes*, p. 2. See also Bridgeman and Hazard, *The Lonely Sky*, p. 194.

17. *D-558 Summary Report*, pp. 20, 21. *D-558-2 #2 PRs*, 29 Aug. 1950; 8 Nov. 1950; 24 Nov. 1950.

18. James Dugan and Carroll Stewart, *Ploesti* (New York: 1962), p. 161. Also Bridgeman and Hazard, *The Lonely Sky*, pp. 62–65, 211–16.

19. Biographical data from Bridgeman and Hazard, *The Lonely Sky*; "Bill and the Little Beast," *Time*, Vol. LXI, No. 17 (April 27, 1953), 68–74; Parrish, *Who's Who in World Aviation, 1955*, p. 40; and Douglas company release "Bill Bridgeman Douglas Test Pilot," n.d.

20. *D-558-2 #3 PR*, 11 Sept. 1950. The account of the first D-558-2 drop flight given by Bridgeman and Hazard in *The Lonely Sky* is actually an account of the D-558-2 #3 flight of 27 Nov. 1950.

21. *D-558-2 #3 PRs*, 4 Oct. 1950; 11 Oct. 1950; 30 Oct. 1950; 8 Nov. 1950; 28 Nov. 1950. Also Bridgeman and Hazard, *The Lonely Sky*, pp. 222–31. See also *D-558-2 #3 PR*, 5 Dec. 1950.

22. *D-558-2 #2 PR*, 20 Dec. 1950.

23. *D-558-2 #2 PR*, 30 Jan. 1951. Bridgeman and Hazard, *The Lonely Sky*, pp. 254–57. Bridgeman cites April 5, 1951, instead of January 26, but the earlier date is correct, and is borne out by NACA and Douglas records.

24. Bridgeman and Hazard, *The Lonely Sky*, pp. 258–61.

25. *Ibid.* Also *D-558-2 #2 PRs*, 2 Feb. 1951; 19 Feb. 1951.

26. *Ibid.*

27. *D-558-2 #2 PRs*, 23 Feb. 1951; 16 March 1951; 30 March 1951; 10 April 1951; 26 April 1951; 14 May 1951. Also Bridgeman and Hazard, *The Lonely Sky*, pp. 277–78.

28. Bridgeman and Hazard, *The Lonely Sky*, p. 277.

29. *Ibid.*, pp. 277–78. Also *D-558-2 #2 PR*, 28 May 1951.

30. Bridgeman and Hazard, *The Lonely Sky*, pp. 278–79.

31. *D-558-2 #2 PR*, 26 June 1951.

32. *D-558-2 #2 PR*, 10 July 1951. Bridgeman and Hazard, *The Lonely Sky*, pp. 287–92. Also William B. Bridgeman, "Supersonic Flight From the Pilot's Seat," paper presented at meeting of the Washington, D.C., section of the Institute for Aeronautical Sciences, 2 Oct. 1951.

33. *Ibid.*

34. *D-558-2 #2 PR*, 21 Aug. 1951. Bridgeman IAS talk, 2 Oct. 1951. Bridgeman and Hazard, *The Lonely Sky*, pp. 279, 293–95. Bridgeman incorrectly places the date for the top-off modification as May–June 1951, but it came after his June 23 flight, and the P2B-1S did not return until July. See *D-558-2 #2 PR*, 10 July 1951.

35. *Ibid.*

36. *D-558-2 #2 PR*, 21 Aug. 1951. Bridgeman IAS talk, 2 Oct. 1951. Bridgeman and Hazard, *The Lonely Sky*, p. 296. See also Martin, "The Record-Setting Research Airplanes," p. 51.

37. *D-558-2 #2 PR*, 30 Aug. 1951. Bridgeman and Hazard, *The Lonely Sky*, pp. 304–05. Also Martin, "The Record-Setting Research Airplanes," p. 52.

38. Letter, A. J. Marchese to Commanding General, AMC, 1 May 1947. See also *Air Force Supersonic Research Airplane XS-1, Report No. 1*, 9 January 1948, p. 45.

39. De E. Beeler, Memo for Chief of Research (NACA), "XS-2 Conference at Bell Aircraft, May 14, 1948," 15 June 1948. Hartley A. Soulé, Memo for Chief of Research (NACA), "Visit to Bell Aircraft Corporation on January 6 and 7, 1949," 8 Jan. 1949. Hartley A. Soulé, Memo for Chief of Research (NACA), "Research airplane projects—Visit to Wright-Patterson Air Force Base on November 17, 1949," 29 Nov. 1949.

40. Soulé memo, 29 Nov. 1949. H. Arthur Carner, Memo for Head, NACA High-Speed Flight Research Station, "Visit to Bell Aircraft Corporation," 18 Nov. 1949.

41. Mulac, X-1-3 flight chronology.

42. Bell Aircraft Corporation, "Comparative Specification Sheet for the X-1 #1, X-1-3, and X-1D aircraft," 23 July 1951. In NASA Historical Archives.

43. Frost interview, 25 May 1972.

44. *Ibid.*

45. Bell spec. sheet for X-1 #1, X-1-3, and X-1D, 23 July 1951.

46. AFFTC, *Experimental Research Aircraft*, p. 28.

47. Flight transcript, X-1-3 glide flight, 20 July 1951. Also Edwards AFB Historical Report, 1 July 1951–31 Dec. 1951, pp. 16, 30. In Air Force Archives, Maxwell AFB.

48. Annual Report for the NACA High-Speed Flight Research Station for 1951. In LaRC files.

49. *Ibid.* Also Edwards AFB Historical Report, 1 July–31 Dec. 1951, pp. 17, 30. Also Mulac, X-1D flight chronology.

50. Everest, *The Fastest Man Alive*, p. 129.

51. *Ibid.*, pp. 129–30. Also *X-1D Accident Report*, 10 Sept. 1951.

52. *Ibid.* Also transcript of X-1D flight, 22 Aug. 1951, by NACA HSFRS.

53. Report of Engineering Officer (Capt. David M. Sharp, USAF). Also NACA HSFRS 1951 annual report.

54. *X-1-3 Accident Report*, n.d. Also Edwards AFB Historical Report, 1 July–31 Dec. 1951, pp. 30–31.

55. *Ibid.*

56. *Ibid.* Also NACA HSFRS 1951 annual report.

57. Crossfield interview, 2 Feb. 1971.

CHAPTER

VIII

MACH 2—

AND BEYOND

S lightly over a week after the X-1D dropped to destruction, Douglas delivered both the D-558-2 #1, BuAer No. 37973, and the
D-558-2 #2, BuAer No. 37974, to the NACA High-Speed Flight Research
Station at Edwards. Nearly 9 months earlier, the company turned over
the D-558-2 #3, BuAer No. 37975. Thus, NACA now had all 3 Skyrockets.
Douglas had not modified the D-558-2 #1 to air-launch configuration,
and when NACA received the plane, it was suitable for ground takeoffs
only. During the contractor program on this particular Skyrocket, the
plane completed a total of 122 flights. Flown primarily to check the results of wind-tunnel studies, the D-558-2 #1 confirmed wind-tunnel
performance predictions, though the plane exhibited less drag above
Mach 0.85 than tunnel tests had predicted.[1]

The NACA placed the D-558-2 #1 in storage, having no desire to
operate the plane in the ground-launched mode. In October 1951, the
Navy Bureau of Aeronautics amended the Douglas D-558 contract to
provide for converting the D-558-2 #1 to all-rocket air-launch configura-

tion, and NACA hoped that eventually the plane might be utilized for external stores—bomb shapes, drop tanks, etc.—testing at supersonic speeds.[2] The NACA gave all three Skyrockets special NACA call signs. The ground-launched D-558-2 #1 became NACA 143. The air-launched all-rocket D-558-2 #2 became NACA 144, and the air-launched jet-and-rocket-propelled D-558-2 #3 became NACA 145. The planned NACA flight programs on the three airplanes differed according to the capabilities of the individual aircraft.

After receiving the jet-and-rocket-powered D-558-2 #3 in December 1950, NACA readied it for flight and, on December 22 and 27, Scott Crossfield completed two NACA familiarization flights, dropping away from the launch P2B-1S and flying down to the lakebed on turbojet power only. Over January and February of 1951, High-Speed Flight Research Station technicians modified the plane to record loads upon the wing slats via pressure-distribution and strain-gauge measurements. On March 26, 1951, Crossfield launched from the Superfortress on the first slat-loads investigation, but the J-34 engine flamed out and he lost considerable altitude before getting a relight, preventing the Skyrocket from acquiring data at altitudes above 25,000 ft. On May 17, 1951, NACA attempted their first jet-and-rocket flight in the airplane, but it was virtually identical to Bill Bridgeman's last contractor flight in the plane. During the climb, the J-34 experienced flame instability and Crossfield shut it down, whereupon the cabin depressurized and ice formed on the windshield. Chase pilots Fitzhugh Fulton and John Konrad began talking Crossfield down for a "blind" landing, but at lower altitudes the ice began to melt and Crossfield brushed away the frozen slush. Unable to get an airstart on the J-34, Crossfield completed a dead-stick landing on the lakebed. NACA technicians pulled the turbojet engine for inspection and replacement.[3] In July, the plane returned to the air, and NACA pilot Walter P. Jones checked out in it. In August, Crossfield flew it to Mach 1.14, and Brig. Gen. Albert Boyd completed a familiarization flight to Mach 1.05. After one more check flight by Jones, NACA prepared the D-558-2 #3 for an extensive pitch-up research program.[4]

The Skyrocket had first encountered pitch-up in August 1949 during NACA flights by Robert A. Champine and John Griffith in the D-558-2 #2, before modification of that airplane to all-rocket air-launch configuration. NACA recognized the seriousness of the pitch-up problem and desired to make a complete investigation of the phenomenon. In conventional aircraft, pitch-up could produce a limiting and dangerous restriction on aircraft performance. For example, a pilot might encounter pitch-up at low speeds at takeoff and landing, where he would have insufficient altitude to effect a recovery before the plane plunged into the ground. Or a fighter pilot might execute a tight wind-up turn to place his airplane on the tail of an enemy plane, and his fighter might pitch up, tumbling out of control, possibly exceeding its load limitations or putting the pilot in a disadvantageous position with his opponents. In September 1951, Walter Jones and Scott Crossfield began a pitch-up investigation program on the D-558-2 #3 that lasted for nearly the next two years, and involved flying the plane with various wing-slat and wing-fence configurations in both steady and maneuvering flight at transonic speeds. At one point, NACA engineers installed a special chord extension giving the D-558-2 #3 a "sawtooth" leading edge, to see if this might alleviate the pitch-up problem.

As always, however, it was the all-rocket research airplanes that captured the imagination rather than the exacting data-gathering missions of their slower brethren. The spectacular speed and altitude marks set by the rocket-research aircraft, figures far in excess of those obtainable in conventional high-performance airplanes, sometimes obscured the fact that these aircraft too were highly instrumented test vehicles designed to acquire aerodynamic data of use to aircraft designers, and not simply expensive experiments in and of their own right.

After Douglas delivered the all-rocket D-558-2 #2 to NACA on August 31, 1952, NACA High-Speed Flight Research Station engineers decided to perform exploratory flights aimed at defining the plane's operational limitations. On September 28, 1951, Scott Crossfield completed the D-558-2 #2's first NACA flight. By the end of the year he made four more familiarization flights in the plane. Then annual rains closed the lakebed until the following June. NACA technicians utilized the time spent on the ground by installing research instrumentation, including a 36-channel oscillograph.[5]

When the all-rocket D-558-2 #2 resumed its flight program in June 1952, Crossfield piloted the aircraft on a series of research flights at moderate supersonic speeds to approximately Mach 1.5. By the end of October 1952, NACA had completed 13 flights in the plane, primarily to acquire data on longitudinal stability and control, wing and tail loads, and evaluation of lift, drag, and buffeting characteristics at supersonic speeds.[6] During turns at supersonic speeds, for example, the Skyrocket's pitch-up problem reappeared, particularly in high-lift conditions around Mach 1.2. Crossfield found that during these and other maneuvers at low supersonic speeds, the Skyrocket exhibited a general decrease in longitudinal stability, resulting in pitching motions.[7]

The winter rains that grounded the Skyrocket in October flooded the lakebed. NACA decided that on future Skyrocket flights the plane would explore lateral stability and control at supersonic speeds, particularly the severe rolling motions at high Mach numbers that plagued the Douglas contractor flights in 1951.[8] When the new year opened, the Skyrocket was no longer the only rocket research airplane flying at Edwards. Bell arrived at Edwards on January 7, 1953, with the X-1A, the second of the advanced turbopump-equipped X-1s to be completed.[9]

Originally, the Air Force planned for the Cornell Aeronautical Laboratory to conduct a stability investigation on the X-1A, serial 48-1384, but, to prevent delays in acquiring the airplane, the Air Force cancelled the Cornell stability program and offered it to the NACA pending successful completion of a Bell contractor program on the airplane. The NACA agreed to the Air Force proposal.[10] Bell assigned company test pilot Jean "Skip" Ziegler to the X-1A project. Ziegler, Bell's chief test pilot, had flown contractor flights on the two Bell X-5 variable-geometry aircraft, the X-2 #2, and the X-1D. On January 24, 1953, Ziegler completed a captive flight with a full load of propellants. On February 14 and 20, he performed two glide flights in the X-1A. On February 21, 1953, Ziegler dropped away from the B-29 launch ship, and fired up the XLR-11 engine. After igniting three cylinders, a fire warning light glared in the cockpit. Ziegler did not know the alarm was false, so as a precaution he shut off the engine, jettisoned the remaining propellants, and glided down to a landing.[11] Skip Ziegler completed three more powered flights in the X-1A by the end of April, none of them faster than Mach 0.94. During the flights he noted an annoying elevator buzz and Bell halted further flight tests in order to instrument the plane to examine the buzz in detail. Ziegler returned to Buffalo.[12]

Subsequent events then changed completely the Bell program on the airplane. Early in 1953, the Bell company completed the X-2 #2, serial 46-675, a potential Mach 3 sweptwing supersonic research airplane. On May 12, 1953, Bell flew a captive flight of the X-2 #2, locked under a B-50 launch plane, over Lake Ontario to test liquid oxygen topping-off procedures. As the B-50 cruised back and forth over the lake at 30,000 ft., with a chase Republic F-47 Thunderbolt off its left wing, Jean Ziegler prepared to check the topping-off system. Suddenly the X-2 exploded in a huge ball of red flame, slamming the B-50 100 ft. vertically and throwing the Thunderbolt into a left bank. On the ground, Bell engineers in the company radio station heard a voice radio, "We lost the beast!" and the chase pilot call, "Okay B-50? Got her under control B-50?"[13]

Inside the B-50, Bell pilots William Leyshon and D. W. Howe struggled to retain control of the mangled bomber. The blast had blown Skip Ziegler out of the bomb bay, probably killing him instantly. What remained of the X-2 dribbled out of the sky into Lake Ontario. A flash fire swept through the bomb bay and one aircrewman, Frank Wolko, bailed out. Either through shock or hypoxia he failed to open his parachute and was lost. Shrapnel from the explosion shredded the inboard sections of the landing flaps and tore into the engine nacelles. But in a superb display of airmanship, Leyshon and Howe brought the crippled launch plane back to an emergency landing at Niagara Falls Airport. That the B-50 survived at all was a testimony to the rugged structure Boeing engineers designed and the capabilities of its crewmen. The explosion had so extensively damaged the bomber that it never flew again.[14]

An accident board, formed to trace the cause of the fatal explosion in the X-2 #2, concluded that an electrical malfunction triggered an explosion of alcohol and oxygen vapors in the propellant tank section of the plane, and that the remaining X-1 and X-2 airplanes should undergo thorough inspection before the Air Force returned them to flight status. As a precaution against further accidents, Bell replaced the nitrogen-tube-bundle assemblies in the X-1A, X-1B, and X-2 #1 with simple spherical nitrogen containers.[15] The X-1A left Edwards for the Bell plant in June 1953 and did not return to the test center until mid-October 1953.[16]

While the X-1A underwent modifications in Buffalo, the all-rocket D-558-2 #2 soldiered on. Early in April 1953, the NACA High-Speed Flight Research Station began working up to higher Mach numbers in the all-rocket Skyrocket as part of the planned lateral-stability-investigation program. Crossfield found that the plane remained fully controllable at moderate angles of attack, but at low angles of attack and low load factors—near or at og—lateral stability decreased markedly.[17] On August 5, 1953, Scott Crossfield reached Mach 1.878, the fastest Skyrocket flight since the Douglas demonstration program. Once again, the D-558-2 #2 was nudging Mach 2.

In mid-summer the Bureau of Aeronautics requested that Marine Lt. Col. Marion Carl, who had set the 650.796 mph speed record in the Skystreak in August 1947, fly the NACA D-558 #2 all-rocket airplane to high altitudes for pressure suit and physiological research. Carl arrived at Edwards in July 1953 and made 2 familiarization flights in the jet-and-rocket D-558-2 #3 before trying his hand with the D-558-2 #2. The Navy hoped to exceed 80,000 ft. on these flights. Carl aborted the first flight attempt because of oxygen-equipment difficulties with the pressure suit, and subsequent flights on August 14 and 18 failed to attain the desired altitudes. But on August 21, 1953, Carl dropped away from the launch P2B-1S Superfortress, tripped the rocket switches controlling the LR-8 engine, and nosed upwards. The Skyrocket kept climbing, beyond Bill Bridgeman's mark of 79,494 ft. The engine consumed the last of its propellants and shut down, but still the rocket plane moved onwards, finally peaking at 83,235 ft., a new unofficial world's altitude record.[18] The Navy now requested an additional 2 flights in the D-558-2 #2 airplane for attainment of the plane's maximum Mach number. Neither attempt, however, succeeded. On the first flight, August 31, 1953, Carl pushed over at a low angle of attack, and the rocket engine cut out. Traveling at Mach 1.5, the Skyrocket began a violent rolling motion reminiscent of Bridgeman's earlier experiences. On the second attempt, the Skyrocket only reached Mach 1.728.[19]

After Carl completed the Navy flights in the airplane, NACA technicians installed nozzle extensions on the LR-8 engine's rocket cylinders. The extensions prevented the expanding rocket gases of the exhaust from impinging upon the rudder at supersonic speeds. They also had the added beneficial effect of boosting the engine thrust 6.5 percent at Mach 1.7 at 70,000 ft. Crossfield completed the D-558-2 #2's first nozzle extension flight on September 17 and streaked to Mach 1.85 at 74,000 ft. On September 25, 1953, Crossfield made another high-Mach flight. Pushing over at a low angle of attack with a 0g load factor, Crossfield noted that the plane developed a severe rolling motion and rolled over on its back at about Mach 1.7. Crossfield attempted to recover using the ailerons, but the ailerons did not have sufficient effectiveness so Crossfield used the stabilizer trim and performed a split-S recovery maneuver. In October, he flew a further 4 lateral-stability investigations in the plane. On October 14, 1953, Crossfield flew the Skyrocket to Mach 1.96, the fastest flight to date of any aircraft.[20]

So it was that six years to the day since Charles Yeager's first Mach 1 flight, man first came close to Mach 2. While the NACA had not formulated any firm studies of the airplane's behavior at speeds near Mach 2, beyond tentative studies during the Douglas contractor program, agency engineers found that changing the Skyrocket's angle of attack at high Mach numbers from around —2° to +2° improved the airplane's lateral stability and the rolling motion became controllable up to Mach 1.96. Beyond this, NACA engineers did not know what might take place. All indications were, however, that the Skyrocket could operate satisfactorily to a Mach number of 2.0.[21]

Thus as the winter of 1953 approached, the band of NACA engineers and research pilots at Edwards conceived flying the all-rocket D-558-2 #2 through Mach 2, the first flight at twice the speed of sound. It was something the engineers at Douglas El Segundo would have thought hardly possible back in 1946. They had designed it to go only half as fast. Nevertheless, early in November 1953, the High-Speed Flight Research Station requested and secured the approval of Dr. Hugh Dryden, NACA Director, to attempt the world's first Mach 2 flight.[22] Once more interest sharpened at Edwards, for if the Skyrocket failed to attain its desired goal, the Air Force was back with the X-1A, with its listed Mach 2+ performance.

NACA had reduced the complexities of Skyrocket operations to routine. Agency pilots and crewmen operated the P2B-1S launch aircraft, and agency technicians readied both the research plane and mother ship for flight. Agency engineers, working with the pilot, planned the flights in the rocket plane, and operated the telemetry-receiving and radar-tracking equipment during the actual flight itself. They reduced the oscillograph film and instrument records to meaningful data in usable form. In preparing the Skyrocket for the world's first Mach 2 manned flight, NACA technicians drew on all their past experience with the plane. NACA D-558-2 project engineer Herman O. Ankenbruck devised a special flight plan for the attempt whereby Crossfield would climb to approximately 72,000 ft., push over gradually, hopefully reaching Mach 2 in a shallow dive. The flight plan followed the shape of a parabola, similar in general method to that followed by Douglas during the contractor program on the D-558-2 #2 in 1951.[23]

To squeeze the maximum performance possible from the D-558-2 #2 Skyrocket, the NACA flight team learned to "cold soak" the plane by loading liquid oxygen in the plane about five hours prior to the scheduled launch, so that even more liquid oxygen could be added just before launch in order to increase the burn time of the engine, thereby boosting the plane's performance. Likewise, the team chilled the alcohol so that more could be carried. In preparation for the Mach 2 attempt, the ground crew covered all panel cracks with masking tape, and gave the plane a heavy coat of wax. They replaced the standard stainless steel jettison pipes with lightweight aluminum tubes bent to protrude in the blast area of the rocket exhaust. During the climb after drop, these tubes—needed only in the event of an abort—would burn away, further lightening the Skyrocket for its record attempt.[24]

Early in the morning of November 20, 1953, NACA prepared the D-558-2 #2 Skyrocket and the P2B-1S launch plane for flight. During filling of the plane's hydrogen peroxide tanks, a spillage occurred showering John Moise, launch panel operator of the NACA P2B-1S, with the volatile liquid. A quick-thinking mechanic sprayed Moise with water, diluting the peroxide, then rushed him to a dispensary. Aside from bleaching his skin white, the peroxide did not seriously injure Moise, and the discoloration disappeared within a few days.[25]

Moise's accident did not delay the Mach 2 flight attempt. In mid-morning, NACA pilot Stanley Butchart guided the P2B-1S from the runway at Edwards and climbed into the sky. Crossfield entered the Skyrocket from the bomb bay of the Superfortress and completed preparations for flight in the rocket plane. After climbing for over an hour, the launch plane reached 32,000 ft., the launch altitude. Butchart positioned the rocket plane for launch; finally, the Skyrocket dropped clear of the bomber. As the D-558-2 #2 fell away, Crossfield ignited the LR-8 rocket engine and began his climb, carefully watching the flight instruments so that the plane would not stray from its preselected flight path, wasting energy and fuel. The Skyrocket climbed up into the stratosphere, streaming a broad white contrail. At 72,000 ft., Crossfield initiated his pushover, and the Skyrocket arced over into a shallow dive. During the dive the plane picked up speed rapidly, edging closer to Mach 2 as the engine continued to fire, the cold soaking having added vital seconds of engine burn time. At 62,000 ft., the D-558-2 #2 crossed Mach 2, attaining Mach 2.005, 1,291 mph. A. Scott Crossfield became the first man to travel at twice the speed of sound. After 207 seconds of burn time, the LR-8 engine starved itself of fuel and shut down. The Skyrocket decelerated, and Crossfield began his recovery. During aileron rolls at Mach 1.95, he felt that the aileron effectiveness was as good as that near Mach 1. Gliding downwards, he set up his approach to the lakebed, extended the landing gear and flaps, and set down in a smooth dead-stick landing.[26]

For his "important contributions in aeronautical flight research, especially at transonic and supersonic speeds up to Mach 2," the Institute of Aeronautical Sciences awarded Scott Crossfield the 1954 Lawrence B. Sperry Award.[27] The D-558-2 #2 never again approached Mach 2 during the remainder of its flight research program. The Mach 2 flight attempt had required extensive and unusual preflight preparations that could not be repeated for every high-Mach flight-research flight. NACA soon planned to receive two airplanes with Mach 2.5 performance, the X-1A and X-1B. With the Mach 2 flight behind them, NACA engineers at the High-Speed Flight Research Station transferred their attention to the Air Force, then preparing the X-1A for flight.

Following the death of Jean Ziegler in the X-2 #2, the Air Force Air Research and Development Command moved rapidly to keep the advanced X-1 and the lagging X-2 programs near schedule. Lt. Col. Frank K. Everest requested and received assignment as project pilot on the X-2, and the Air Force Flight Test Center at Edwards assigned Maj. Charles E. Yeager to complete the remaining contractor flights—commonly termed "Phase I" flights—on the X-1A.[28] After the X-1A arrived back at Edwards AFB from Bell's Buffalo plant on October 16, 1953, Air Force technicians installed nitrogen-storage tanks to replace the "tube bundle" storage system removed by Bell. Then, NACA engineers from the Edwards High-Speed Flight Research Station installed research instrumentation in the plane. On November 21, 1953, the day after Crossfield's Mach 2 flight, Chuck Yeager went aloft on the X-1A's first powered flight since modification.[29]

On the first powered flight, Yeager reached Mach 1.15; on the second he attained Mach 1.5. On the latter flight he found the stick forces for aileron control so high that he subsequently recommended installation of a control wheel for better pilot advantage. The Air Force now decided to initiate the plane's high-speed research program. On December 8, 1953, Yeager flew the X-1A and reached Mach 1.9 at 60,000 ft., during a slight climb. Four days later, December 12, 1953, Maj. Harold Russell took off from Edwards with the B-29 and X-1A. During the climb to altitude, Lt.

Col. Jack Ridley and Maj. Arthur "Kit" Murray joined up in two F-86 Sabre chase airplanes. At 30,500 ft., Yeager dropped free from the B-29, fired 3 cylinders of the LR-11 engine, and accelerated away from the bomber as NACA radar tracked him from the ground and Bell company technicians listened in from a mobile radio van.

Climbing rapidly, Yeager fired the remaining rocket cylinder at 45,000 ft. and, under full power, the X-1A climbed to 70,000 ft. At that altitude the pilot began his pushover to level flight. In level flight at approximately 76,000 ft., the X-1A accelerated rapidly through Mach 2 and beyond. The X-1A easily exceeded the Skyrocket's maximum speed and pressed on through Mach 2.3. During preflight briefings, Bell engineers warned Yeager that the X-1A might lose stability and go out of control at speeds above Mach 2.3. Now the rocket airplane violently proved the correctness of the Bell engineers' hunches. Ten seconds after leveling out on its high-speed run, the X-1A began a slow roll to the left. Yeager applied aileron and then rudder to correct the motion and the X-1A rolled violently to the right. Attempting to correct this, Yeager found the plane snapped into a left roll again. Sensing that the plane was going rapidly out of control, he shut off the rocket engine. Still moving at about Mach 2.44, the X-1A tumbled completely out of control, throwing Yeager around in the cockpit. The X-1A's motions resembled an oscillatory spin, with frequent reversals in roll direction.

On the ground, the Bell radio truck monitored the urgent calls of Ridley and Murray as they tried to raise Yeager by radio. In the cockpit, Yeager was fighting for his life as the rocket plane lost altitude rapidly. As the plane fell it decelerated, finally winding up in a subsonic inverted spin at 34,000 ft. At 29,000 ft., Yeager—groggy, battered, and semiconscious—recovered to a normal spin, then recovered from that into level flight at 25,000 ft. Then he called the chase: he was over Tehachapi at 25,000 ft., uncertain he could limp back to Edwards. Incredulous, Murray and Ridley asked him for his position again, then swung their Sabres off for Tehachapi, sixty miles from the dry lake. Still dazed—for during the 50,000-ft. drop, he had cracked the hard inner shell of the canopy with his helmet—Yeager jettisoned the remaining propellants, dropped his landing gear and flaps, and descended to the lakebed, with Kit Murray riding off his wing to call out the altitude on landing.

As the X-1A touched down in a plume of dust, Yeager summed up his feelings about the flight. "You know," he radioed, "if I'd a [ejection] seat, you wouldn't still see me in this thing." The young pilot got out of the rocket plane, having completed one of the wildest, roughest, yet shortest flights in aviation history.[30] For the flight, Yeager later received the Harmon Trophy. On the flight, NACA radar tracking records indicated the plane attained a peak speed of 1,612 mph at 74,200 ft.[31] Later analysis of his flight by NACA scientists led to the conclusion that decreasing directional stability and damping in roll at high Mach numbers led to a phenomenon of "coupled" motions, combined longitudinal and lateral motions first predicted by NACA scientist William H. Phillips in 1948. The plane's difficulties led to immediate recognition that airplanes flying beyond Mach 2.3 would require much larger vertical and horizontal stabilizer surfaces to retain adequate stability at high Mach numbers.[32] Following Yeager's wild flight, the Air Force decided to limit the airplane to speeds no greater than Mach 2, and initiate a high-altitude research program in an attempt to attain altitudes in excess of 90,000 ft.[33]

Yeager's Mach 2.44 flight represented the high-water mark of the entire X-1 program. No X-1 airplane ever equaled or exceeded this speed mark. In February 1954, the Air Force secured permission from the NACA to conduct limited tests with the plane before turning it over to the NACA, and assigned Maj. Arthur Murray to make the altitude flights. Murray had a reputation as a skilled and cautious pilot. During a delivery flight of a North American B-45 Tornado jet bomber, the plane caught fire in mid-air. Rather than abandon the stricken plane over Los Angeles, Murray stayed with the plane until he could make an emergency landing at L.A. International. On another occasion, during a night accelerated service test flight in a Lockheed F-94 interceptor, Murray struck an unlighted radio range tower, shearing off the top 10 feet. He remained with the jet and made a wheels-up landing on the lakebed with severe wing damage.

During the spring and summer of 1954, B-29 45-21800 hauled the X-1A and Murray up to altitude for a number of flight attempts. Out of 14 attempts, only 4 flights were really successful. One was Murray's checkout flight. The rest were altitude tries. On May 28, 1954, Murray exceeded Marion Carl's Skyrocket record by shooting to 87,094 ft. Slightly over one week later, on June 4, 1954, Murray reached 89,750 ft., but on this flight he experienced the same violent tumbling Yeager had felt more than 6 months previously. Slightly over 80,000 ft. and Mach 1.97, the X-1A began a roll to the left. Murray corrected with his ailerons and rudder, and the plane rolled right. He shut down the rocket engine, but the plane continued rolling as it climbed. Finally, as with Yeager, it went completely out of control, but at a higher altitude and lower airspeed than the earlier flight. After tumbling over 20,000 feet, Murray finally recovered control at 65,000 ft. He continued down to a landing.[34] More than 2 months later, on August 26, 1954, Murray cautiously extended the X-1A's altitude record to 90,440 ft.[35]

During September 1954, the Air Force turned over the X-1A to the NACA. The engineers at the NACA facility—now operating out of new buildings of their own rather than leased Air Force structures, and renamed the NACA High-Speed Flight Station—returned the plane to Bell for installation of an ejection seat as a precaution against the X-1A's poor stability and control characteristics at high Mach numbers.[36]

By the fall of 1954, then, both the D-558-2 and the advanced X-1 series had passed the peak of their performance potential. The Skyrocket never exceeded Carl's altitude figure and Crossfield's maximum speed. The advanced X-1's never flew beyond Yeager's record Mach 2.44 or Murray's 90,440 ft. Thus, the image of the 2 aircraft types extending the borders of speed and altitude died away, for all their other flights fell well within the earlier marks mapped out by Carl, Crossfield, Yeager, and Murray. As the speed and altitude marks set by the Skyrocket fell to the X-1A, so did the latter's fall to another research airplane, the all-rocket X-2 #1. But the X-1A did not bequeath its laurels as quickly as had the Skyrocket, for the X-2 did not break the earlier marks until the summer of 1956, 2½ years after Yeager reached Mach 2.44, and slightly more than 2 years after Murray approached the purple-black void of space.

Though the Skyrocket and the X-1's are best known for their pioneering flights into the unknown, the records they set in 1953 and 1954 did not terminate their usefulness. None of the research airplanes built were fabricated for setting records. Rather, they were designed as research tools. Though they set some spectacular records in the course of their research, their main function remained unchanged: the acquisition via flight instrumentation of data on a variety of areas. While the record-breaking flights served to bring the Skyrocket and X-1 programs into sharp focus, they often tended to diminish, in the public eye, the very great benefits accruing from dozens of "routine" flights at now unspectacular speed and altitude figures. The new glamour ship awaited at Edwards was the X-2. The X-1's and Skyrockets, though they continued flying, gradually faded from the limelight.

NACA'S SKYROCKETS: THE TWILIGHT YEARS

The Skyrockets and X-1's kept going into the latter half of the decade. Of the two, the Skyrocket series flew most extensively. The jet-and-rocket D-558-2 #3, BuAer No. 37975, did not have the performance potential of the all-rocket D-558-2 #2, BuAer No. 37974. Accordingly, engineers at the NACA High-Speed Flight Station utilized the jet-and-rocket airplane primarily for transonic research. By the fall of 1954, NACA had concluded the pitch-up investigation program started on this airplane in 1951. Engineers had tested the plane with the wing slats locked open in various positions, with inner and outer wing fences, with a leading edge extension. The attempt to find possible cures for the pitch-up problem was not entirely successful, however. Only with the configuration having the wing slats locked fully open did an improvement in the plane's longitudinal stability take place. Fully open slats eliminated pitch-ups except around Mach 0.8–0.85. With the slats half open, and with or without wing fences, no improvement occurred. Wind-tunnel tests of a Skyrocket model indicated that a chord extension over the outer 32 percent of the wing panels might eliminate pitch-up, but flight tests of the extensions on the D-558-2 #3 disproved the wind-tunnel test results. In fact, Crossfield felt the pitch-up even more objectionable with the extensions than without.[37] NACA restored the D-558-2 #3 to its original configuration and embarked on another research program.

In the summer of 1954, NACA installed external-stores pylons on the D-558-2 #3 and began flying it to investigate the effects of external stores upon the airplane's transonic behavior. The tests started using 120-inch 1,000-lb. bomb shapes, but the engineers felt that these were too small and later substituted Douglas-designed 180-inch-long, 150-gallon external fuel tanks. NACA pilot Scott Crossfield began the stores investigation, but when he left NACA to join North American on the X-15 program, NACA assigned research pilot John B. "Jack" McKay to complete the stores program. McKay and NACA pilot Stanley Butchart completed the stores-investigation program in early December 1955, and NACA scheduled only 2 more flights in the plane before its retirement. Due to a flooded lakebed and maintenance and repair work on the NACA-operated P2B-1S mother ship, the High-Speed Flight Station did not complete these flights until August 1956. The D-558-2 #3 made its last research flight, to obtain wing-loads data in "clean" configuration, on August 28, 1956, piloted by Jack McKay.[38]

NACA believed it desirable to investigate the effects of external stores upon airplane behavior at moderate supersonic speeds, but could not modify the D-558-2 #2 all-rocket airplane for stores research because of the need for this plane for pure aerodynamic research. However, provision had been made in the Skyrocket contract for modification of the old ground-launched D-558-2 #1, BuAer No. 37973, to air-launch configuration. In 1954, NACA delivered the plane to Douglas for all-rocket air-launch modification, with provisions for external-stores pylons. It arrived back at Edwards on November 15, 1955. Operational and instrumentation work kept the D-558-2 #1 grounded until September 1956. On September 17, 1956, John B. McKay completed this plane's first air-launch flight, flying it in "clean" configuration without either the pylons or external stores. NACA then set about preparing the plane for a stores-investigation program beginning in January 1957, but a wet lakebed forced cancellation of planned flights and shifting priorities caused NACA to cancel the external-stores program. In March 1957, the D-558-2 #1,

BuAer No. 37973, NACA 143, returned to the limbo of retirement from which it had briefly emerged.[39]

Following Scott Crossfield's epic Mach 2 flight in November 1953, NACA continued stability and control research in the all-rocket air-launched D-558-2 #2, BuAer No. 37974. NACA engineers obtained data on lateral and longitudinal stability and control, wing and tail loads, pressure distribution on the wing and horizontal tail, and lift and drag. Air Force Lt. Col. Frank K. Everest flew the Skyrocket on May 5, 1955, attaining Mach 1.46 at 68,000 ft., in a training flight in preparation for the upcoming X-2 program. In June 1955, the D-558-2 #2 concluded its pressure-distribution research, and NACA removed the plane's manometer installation. Scott Crossfield left the Skyrocket program in September 1955 to join North American in designing the X-15. McKay carried the NACA Skyrocket program onward.

NACA attempted a brief structural-heating program on the plane in November 1955, but concluded it in January 1956 when test engineers discovered the Skyrocket could not remain at high Mach numbers long enough for the temperatures of the plane's structure to stabilize, permitting accurate measurements.[40] Then, on March 22, 1956, the D-558-2 #2 left the Edwards runway tucked under the P2B-1S launch airplane for its 67th flight. What no one knew was that the plane would undergo the most serious inflight emergency to occur during the entire high-speed flight-research program, with the exception of the inflight rocket-plane explosions.

Aside from the rocket-research pilot, the most difficult job was that of launch-plane commander. He had to have all preparations completed on the rocket plane, the launch plane at proper altitude, and the launch plane over the correct geographic position in case the rocket pilot had a "no light" condition. He had to have all of these preparations completed simultaneously by launch. Unlike normal heavy-aircraft operation, the left-seat pilot served as mission commander. The right-seat pilot acted as pilot of the launch plane. It was impossible for the left-seat pilot both to fly the launch plane and to control the mission simultaneously. During the launch flights, the B-29 used for the X-1s and the P2B-1S used for the Skyrockets did not experience control problems, but they did have serious performance problems. Engine cooling was the most serious problem, for the planes climbed very slowly, almost too slowly for adequate cooling. As a result, the launch planes frequently lost engines on launch flights.

On the March 22, 1956, flight attempt, Stanley Butchart rode the left seat as mission commander, and NACA research pilot Neil A. Armstrong rode the right seat as P2B-1S pilot. A few minutes before the scheduled drop, the Skyrocket experienced a systems malfunction, scrubbing the launch. Then the Superfortress' number four engine, the outer engine on the right wing, "ran away." As previously agreed, should an emergency occur to the launch ship, Butchart and Armstrong released McKay in the Skyrocket. As the rocket plane fell earthwards, McKay jettisoned propellants and glided down to a safe landing on the lakebed. No sooner had the launch crew dropped the D-558-2 #2, then the propeller from the ailing engine tore loose from its shaft, sawed across the underside of the wing and fuselage, cutting into the bomb bay. Had the propeller cut into the Skyrocket before it dropped away, both the rocket plane and launch airplane would have crashed. As it was, the propeller cut all the controls on the left side of the plane so that Butchart's control column flopped back and forth uselessly. But Neil Armstrong still retained control, and brought the P2B-1S down for a safe emergency landing on the dry lake.[41] The incident grounded the launch plane four months for repairs.

In August 1956, the D-558-2 #2 returned to flying status, completing its loads and stability program by November. NACA instrumented the plane in November 1956 for an aerodynamic noise-investigation program to measure overall noise levels at supersonic speeds. After two noise investigations in December by Jack McKay, NACA engineers removed the research instrumentation from the plane and prepared it for a brief pilot-familiarization program for NACA and military pilots. NACA planned familiarization flights in all the D-558-2 airplanes. But in March 1957, NACA cancelled the planned familiarization program, and retired all three planes. After almost nine years of research flying, the D-558-2s joined the two surviving D-558-1s in retirement.

NACA'S X-1'S: EXPLOSIVE GASKETS, A PHOENIX, AND CONTROLS FOR SPACE

Though not as extensive as the Skyrocket program, the X-1 program after 1954 lasted through December 1958, until the dawn of the hypersonic X-15. The Bell X-1B, serial 48-1385, arrived at Edwards on June 20, 1954. NACA planned to use this airplane for aerodynamic heating research, following a brief Air Force program for pilot familiarization. The Air Force had little need for the plane since it offered no performance advantages over the X-1A, and so planned pilot-familiarization flights in the plane in preparation for the upcoming X-2 program. Because of the marked instability encountered by Yeager and Murray in the X-1A, the Air Force had no desire to explore the X-1B's maximum performance limitations. In September and October 1954, the X-1B completed two glide flights. On October 8, 1954, Maj. Arthur Murray completed the plane's first powered flight. Between then and the end of November, the plane made six more flights for pilot familiarization.[42]

Late in November, after making a familiarization flight in the X-1B, Lt. Col. Frank K. Everest secured permission to attempt a maximum speed run in the X-1B. Everest felt that the high-Mach experience would serve him well in the upcoming X-2 program, since he was the designated X-2 project pilot. Everest flew the mission on December 2, 1954, attaining approximately Mach 2.3 at 65,000 ft. During the flight, at speeds above Mach 2, the X-1B began rolling and yawing, the wings dipping as much as 70°. After Everest reduced power, the motions slowly ceased as the X-1B decelerated. The next day, the Air Force delivered the plane to the NACA High-Speed Flight Station. NACA engineers planned to use the X-1B for heating research and the sister X-1A for high-altitude high-Mach research. They shipped the X-1B to NACA's Langley Laboratory on December 14 for instrument installation. It did not arrive back at Edwards until August 1, 1955.[43]

The Bell X-1A returned to Edwards with a newly installed ejection seat on February 23, 1955. NACA engineers began preparations for its NACA flight-research program, but instrument installation and systems inspection kept the plane grounded until July. On July 20, 1955, NACA research pilot Joseph A. Walker made a familiarization flight in the airplane, encountering severe aileron buzz from Mach 0.90 to 0.92. He continued the flight to Mach 1.45 at 45,000 ft. Later in the month he attempted a second flight, but operational difficulties forced an abort before launch.[44] On August 8, 1955, Walker went aloft in the B-29 preparatory to another X-1A flight attempt. At 8,000 ft., he entered the cockpit of the rocket plane, closed the stepped canopy, and readied the rocket plane for flight. At 31,000 ft., one minute prior to launch, the X-1A's liquid oxygen tank exploded. A white cloud of liquid oxygen vapor erupted from the lower center section of the rocket plane. Debris from the explosion shattered the canopy on Kit Murray's chase F-86. Fortunately, the explosion was of low order, nothing like the catastrophic blast with the X-2 #2 over Lake Ontario. Walker scrambled from the X-1A's cockpit into the bomb bay of the B-29 launch plane. Then B-29 pilot Stanley Butchart, copilot Jack McKay, Joseph Walker, and Arthur Murray, together with the rest of the B-29 drop crew and NACA chase pilot Neil A. Armstrong in an F-51 Mustang tried to figure how to save the crippled X-1A for further research flights.

The explosion had caused the X-1A's landing gear to extend, and the rocket plane appeared to have dropped a few inches. Further, the plane still retained a full load of fuel and volatile hydrogen peroxide that would have to be jettisoned if Butchart and McKay hoped to make a safe landing. NACA X-1A crew chief Richard Payne entered the B-29 bomb bay and examined the cockpit of the X-1A. He noted that the landing gear handle was still in the retracted position. He attempted to jettison the fuel and peroxide using the remaining nitrogen supply, but Kit

Murray observed only a small amount of fuel before the flow stopped. If Butchart wanted to land with the X-1A, he would have to do it with a dragging landing gear and a full load of propellants in the rocket plane. On the ground, NACA Operations chief Joseph R. Vensel radioed Butchart with the only possible answer: "Butch, you might as well drop it. Pick a good place." Butchart swung the bomber over the Edwards bombing range, and jettisoned the research plane. Out of balance from the explosion, the X-1A entered a tail-down flat spin and exploded when it hit the desert, starting a brush fire. NACA and the Air Force immediately established a joint accident board to investigate the cause of this incident, the fourth of a long series of mysterious explosions that had claimed the X-1-3, X-1D, X-2 #2, and now the X-1A.[45]

Unlike the 3 earlier victims, the X-1A did not have a tube-bundle nitrogen storage system. Bell had replaced the tube-bundle system on the X-1A and X-1B with 3 cylindrical nitrogen storage tanks. These tanks survived the inflight explosion and subsequent ground impact, and thus could not be the cause of the explosion. NACA engineers assembled the wreckage of the X-1A in the High-Speed Flight Station, and placed the X-1B next to it to facilitate examination of the wreckage. During removal of the X-1B's liquid oxygen tank-access doors, technicians discovered an oily substance inside the tank and the liquid oxygen supply lines to the rocket engine. Analysis revealed the liquid to be tricresyl phosphate, a substance used to impregnate leather. The treated leather, called Ulmer leather, found application on the X-1s as gasket material in their liquid oxygen tanks. The accident board consulted a commercial air-products company, which advised that Ulmer leather should not be used in proximity to liquid oxygen, since at low temperatures it readily detonated under comparatively low impact. The accident board then placed pieces of Ulmer leather and frozen drops of tricresyl phosphate on an anvil, and dropped a 5-lb. steel bar from 10 ft. above the anvil. In each of 30 tests, the leather and frozen tricresyl phosphate exploded when hit by the bar. The board theorized that under the jolt of pressurization, the gaskets exploded, fatally crippling the X-1A. The accident board noted the great similarity between the loss of the previous 3 research airplanes and the X-1A. In each case, the explosion occurred near the liquid oxygen tanks during pressurization. The accident report suggested Ulmer leather as the possible cause of the previous accidents since all of the destroyed planes used Ulmer leather gaskets.[46]

The board recommended in its accident report that the Ulmer leather gaskets be removed from the remaining research airplanes, and NACA and the Air Force quickly complied. NACA awarded B-29 crewmen Charles W. Littleton and John W. Moise the NACA Distinguished Service Medal for "outstanding bravery beyond the call of duty." Stanley Butchart, Joseph Walker, and Richard Payne received the NACA Exceptional Service Medal; and Jack McKay, Rex L. Cook, Richard A. DeMore, and Merle C. Woods received letters of commendation. Jerome Hunsaker, former NACA chairman, sent Maj. Arthur Murray a letter of commendation for aiding the B-29 crew despite severe damage to his own chase plane.[47]

NACA still had two advanced X-1s left, the X-1B and the X-1E. The X-1B was a sister ship to the X-1A. Following the X-1A accident, technicians removed its Ulmer leather gaskets. The X-1B aerodynamic-heating program did not get under way until the fall of 1956. In August, Jack McKay completed two familiarization flights marred by minor malfunctions, including the recurrence of the X-1's traditional nosewheel-collapse-on-landing problem. McKay completed the heating program in January 1957, after a Mach 1.94 flight. Preliminary data showed a maximum heating rate of about 3°F. per second. Maximum recorded temperature was 185°F. on the forward point of the X-1B's nose. Calculated temperatures agreed closely with those recorded in flight and were felt to be representative of heating conditions that could be expected on future fighter and interceptor aircraft.[48]

Because of the loss of the X-1A, NACA decided to employ the X-1B for high-altitude research in areas of low dynamic pressure where ordinary control surfaces lost effectiveness, preventing the pilot from controlling the motion of the airplane. This had been shown most dramatically on Air Force Capt. Iven Kincheloe's 126,200 ft. altitude flight in the Bell X-2 #1 on September 7, 1956. During the flight, the X-2 described a ballistic arc. During its high-altitude journey, Kincheloe could not have altered its path in the slightest by use of his ailerons, elevator, or rudder controls. When the X-2 descended to lower, denser levels, once more the control surfaces could "grip" the air. The obvious solution for control at high altitudes where ordinary surface controls proved ineffective was in the use of reaction controls, small thruster rockets utilized to control the attitude of the plane. The NACA High-Speed Flight Station decided to install a prototype reaction-control system on the X-1B to gain information and experience that might be of great value in preparation for the upcoming X-15 program.[49]

Pending installation of the reaction controls, Jack McKay completed a brief series of stability and control investigations to Mach 1.65. On August 8, 1957, he made his last flight in the plane. Neil A. Armstrong checked out in the plane on August 15, attaining Mach 1.32 at 45,000 ft. In preparation for the reaction-control program, Armstrong "flew" a ground simulator, the "Iron Cross." It was in the shape of an X, and matched the dimensions and inertial characteristics of the X-1B aircraft. The "fuselage" leg consisted of a "cockpit" for the pilot at one end, and pitch and yaw reaction controls at the other end of the "fuselage" leg. The "wing" bar housed reaction controls for rolling (lateral) motion in the right "wing tip." The simulator used nitrogen gas for motion, and rested on a short tower that permitted motion about all 3 axes.[50]

Armstrong began the X-1B's reaction control program in November 1957, and in support of the X-1B program flew a NACA F-100A Super Sabre on zoom simulation flights to simulate X-1B trajectories and positioning over the lakebed. On January 23, 1958, he completed the X-1B's seventeenth NACA flight. Winter rains then closed the lakebed to further operations, and NACA installed a modified engine and ventral fins, the latter to improve directional control above Mach 1.6. Then during a preflight inspection in May 1958, NACA technicians discovered four fatigue cracks in the bottom of the X-1B's liquid oxygen tank. They welded the cracks shut, but X-ray inspection revealed flaws in the welds. Had the welds been perfect, NACA engineers still felt that safety factors for tank pressure were not high enough to permit use of the tank with welded cracks. So, in June 1958, NACA retired the X-1B. Engineers transferred the reaction-control program from the X-1B to a NACA F-104A Starfighter, and this plane later served as a pilot trainer for the X-15 program.[51]

Though it had not made any spectacular contributions to the high-speed-flight research program, the X-1B did make two important contributions to the sum of knowledge acquired through the research-aircraft program. It returned the first detailed data on structural heating at supersonic speeds, and it was the first airplane to employ hydrogen peroxide reaction controls for use during semiballistic flight in regions of low dynamic pressure. Though events prevented the X-1B from using its reaction controls in high-altitude research, the development of the controls for the airplane and the limited flight testing with them provided valuable experience that aided the initiation of the X-15 program in 1959.

The remaining X-1 aircraft, the X-1E was informally known among NACA personnel as "Little Joe." Perhaps a better appellation would have been "The Phoenix." After grounding the X-1 #2, serial 46-063, in late 1951, NACA engineers concluded the plane should be rebuilt with a low-pressure turbopump fuel system to replace the former high-pressure nitrogen fuel-feed system. In April 1952, NACA engineers at Edwards began design of the new fuel system using ideas gleaned from the turbopump installations on the D-558-2, and the ill-fated X-1D and X-1-3. At the same time, the Air Force and NACA reached a joint agreement whereby the Air Force would procure a new thin—4 percent thickness-chord ratio—wing with an aspect ratio of 4.[52] With the low-pressure fuel system and the new thin wing in contrast to the old "thick" wing, the modified X-1 #2 would be able to fly around Mach 2.5.

To develop the special wing, the NACA and Air Force turned to the Stanley Aviation Corporation, founded by Robert M. Stanley, the former Bell Vice-President for Engineering so closely associated with the original XS-1 program. Among its personnel, the firm counted Richard H. Frost, former XS-1 project engineer at Muroc. The Stanley engineers designed the wing with a span of 22.79 ft., a root chord of 7.62 ft., a tip chord of 3.81 ft., and used a modified NACA 64A-004 symmetrical airfoil section. The construction of the wing posed difficult problems for the Stanley technicians. Maximum thickness of the wing at the root was only 3⅜ in., and the Stanley engineers had to guard against aeroelastic effects at high Mach numbers. They achieved maximum torsional stiffness by using multiple spars of rectangular cross section with tapered milled wing skins bolted to the spars and rips. The wing contained over 200 orifices for pressure distribution studies, as well as 343 gauges baked onto the wing surface for measurement of structural loads and aerodynamic heating.[53]

As well as changing the wing configuration and propellant feed system, NACA modified the cockpit section of the plane. Technicians installed a stepped canopy closely resembling the hooded enclosure of the D-558-2 Skyrocket, and installed an ejection seat formerly used on the Northrop X-4 #2 airplane before that research plane retired. The resulting plane was a composite aircraft. NACA designed and fabricated the rocket system, and reworked and rebuilt the cockpit. Stanley furnished the wing. Bell, the original builders of the airplane, only claimed responsibility for those components that Bell had furnished, namely the tail group, forward fuselage shell, and landing gear. Everything else was new. The plane owed much to the Skyrocket rocket system—in fact, the modified research aircraft used a RMI LR-8 engine originally assembled for the Navy D-558-2. Rather than any indigenous Bell product, the modified plane's development closely paralleled that of the composite General Motors XP-75 fighter, the "Fisher Eagle" of World War II. Recognizing the distinct character of the airplane, NACA formally designated it as the X-1E in March 1954.[54]

NACA completed engineering work and assembly of the plane in mid-1955. Following instrumentation and final checks on the plane's systems, the High-Speed Flight Station readied it for its flight program. The first attempt at flight came on December 3, 1955, but loss of source pressure forced an abort before launch. On December 12, 1955, nine years after its original powered flight, the X-1E dropped from the launch B-29—the same one, 45-21800, that launched it nine years earlier—on its first glide flight, piloted by NACA research pilot Joseph Walker. Three days later, on Dec. 15, 1955, Walker completed the X-1E's first powered flight. After further general handling-qualities and familiarization flights in April and May 1956, Walker completed the X-1E's first faster-than-sound flight on June 7, 1956, accelerating in the little rocket airplane to Mach 1.55, approximately 1,020 mph. Two months later, on August 31, 1956, Joe Walker reached Mach 2.[55]

Following a Mach 2 flight on May 15, 1957, the X-1E suffered severe damage during a landing accident. Walker's helmet face plate distorted his vision upon landing. He landed hard and the nose gear snapped off. The X-1E also received damage to its main gear, fuselage skin, and ventral fairing. Engineers at the High-Speed Flight Station decided to replace the nitrogen cockpit-pressurization system with an air system so that the pilot could remove his face piece to improve his vision for landing. While technicians repaired and modified the airplane, NACA engineers published preliminary data from its aerodynamic heating investigations made over the previous year.[56]

In August 1957, the airplane returned to flight status. On October 8, 1957, Walker streaked to Mach 2.24, approximately 1,480 mph. Because Langley Laboratory wind-tunnel studies had shown the X-1E to have very low directional stability at speeds above Mach 2, NACA engineers at the High-Speed Flight Station devised a ventral fin configuration for the plane to improve its directional stability at high Mach numbers. Technicians installed two ventral fins on the airplane in December 1957, and Walker made the first flight in the plane with the ventrals added in May 1958. He found that the ventral fins markedly improved stability, but decreased the plane's maneuverability over the entire speed range.[57]

The loss of the Bell X-2 #2 in September 1956, following Capt. Milburn G. Apt's ill-fated flight to Mach 3.2—the first Mach 3 manned flight ever made—left the X-1B and the X-1E the only two high-performance rocket-research airplanes still flying, pending the delivery of the North American X-15. Following its Air Force program, the X-2 was to have joined the NACA stable as an aerodynamic heating-research aircraft. To fill the gap caused by its loss, NACA High-Speed Flight Research Station engineers Hubert M. Drake and Donald R. Bellman suggested in November 1957 that the performance capabilities of the X-1E be boosted from its design speed of Mach 2.7 to about Mach 3 by boosting engine chamber pressure in the RMI LR-8 engine from 250 psi to 300 psi. They would also replace the alcohol fuel with a more powerful fuel called Hidyne or U-deta, consisting of a mixture of 60 percent unsymmetrical dimethylhydrazine and 40 percent diethylene triamine. Following another landing accident to the X-1E on June 10, 1958, when it again lost its nose gear, NACA decided to undertake the U-deta program and install a new stabilizer bell crank to increase stabilizer travel, thus improving longitudinal maneuverability that the ventral fins had decreased.[58]

In September 1958, the plane flew again, making the last two flights by Joseph Walker. John McKay checked out in the rocket plane on September 19, 1958, and flew it on the remainder of its research program. In October, he made two flights in the plane at increased engine pressure. On November 6, 1958, McKay launched from the Boeing B-29 Superfortress on the first check flight using U-deta as a propellant. Fourteen minutes after launch the X-1E touched down on the smooth surface of the dry lake, having completed its twenty-sixth flight.[59]

Though no one knew it, it was the last research flight ever made by the X-1 series of airplanes. In November 1958, High-Speed Flight Station engineers grounded the plane for replacement of its ejection system. The ejection seat, a holdover from the X-4 program, was not compatible with a pilot wearing a high-altitude pressure suit. In December 1958, an X-ray inspection revealed cracks in the plane's alcohol tank. Serious enough separately, the 2 deficiencies spelled the end of the X-1E's research program. The X-1E joined the X-1 #1 and X-1B in retirement in April 1959.[60] After more than 12 years of research flying, the X-1s disappeared from the skies.

NOTES

1. *D-558 Summary Report*, p. 43. Also Mulac, D-558-2 #1 flight chronology.

2. Van Wyen, *D-558 Program Notes*, p. 2. NACA HSFRS 1951 annual report.

3. *D-558 Summary Report*, p. 23. D-558-2 #3 PRs, 20 Dec. 1950; 12 Jan. 1951; 30 Jan. 1951; 2 Feb. 1951; 19 Feb. 1951; 23 Feb. 1951; 16 March 1951; 30 March 1951; 10 April 1951; 26 April 1951; 14 May 1951; 29 May 1951; 12 June 1951. Mulac, D-558-2 #3 flight chronology. Crossfield, *Always Another Dawn*, pp. 45–52.

4. *D-558-2 #3 PRs*, 26 June 1951; 10 July 1951; 19 July 1951; 1 Aug. 1951; 15 Aug. 1951; 31 Aug. 1951. Also Mulac, D-558-2 #3 flight chronology.

5. *D-558-2 #2 PRs* from 16 October 1951 through 3 June 1952. Also Mulac, D-558-2 #2 flight chronology.

6. *D-558-2 #2 PRs* from 26 June 1952 through 7 January 1953.

7. *D-558-2 #2 PR*, 21 Nov. 1952. Mulac, D-558-2 #2 flight chronology.

8. NACA HSFRS 1952 annual report.

9. Edwards AFB Historical Report, 1 Jan.–30 June 1953, Vol. 5, p. 22. In Air Force Archives, Maxwell AFB.

10. NACA HSFRS 1953 annual report.

11. Edwards AFB Historical Report, 1 Jan.–30 June 1953, Vol. 5, pp. 22–23.

12. *Ibid*. Also NACA HSFRS 1953 annual report.

13. Tape transcription of air-ground communications. In Tab C, X-2 #2 *Accident Report*, Vol. 1.

14. *Ibid*.

15. X-2 #2 *Accident Report*, Vol. 1, esp. "Memorandum Report," 26 May 1953. Also NACA HSFRS 1953 annual report.

16. Edwards AFB Historical Report, 1 Jan–30 June 1953, Vol. 5, p. 26. Also Edwards AFB Historical Report, 1 July–31 Dec. 1953, Vol. 1, pp. 87–88. In Air Force Archives, Maxwell AFB.

17. *D-558-2 #2 PRs*, 9 April 1953; 11 May 1953, 10 June 1953; 14 July 1953. Also NACA HSFRS 1953 annual report.

18. *D-558-2 #2 PR*, 2 Sept. 1953. Mulac, D-558-2 #2 flight chronology. Martin, "The Record-Setting Research Airplanes," p. 52. Also Askins, "The Ultimate Fighter Pilot," p. 77.

19. *Ibid.* Also *D-558-2 #2 PR*, 6 Oct. 1953.

20. *D-558-2 #2 PR*, 12 Nov. 1953. Also Mulac, D-558-2 #2 flight chronology, and NACA HSFRS 1953 annual report.

21. *Ibid.*

22. Crossfield, *Always Another Dawn*, pp. 169, 173–174.

23. *Ibid.*

24. *Ibid.*

25. *Ibid.*, pp. 173–74.

26. *Ibid.*, pp. 175–79. *D-558-2 #2 PR*, 7 Dec. 1953. Martin, "The Record-Setting Research Airplanes," p. 51. Also Mulac, D-558-2 #2 flight chronology.

27. Emme, *Aeronautics and Astronautics*, p. 194.

28. Edwards AFB Historical Report, 1 July—31 Dec. 1953, Vol. 1, pp. 87–88. Also letter, Brig. Gen. Charles E. Yeager to author, 12 Oct. 1971.

29. *Ibid.*

30. Data on Yeager's flight is from letter, Brig. Gen. Charles E. Yeager to author, 12 Oct. 1971; Hubert M. Drake and Wendell H. Stillwell, "Behavior of the Bell X-1A Research Airplane During Exploratory Flights at Mach Numbers Near 2.0 and at Extreme Altitudes," NACA RM H55G25, 7 July 1955; Lundgren, *Across the High Frontier*, pp. 278–84. NACA HSFRS 1953 annual report.

31. Martin, "The Record-Setting Research Airplanes," p. 52.

32. Letter, Brig. Gen. Charles E. Yeager to author, 12 Oct. 1971.

33. NACA HSFRS 1953 annual report.

34. Mulac, X-1A flight chronology. Also Drake and Stillwell, "Behavior of the Bell X-1A Research Airplane During Exploratory Flights at Mach Numbers Near 2.0 and at Extreme Altitudes." Additionally, see NACA HSFS 1954 annual report.

35. Martin, "The Record-Setting Research Airplanes," p. 52.

36. NACA HSFS 1954 annual report. Also *X-1A PR*, 6 Oct. 1954.

37. Data on NACA pitch-up program on D-558-2 #3 is in Mulac, D-558-2 #3 flight chronology, and *D-558-2 #3 PRs*, 28 Sept. 1951, 6 Nov. 1951, 21 Nov. 1951, Nov. 1951–Dec. 1952, 12 March 1953, 9 April 1953, 11 May 1953. The conclusions were presented by A. Scott Crossfield, Hubert M. Drake, Jack Fischel, and Joseph A. Walker, in "Additional Investigation of the Handling Qualities of Airplanes at High Speeds," paper presented at the NACA Conference on Aerodynamics of High Speed Aircraft at the Ames Aeronautical Laboratory, Moffet Field, California, July 8–10, 1953.

38. NACA HSFS 1954 annual report. Also *D-558-2 #3 PRs*, May 1954–Sept. 1956. Also Mulac, D-558-2 #3 flight chronology.

39. NACA HSFS 1954 annual report. *D-558-2 #1 PRs*, July 1956–March 1957. Also Mulac, D-558-2 #1 flight chronology.

40. NACA HSFS 1953 and 1954 annual reports. *D-558-2 #2 PRs* Nov.

1953–Feb. 1956. Mulac, D-558-2 #2 flight chronology. ARDC letter to NACA, 24 Sept. 1954, cited in letter, J. W. Crowley to Commander, ARDC, 22 Oct. 1954. Also Everest flight report for D-558-2 flight, 9 May 1955.

41. Interview of Neil A. Armstrong by the author, 26 Jan. 1972. *D-558-2 #2 PR*, 5 April 1956. Mulac, D-558-2 #2 flight chronology. Crossfield, *Always Another Dawn*, pp. 201–202.

42. NACA HSFS 1954 annual report. Mulac, X-1B flight chronology. Charles V. Eppley, *The Rocket Research Aircraft Program 1946–1962*, TDR No. 63-3, February 1963, AFFTC, Air Force Systems Command, p. 11.

43. *Ibid*. Also Everest, *The Fastest Man Alive*, pp. 135–40. Additionally, see *X-1B PR*, 7 Sept. 1955.

44. *X-1A PRs*, Jan.–Sept. 1955. Walker pilot report, 20 July 1955. Mulac, X-1A flight chronology.

45. NACA HSFS, "Report of Investigation into the Loss of the X-1A Research Airplane on August 8, 1955," Nov. 1955.

46. *Ibid*.

47. *Ibid*. Also NACA release 26 Nov. 1956, "NACA Honors Staff Members in X-1A Incident."

48. *X-1B PRs*, Oct. 1955–Jan. 1957. Mulac, X-1B flight chronology. Richard D. Banner, "Flight Measurements of Airplane Structural Temperatures at Supersonic Speeds," NACA RM H57D18b, 7 June 1957.

49. *X-1B PRs*, 5 March 1957 and 5 April 1957. Hubert M. Drake, "Flight Research at High Altitude," Proceedings of the Seventh AGARD General Assembly, Washington AGARD Conference, 18–26 Nov. 1957.

50. *X-1B PRs*, June–Sept. 1957. Mulac, X-1B flight chronology. Drake, "Flight Research at High Altitude." Armstrong interview, 26 Jan. 1972.

51. Armstrong interview, 26 Jan. 1972. Mulac, X-1B flight chronology and F-100A flight chronology. *X-1B PRs*, Nov. 1957–June 1958. James E. Love, Memo for Chief, HSFS, "Unsafe Condition of Liquid Oxygen Tank of the X-1B Airplane," 14 Aug. 1958. Walter C. Williams, Memo for Research Airplane Projects Leader, "Retirement of the X-1B from flight status," 27 Aug. 1958. Letter, De E. Beeler to Directorate of Systems Management, ARDC, 20 Feb. 1959.

52. *X-1 #2 PRs*, 6 March 1952–9 May 1952.

53. For wing data see Norman V. Taillon, "Flow Characteristics About Two Thin Wings of Low Aspect Ratio Determined From Surface Pressure Measurements Obtained in Flight at Mach Numbers From 0.73 to 1.90," NASA Memo 5-1-59H, May 1959. Also "Thinner Wing to Raise X-1 Mach Limit," *Aviation Week*, LXII, No. 17 (April 25, 1955), 42.

54. *X-1 #2 PRs*, May 1952–Feb. 1954. *X-1E PRs*, March–May 1954. *X-1E PRs* did not resume until Jan. 1956, until the plane began flying. See also letter, Walter C. Williams to Walter T. Bonney, 4 Jan. 1956.

55. *X-1E PRs*, Jan.–Aug. 1956. Mulac X-1E flight chronology. De E. Beeler, Memo for Research Airplane Projects Leader, "First Supersonic Flight of the X-1E Airplane," 20 June 1956. Joseph A. Walker, Memo for Files, "X-1E Landing Accident," 29 June 1956.

56. *X-1E PRs*, Sept. 1956–July 1957. Mulac, X-1E flight chronology. Let-

ter, W. C. Williams to NACA Hq., 9 July 1957. Banner, "Flight Measurements of Airplane Structural Temperatures at Supersonic Speeds," 7 June 1957.

57. *X1-E PRs*, Aug. 1957–June 1958. Mulac, X-1E flight chronology.

58. *X-1E PRs*, July–Aug. 1958. Hubert M. Drake and Donald R. Bellman, Memo for Chief, High-Speed Flight Station, "Recommendations for Performance Improvements for the X-1 Airplanes," 20 Nov. 1957.

59. *X-1E PRs*, Sept–Nov. 1958. Mulac, X-1E flight chronology.

60. *X-1E PRs*, Dec. 1958–April 1959. Letter, Walter C. Williams to Richard H. Frost, 4 June 1959.

EPILOGUE

Today the surviving X-1 and D-558 airplanes are on display or in storage awaiting display. The X-1 #1 resides in the Smithsonian National Air and Space Museum. The X-1B, with its reaction controls, rests in the Air Force Museum, Wright-Patterson AFB, Ohio. The X-1E née X-1 #2 is mounted in characteristic attitude on a concrete pedestal in front of the former NACA High-Speed Flight Station, now the NASA Flight Research Center at Edwards AFB, a fitting reminder of the X-1s and D-558s that flew from the exotic dry lake. The Navy displays the Douglas D-558-1 #1 Skystreak at the Naval Aviation Museum, Pensacola, Florida, repainted in brilliant red. The only other surviving Skystreak, the D-558-1 #3, "NACA 142," is in storage at the Marine Corps base at Quantico, Virginia. The first Skyrocket, the D-558-2 #1, is on display at the Ontario Air Museum, Ontario, California. The record-setting D-558-2 #2 is in storage at the Smithsonian's Silver Hill, Maryland, storage facility. The workhorse D-558-2 #3 rests on a steel pedestal at the Antelope Valley College, Lancaster, California, presented to the school by NASA.

The X-1 and D-558 aircraft could serve as models for research-aircraft procurement. Generally speaking, leading aerodynamicists and engineers like Ezra Kotcher and John Stack recognized the need for a transonic and supersonic research airplane at least five years prior to government and industry efforts to procure such a plane. When the NACA, AAF, and Navy issued authorization for companies to develop the research airplanes, the goals stipulated were modest, despite the radical mission of the planes. Essentially, the companies had to design the aircraft to attain or approach Mach 1, the speed of sound. The design of the planes should not be hindered by existing requirements for design or by military requirements. But though the contractor had a free hand in the development of an airframe, the plane should be as simple and conventional as possible, so that its results from research could be applied in the design of new conventional-type aircraft. This development approach led to an almost phenomenally rapid development and delivery schedule. Within one year from Robert Woods' original discussion with Ezra Kotcher, Bell had the first XS-1 ready for its initial glide flights. Within two years from initial discussions with the Navy, Douglas had the first D-558-1 flying at Muroc.

Both designs reflected good engineering and careful development. Neither the XS-1 nor the D-558-1 and D-558-2 required extensive modifications or corrections following flight testing. They all met their contract specifications. The only difficulty in the 2 programs centered around the designing of a reliable turbopump installation to feed propellants to the rocket engines. Bell wisely decided to adopt an interim high-pressure system that could still permit the airplane to attain the required 800 mph at 35,000 ft. Since Skyrocket development started at a later date, Douglas could afford the luxury of waiting for the turbopump to come through. Both design teams kept the designs flexible enough to permit adoption of the basic airframe for additional capabilities. In the X-1s, this meant lengthening the basic design to incorporate additional fuel giving the plane Mach 2.5 performance. In the D-558-2, this meant that Douglas could modify the plane into an all-rocket air-launched aircraft. The discovery that the modified or advanced airplanes encountered severe stability and control problems around Mach 2 did not reflect on the design teams, but rather indicated new problems in supersonic flight, potentially affecting all high-performance aircraft, that scientists and engineers would have to solve or alleviate before practical Mach 2 aircraft became a reality. It must be remembered at all times that these aircraft, the D-558s and the X-1s, were originally designed for speeds around Mach 1. This was the design goal, despite predictions by some that they might go even faster. Finally, engineers not only designed the aircraft to fulfill their research mission, but at the same time did not sacrifice the plane's flying qualities. Pilots of both the X-1 and D-558 series continually stated that the planes had very satisfactory flying qualities both at subsonic and transonic velocities.

Of the original two designs, the XS-1s were the most radical, since they incorporated a rocket power plant. This of itself implied the planes might undergo a prolonged flight program before the rocket engine proved itself a reliable system. However, the Reaction Motors engineers developed a highly satisfactory engine that did not require extensive development testing and that did not disrupt the X-1 or D-558 development programs. Drawing on their previous experience with liquid oxygen-

and-alcohol-fueled engines, the small firm built a reliable power plant that, more than a decade later, propelled the North American X-15 on its initial contractor flights. Though frozen valves and the like occasionally plagued X-1 and D-558-2 flights, the difficulties did not stem from any inherent flaw or fault in the design of the engine. This simple approach taken in the design of the X-1s and D-558-2s, together with the resulting success of the two programs, contrasts sharply with other research-aircraft programs undertaken at later dates and plagued by problems in airframe and power plant design.

At the time of their initial formulation, both the X-1 and D-558 aircraft were conceived for research in the vicinity of Mach 1. It would seem a duplication of effort to develop both planes. However, the D-558 represented closely a service-type airplane, while the XS-1 was more radical in that it required air launching, special fuels, and the like. In effect, the D-558 was insurance against the possible failure of the XS-1 to emerge as a successful design. When the two types began flying, however, the D-558, with its high transonic speeds, freed the XS-1s to concentrate on supersonic flight research. This meant that the XS-1s could obtain data on supersonic flight that much faster, without having to fly an extensive transonic flight program as well. Further, the development of the sweptwing D-558-2 opened up a whole new field of research, that of sweptwing behavior at transonic and supersonic speeds. Had the D-558 been dropped in favor of the X-1, derivation of data on sweptwing behavior might have come only at a later date, through development of a wholly new airplane.

Aside from direct technical contributions, the most important contribution of the X-1 was in eliminating the myth of a "sound barrier" from the minds of most aeronautical engineers. It changed thinking from subsonic to supersonic, and forced engineers and pilots to look upon supersonic flight as just as real a possibility as subsonic flight. The fact that the nation possessed an airplane that could actually fly through the "barrier" caused the barrier to melt away. It gave aircraft designers and manufacturers confidence in developing transonic and supersonic airplanes. Less than a year after Yeager exceeded Mach 1, Air Force pilots regularly dove faster than the speed of sound in production F-86 Sabres. On May 25, 1953, North American test pilot George Welch completed the first flight of the prototype North American F-100A Super Sabre, the first Western supersonic fighter. Its design dated to 1949. Before the X-1s retired in 1958, production F-100s and Mach 2 Lockheed F-104s regularly flew chase for the rocket planes.

Technically, the X-1 and D-558 series made valuable contributions to the state of aeronautical science. Primarily, the development of the XS-1 enabled NACA and Air Force engineers to give focus to the whole problem of transonic and supersonic flight. It gave them a real vehicle to work on, and enabled them to bring together in one design the best aero-dynamic data and ideas concerning transonic and supersonic aerodynam-ics that they had at the time. The X-1 came at a time when ground-based research methods could not generate the necessary data to permit designers to configure airplanes for safe transonic and supersonic flight. Aerodynamicists sought to reach a desired technology level permitting them to design airplanes for flight at Mach 1. Not content to wait for ground-research methods to reach the state of the art whereby reliable high-speed aerodynamic data could be acquired, they elected to develop a research aircraft that could jump above the state of the art until ground-research methods could catch up to the same level of technologi-cal sophistication. The place of the X-1 and D-558, then, can be set on a graph of time versus the level of technological capability.

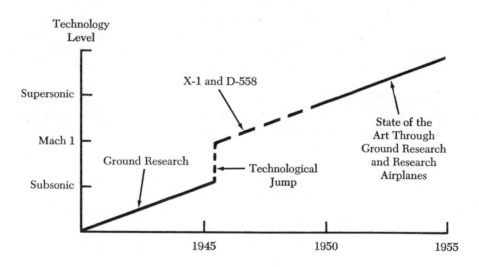

In time, ground-research methods did catch up. In part, this was in response to an increased need for accurate aerodynamic data in the design of the X-1 and D-558. Wind-tunnel technology underwent an evolutionary process aimed at developing transonic-research methods. First came the development of the "splitter plate" method, then the emergence of the sting model support system, used for testing the XS-1 and D-558. In 1945, Coleman du Pont Donaldson invented the annular transonic tunnel for airfoil testing to Mach 1.1. The next year, Ray Wright and Vernon Ward at NACA's Langley Laboratory arrived at the basic theory supporting the "slotted throat" wind tunnel. Testing began on January 8, 1947, and during December 1949 NACA achieved the first continuous transonic flow using the slotted-throat technique in the Langley 8-ft. high-speed tunnel. The mysterious gap from Mach 0.75 to Mach 1.3 in wind-tunnel testing was no more. John Stack and his associates at Langley received the Robert J. Collier trophy for 1951 for the development of the slotted-throat wind tunnel.

During the flight testing of the X-1 and D-558 research airplanes, engineers gained insight into new problems affecting aircraft design. One was the marked loss of elevator effectiveness at Mach 1 and above. X-1 pilots found the stabilizer to be 20 times more effective than the elevator. This led directly to the development of the all-moving or "flying" tail for supersonic aircraft that appeared first on the North American F-86D Sabre interceptor. Provisions for an adjustable stabilizer together with the elevators on the regular F-86 fighter contributed greatly to its excellent transonic behavior in contrast to the MiG-15. Transonic buffet investigations with the X-1 and D-558-1 confirmed the desirability of using thin wing sections on high-speed airplanes. Using a thin wing, for example, the Lockheed F-94C Starfire interceptor could exceed Mach 1 in a dive, something the earlier F-94A and F-94B aircraft could not do. The pitch-up phenomena, first encountered and studied by the D-558-2 Skyrocket, plagued subsequent high-performance sweptwing aircraft, particularly, for example, in the McDonnell F-101 Voodoo fighter-interceptor. The only cure appeared in changing the tail configuration so that the horizontal stabilizer emerged very low on the side of the fuselage. This became a standard design feature on such aircraft as the North American F-100, Grumman F11F Tiger, and Vought F-8 Crusader. At one point, NACA gave serious consideration to adding a low horizontal tail to the Skyrocket.

Once the advanced X-1s and the all-rocket D-558-2 began explorations at speeds above Mach 1.5, other problems appeared. The most serious were the loss of directional stability and the phenomenon of coupled motions, such as combined pitching, rolling, and yawing motions. This led to greater study of tail effectiveness at supersonic speeds and the introduction of analog studies using flight-test results to predict aircraft behavior at higher speeds. The advanced capabilities of the aircraft for speeds at Mach 2 and altitudes above 80,000 ft. led to the investigation of aerodynamic heating and the development of prototype-reaction controls for control of the aircraft in a near-space environment. The X-15 employed reaction controls during its flight-test program, and they were standard equipment on the Mercury, Gemini, and Apollo spacecraft.

One area in which the research-aircraft program contributed to the future was that of research organization. When the research program began in 1946, with the detailing of the NACA engineers to Muroc, Walter C. Williams, head of the little group, reported back to Hartley A. Soulé, head of the Stability Research Division at Langley Laboratory. As the research activities of the X-1 and D-558 at Muroc expanded, so did the need for tighter organization, with the activities of the NACA Muroc unit tied into the activities of the other NACA research centers. Accordingly, NACA designated Soulé as Research Airplane Projects Leader in August 1948. A month later, he recommended formation of a Research Airplane Projects Panel with representatives from the various NACA laboratories. NACA formed the panel and appointed Soulé as chairman. Later, in 1954, when initiating development of the X-15, NACA, the Air Force, and the Navy formed a special three-man X-15 steering committee better to administer the development program on the airplane. Of particular importance, however, was the tight organizational relationship between NACA, the military services, and private industry in the development and testing of the research airplanes. In the meantime, at Edwards, the personnel of the NACA High-Speed Flight Station developed organization and mission planning to a high level of competence, from engineering planning on the airplanes, through administration, flight planning, flight testing, ground tracking, interpretation of data, and maintenance. This found its fullest expression in the special "High Range" tracking network established specifically for the X-15. It was a long way from the original two SCR-584 gun radars that tracked the XS-1 and D-558 back in 1946 and 1947.

All of this backlog of program management paid off in the manned spacecraft program, a strange byproduct of a program beginning with the transonic D-558 and supersonic XS-1. When the time came for NASA to form a team for Project Mercury, the first American manned-spacecraft venture, the agency called on those individuals most closely associated with the research-aircraft program. Robert R. Gilruth, who developed the wing-flow method of research and who favored the use of a thin wing for the X-1, became Director of the Space Task Group, with responsibility for the development of Project Mercury. Walter C. Williams, Chief of the NACA High-Speed Flight Station, later the NASA Flight Research Center, became Operations Director of Project Mercury and Associate Director of the Manned Spacecraft Center. Hartley A. Soulé, former Research Airplane Projects Leader, became project director for establishing a world-wide tracking network for Project Mercury. Gerald M. Truszynski, Chief of the Instrumentation Division at the NACA High-Speed Flight Station, became Deputy Associate Administrator for Tracking and Data Acquisition for the Mercury program. It seems fitting, then, that the first man to set foot on the moon was a former NACA research pilot who had flown the X-1B, X-5, and X-15, and who had served as launch pilot on the NACA B-29 and P2B-1S, Neil A. Armstrong.

Writing in the early seventeenth century, Sir Francis Bacon stated, "By far the greatest obstacle to the progress of science and to the undertaking of new tasks and provinces therein, is found in this—that men despair and think things impossible." The men who designed, maintained, and flew the X-1s and D-558s did not despair and think their task impossible. Through them aviation science crossed the invisible threshold to flight faster than sound.

APPENDIX ONE

Technical Specifications for the X-1s and D-558s

BELL XS-1 (X-1)

ENGINE: One Reaction Motors Inc. XLR-11-RM-3 (Model A6000C4) four-chamber rocket engine rated at 6,000 pounds static thrust.

PROPELLANTS: Liquid oxygen (311 gallons) and diluted ethyl alcohol (293 gallons).

WEIGHTS: Launch configuration with 8-percent wing: 12,250 lbs. Launch configuration with 10-percent wing: 12,000 lbs. Landing configuration with 8-percent wing: 7,000 lbs. Landing configuration with 10-percent wing: 6,750 lbs.

HEIGHT: 10.85 feet.

LENGTH: 30.90 feet.

WING: Straight with a NACA 65-108 (XS-1-1) or NACA 65-110 (XS-1-2) airfoil section.
Span: 28 ft.
Area: 130 sq. ft. (including fuselage section)
Root Chord: 74.2 in.
Tip Chord: 37.1 in.
Flap Area: 11.6 sq. ft.
Aileron Area (each aileron): 3.15 sq. ft.

HORIZONTAL TAIL: Area: 26.0 sq. ft. Elevator Area: 5.2 sq. ft.

VERTICAL TAIL: Area: 25.6 sq. ft. Rudder Area: 5.2 sq. ft.

APPROXIMATE MAXIMUM PERFORMANCE: Mach 1.45 at 35,000 feet (960 miles per hour).

Specification is applicable to the XS-1-1 (serial 46-062) and XS-1-2 (serial 46-063).

BELL X-1-3

ENGINE: One Reaction Motors Inc. XLR-11-RM-5 (Model E6000C4) four-chamber rocket engine rated at 6,000 pounds static thrust.

PROPELLANT: Liquid oxygen (437 gallons) and diluted ethyl alcohol (498 gallons). Hydrogen peroxide (for turbine pump) (31 gallons).

WEIGHTS: Launch configuration: 14,751 lbs. Landing configuration: 6,847 lbs.

HEIGHT: 10.85 ft.

LENGTH: 30.90 ft.

WING: Straight with a NACA 65-108 airfoil section.
> Span: 28 ft.
> Area: 130 sq. ft. (including fuselage section)
> Root Chord: 74.2 in.
> Tip Chord: 37.1 in.
> Flap Area: 11.6 sq. ft.
> Aileron Area (each aileron): 3.15 sq. ft.

HORIZONTAL TAIL: Area: 26.0 sq. ft. Elevator Area: 5.2 sq. ft.

VERTICAL TAIL: Area: 25.6 sq. ft. Rudder Area: 5.2 sq. ft.

APPROXIMATE MAXIMUM PERFORMANCE: Mach 2.44 at 70,000 ft. (1,612 miles per hour).

Specification is applicable to the X-1-3 (serial 46-064).

BELL X-1A

ENGINE: One Reaction Motors Inc. XLR-11-RM-5 (Model E6000C4) four-chamber rocket engine rated at 6,000 pounds static thrust.

PROPELLANTS: Liquid oxygen (500 gallons) and diluted ethyl alcohol (570 gallons). Hydrogen peroxide (for turbine pump) (37 gallons).

WEIGHTS: Launch configuration: 16,487 lbs. Landing configuration: 7,266 lbs.

HEIGHT: 10.70 feet.

LENGTH: 35.55 feet.

WING: Straight with a NACA 65-108 airfoil section.
> Span: 28 ft.
> Area: 130 sq. ft. (including fuselage section).
> Root Chord: 74.2 in.
> Tip Chord: 37.1 in.
> Flap Area: 11.46 sq. ft.
> Aileron Area (each aileron): 3.21 sq. ft.

HORIZONTAL TAIL: Area: 26.0 sq. ft. Elevator Area: 5.2 sq. ft.

VERTICAL TAIL: Area: 25.6 sq. ft. Rudder Area: 5.2 sq. ft.

APPROXIMATE MAXIMUM PERFORMANCE: Mach 2.47 at 70,000 feet (1,635 miles per hour).

Specification is applicable to the X-1A (serial 48-1384),X-1B (serial 48-1385), and X-1D (serial 48-1386).

DOUGLAS D-558-1 SKYSTREAK

ENGINE: One Allison J-35-A-11 (developed by General Electric as the TG-180) turbojet rated at 5,000 pounds static thrust.

PROPELLANTS: Aviation fuel (kerosene) (230 gallons).

WEIGHTS: Takeoff configuration: 10,105 lbs. Landing configuration: 7,711 lbs.

HEIGHT: 12 feet 1.7 inches.

LENGTH: 35 feet 8.5 inches.

WING: Straight with a NACA 65-110 airfoil section.
Span: 25 feet.
Area: 150.7 square feet.

APPROXIMATE MAXIMUM PERFORMANCE: Mach 0.832 at sea level (632 miles per hour).

Specification is applicable to the D-558-1 #1 (BuAer No. 37970), the D-558-1 #2 (BuAer No. 37971), and the D-558-1 #3 (BuAer No. 37972).

DOUGLAS D-558-2 SKYROCKET
(Turbojet Ground-Launched Version)

ENGINE: One Westinghouse J-34-40 turbojet engine rated at 3,000 pounds static thrust.

PROPELLANTS: Aviation fuel (gasoline—not kerosene) (260 gallons).

WEIGHTS: Takeoff configuration: 10,572 lbs. Landing configuration: 7,914 lbs.

HEIGHT: 12 feet 8 inches.

LENGTH: 42 feet.

WING: Swept (35 degrees at 30-percent chord) with a NACA 63-010 airfoil section at the root and a NACA 63-012 airfoil section at the tip.
Span: 25 ft.
Area: 175 sq. ft.
Root Chord: 108.51 in.
Tip Chord: 61.18 in.
Flap Area: 12.58 sq. ft.
Aileron Area: 9.8 sq. ft.

HORIZONTAL TAIL: Area: 39.9 sq. ft. Elevator Area: 9.4 sq. ft.

VERTICAL TAIL: Area: 36.6 sq. ft. Rudder Area: 6.15 sq. ft.

APPROXIMATE MAXIMUM PERFORMANCE: Mach 0.825 at 20,000 feet (585 miles per hour).

Specification is applicable to the ground-launched, turbojet-powered D-558-2 #1 (BuAer 37973) prior to installation of its RMI rocket engine, but may be considered applicable to the ground-launched D-558-2 #2 (BuAer 37974) prior to its modification in 1950 to all-rocket air-launched configuration.

DOUGLAS D-558-2 SKYROCKET
(All-Rocket Air-Launched Version)

ENGINE: One Reaction Motors Inc. XLR-8-RM-6 (Model A6000C4) four-chamber rocket engine rated at 6,000 pounds static thrust.

PROPELLANTS: Liquid oxygen (345 gallons) and diluted ethyl alcohol (378 gallons).

WEIGHTS: Launch configuration: 15,787 lbs. Landing configuration: 9,421 lbs.

HEIGHT: 12 feet 8 inches.

LENGTH: 42 feet.

WING: Swept (35 degrees at 30-percent chord) with a NACA 63-010 airfoil section at the root and a NACA 63-012 airfoil section at the tip.
Span: 25 ft.
Area: 175 sq. ft.
Root Chord: 108.51 in.
Tip Chord: 61.18 in.
Flap Area: 12.58 sq. ft.
Aileron Area: 9.8 sq. ft.

HORIZONTAL TAIL: Area: 39.9 sq. ft. Elevator Area: 9.4 sq. ft.

VERTICAL TAIL: Area: 36.6 sq. ft. Rudder Area: 6.15 sq. ft.

APPROXIMATE MAXIMUM PERFORMANCE: Mach 2 at 62,000 feet (1,290 miles per hour).

Specification is applicable to the air-launched D-558-2 #2 (BuAer No. 37974), but also applies to the D-558-2 #1 BuAer No. 37973 as modified in 1955.

DOUGLAS D-558-2 SKYROCKET
(Jet-and-Rocket Air-Launched Version)

ENGINES: One Reaction Motors Inc. XLR-8-RM-5 four-chamber rocket engine rated at 6,000 pounds static thrust. One Westinghouse J-34-40 turbojet engine rated at 3,000 pounds static thrust.

PROPELLANTS: Rocket Engine: Liquid oxygen (170 gallons) and diluted ethyl alcohol (192 gallons). Turbojet Engine: Aviation fuel (gasoline—not kerosene) (260 gallons).

WEIGHTS: Launch configuration: 15,266 lbs. Landing configuration: 9,500 lbs.

HEIGHT: 12 feet 8 inches.

LENGTH: 42 feet.

WING: Swept (35 degrees at 30-percent chord) with a NACA 63-010 airfoil section at the root and a NACA 63-012 airfoil section at the tip.
Span: 25 ft.
Area: 175 sq. ft.
Root Chord: 108.51 in.
Tip Chord: 61.18 in.
Flap Area: 12.58 sq. ft.
Aileron Area: 9.8 sq. ft.

HORIZONTAL TAIL: Area: 39.9 sq. ft. Elevator Area: 9.4 sq. ft.

VERTICAL TAIL: Area: 36.6 sq. ft. Rudder Area: 6.15 sq. ft.

APPROXIMATE MAXIMUM PERFORMANCE: Mach 1.08 at 40,000 feet (720 miles per hour).

Specification is applicable to the air-launched, jet-and-rocket-powered D-558-2 #3 (BuAer 37975), but may be considered applicable to the ground-launched D-558-2 #1 (BuAer 37973) prior to its modification in 1955 to all-rocket air-launched configuration.

Flight Chronologies of the
Research Airplanes

I. XS-1 #1 (X-1-1), SERIAL 46-062, FLIGHTS

A. Bell Contractor Flights

At Pinecastle AAF, Florida

Jan. 19, 1946	Bell flight 1, Jack Woolams, pilot. Familiarization.
Feb. 5, 1946	Bell flight 2, Woolams.
	Bell flight 3, Woolams.
Feb. 11, 1946	Bell flight 4, Woolams. Gear retracted, left wing damaged.
Feb. 19, 1946	Bell flight 5, Woolams. Nosewheel retracted on landing runout. Landing-gear door damaged.
Feb. 25, 1946	Bell flight 6, Woolams. Static directional stability investigation.
	Bell flight 7, Woolams. Longitudinal and directional stability investigation.
Feb. 26(?), 1946	Bell flight 8, Woolams. Dynamic stability check.
Feb. 26, 1946	Bell flight 9, Woolams. Rate of roll investigation.
March 6(?), 1946	Bell flight 10, Woolams. Static longitudinal stability investigation.

At Muroc Dry Lake, California

April 10, 1947	Bell flight 11, Chalmers Goodlin, pilot. Glide flight and stall check.
April 11, 1947	Bell flight 12, Goodlin. Nosewheel damaged. First powered flight of the XS-1 #1 aircraft.
April 29, 1947	Bell flight 13, Goodlin. Handling qualities check.
April 30, 1947	Bell flight 14, Goodlin. Same as flight 13.
May 5, 1947	Bell flight 15, Goodlin. Same as flight 13.
May 15, 1947	Bell flight 16, Goodlin. Buffet-boundary investigation. Aileron-damper malfunction.
May 19, 1947	Bell flight 17, Goodlin. Buffet boundary investigation.
May 21, 1947	Bell flight 18, Goodlin. Same as flight 17.
June 5, 1947	Bell flight 19, Goodlin. Demonstration flight for Aviation Writers Association.

B. Air Force Flights

Aug. 6, 1947	AF glide flight 1, Capt. Charles E. Yeager. For pilot familiarization.
Aug. 7, 1947	AF glide flight 2, Yeager. Same as flight 1.
Aug. 8, 1947	AF glide flight 3, Yeager. Same as flight 1.

Aug, 29, 1947	AF powered flight 1, Yeager. Mach 0.85.
Sept. 4, 1947	AF flight 2, Yeager. Approx. Mach 0.89. Telemeter failure required a repeat of this flight.
Sept. 8, 1947	AF flight 3, Yeager. Repeat of flight 2.
Sept. 10, 1947	AF flight 4, Yeager. Mach 0.91. For stability and control investigation.
Sept. 12, 1947	AF flight 5, Yeager. Mach 0.92. Check of elevator and stabilizer effectiveness. Also buffet investigation.
Oct. 5, 1947	AF flight 6, Yeager. Same as flight 5.
Oct. 8, 1947	AF flight 7, Yeager. Airspeed calibration flight. Plane attained Mach 0.925.
Oct. 10, 1947	AF flight 8, Yeager. Stability and control investigation. Plane attains Mach 0.997.
Oct. 14, 1947	AF flight 9, Yeager. World's first supersonic flight by a manned aircraft. XS-1 #1 attained Mach 1.06 at 43,000 ft., approximately 700 mph.
Oct. 27, 1947	AF flight 10, Yeager. Electrical power failure. No rocket.
Oct. 28, 1947	AF flight 11, Yeager. Telemeter failure.
Oct. 29, 1947	AF flight 12, Yeager. Repeat of flight 11.
Oct. 31(?), 1947	AF flight 13, Yeager.
Nov. 3, 1947	AF flight 14, Yeager.
Nov. 4, 1947	AF flight 15, Yeager.
Nov. 6, 1947	AF flight 16, Yeager. Mach 1.35 at 48,600 ft.
Jan. 16, 1948	AF flight 17, Yeager. Airspeed calibration. M = 0.9.
Jan. 22, 1948	AF flight 18, Yeager. Pressure distribution survey. Mach 1.2.
Jan. 30, 1948	AF flight 19, Yeager. Same as flight 18. M = 1.1.
Feb. 24, 1948	AF flight 20, Capt. James T. Fitzgerald, Jr. pilot. Engine fire after launch forced jettisoning of propellants; completed as a glide flight.
March 11, 1948	AF flight 21, Yeager. Attained Mach 1.25 in dive.
March 26, 1948	AF flight 22, Yeager. Attained Mach 1.45 at 40,130 ft. (approx. 957 mph) during dive. Fastest flight ever made in original XS-1 airplanes.
March 31, 1948	AF flight 23, Yeager. Engine shutdown after launch. Propellants jettisoned, completed as glide flight.
April 6, 1948	AF flight 24, Fitzgerald. Pilot-check flight. Mach 1.1, during 4-cylinder run at 41,000 ft.
April 7, 1948	AF flight 25, Maj. Gustav E. Lundquist. Glide flight only.
	AF flight 26, Fitzgerald. Familiarization flight.
April 9, 1948	AF flight 27, Lundquist. Powered pilot-check flight.
April 16, 1948	AF flight 28, Lundquist. Pressure distribution survey. Only cylinders 2 and 4 ignited.
April 26, 1948	AF flight 29, Fitzgerald. Aborted because of inconsistent rocket operation. Reached Mach 0.9.

April 29, 1948	AF flight 30, Lundquist. Pressure distribution survey. Attained Mach 1.18.
May 4, 1948	AF flight 31, Fitzgerald. Same as flight 30. Mach 1.15.
May 21, 1948	AF flight 32, Lundquist. Stability and control and buffeting investigation, Mach 0.92.
May 25, 1948	AF flight 33, Fitzgerald. Buffet investigation, wing and tail loads. Mach 1.08.
May 26, 1948	AF flight 34, Yeager. Same as flight 33. Mach 1.05.
June 3, 1948	AF flight 35, Lundquist. Left main gear door opened in flight. Nosewheel collapsed on landing.
Dec. 1, 1948	AF flight 36, Yeager (?). Handling qualities and wing and tail loads at Mach 1.
Dec. 13, 1948	AF flight 37, Yeager (?). Same as flight 36.
Dec. 23, 1948	AF flight 38, Yeager. Wing and tail loads during supersonic flight at high altitudes. Mach 1.09.
Jan. 5, 1949	AF flight 39, Yeager. Rocket takeoff from the ground.
March 11, 1949	AF flight 40, Capt. Jack Ridley, pilot. Familiarization flight. Mach 1.23 at 35, 000 ft. Small engine fire due to loose igniter.
March 16, 1949	AF flight 41, Col. Albert Boyd, pilot (?). Familiarization flight. Inflight engine fire and shutdown.
March 21, 1949	AF flight 42, Maj. Frank Everest, pilot. Familiarization flight. Mach 1.22 at 40,000 ft.
March 25, 1949	AF flight 43, Everest. Check of pressure suit for altitude operation. Mach 1.24 at 48,000 ft. Rocket fire and automatic engine shutdown.
April 14, 1949	AF flight 44, Ridley. Accelerated stall check at transonic speeds. Mach 1.1 at 40,000 ft.
April 19, 1949	AF flight 45, Everest. Altitude attempt. Only two cylinders fired.
April 29, 1949	AF flight 46, Ridley (?). Stability and control investigation to high Mach numbers.
May 2, 1949	AF flight 47, Everest. Engine chamber explodes, jamming rudder. Everest lands safely.
July 25, 1949	AF flight 48, Everest. Altitude attempt. Everest attains 66,846-ft. altitude.
Aug. 8, 1949	AF flight 49, Everest. Altitude attempt. Everest attains 71,902-ft. altitude.
Aug. 25, 1949	AF flight 50, Everest. First use of partial pressure suit to save life of pilot during flight at high altitude. X-1 #1 lost cockpit pressurization about 69,000 ft. Everest made safe emergency descent.
Oct. 6, 1949	AF flight 51, Lt. Col. Patrick Fleming, pilot. Pilot familiarization; attained Mach 1.2.
Oct. 26, 1949	AF flight 52, Maj. Richard L. Johnson, pilot. Pilot familiarization.

Nov. 29, 1949	AF flight 53, Everest (?). High-altitude wing-and-tail-loads investigation.
Dec. 2, 1949	AF flight 54, Everest (?). Same as flight 53.
Feb. 21, 1950	AF flight 55, Everest. Wing-and-tail-loads investigation.
April 25, 1950	AF flight 56, Yeager. Lateral stability and control investigation.
April (?), 1950	AF flight 57, Ridley (?). Buffeting, wing and tail loads.
May 8, 1950	AF flight 58, Ridley (?). Same as flight 57.
May 12, 1950	AF flight 59, Yeager. Last flight of the X-1 #1. Flight made for camera footage for the motion picture *Jet Pilot*. Aircraft subsequently retired and presented to the Smithsonian Institution.

II. XS-1 #2 (X-1-2), SERIAL 46-063, FLIGHTS

A. BELL CONTRACTOR FLIGHTS

Oct. 11, 1946	Bell flight 1, Chalmers Goodlin pilot. Glide flight for pilot familiarization.
Oct. 14, 1946	Bell flight 2, Goodlin. Glide flight.
Oct. 17, 1946	Bell flight 3, Goodlin. Glide flight. Stall check.
Dec. 2, 1946	Bell flight 4, Goodlin. Glide flight for check of fuel jettison system.
Dec. 9, 1946	Bell flight 5, Goodlin. First XS-1 powered flight. Mach 0.79 at 35,000 ft. Minor engine fire.
Dec. 20, 1946	Bell flight 6, Goodlin. Familiarization powered flight.
Jan. 8, 1947	Bell flight 7, Goodlin. Buffet boundary investigation. Mach 0.80 at 35,000 ft.
Jan. 17, 1947	Bell flight 8, Goodlin. Same as flight 7. Full power climb. Plane reached Mach 0.82.
Jan. 22, 1947	Bell flight 9, Goodlin. Same as flight 8. Telemetry failure.
Jan. 23, 1947	Bell flight 10, Goodlin. Same as flight 8.
Jan. 30, 1947	Bell flight 11, Goodlin. Accelerated stalls. Partial power due to faulty engine igniters. Mach 0.75.
Jan. 31, 1947	Bell flight 12, Goodlin. Same as flight 7. M = 0.7.
Feb. 5, 1947	Bell flight 13, Goodlin. Machmeter calibration.
Feb. 7, 1947	Bell flight 14, Goodlin. Same as flight 7.
Feb. 19, 1947	Bell flight 15, Goodlin. Accelerated stalls.
Feb. 21, 1947	Bell flight 16, Goodlin. Flight aborted after drop because of low engine-chamber pressure.
May 22, 1947	Bell flight 17, Alvin M. Johnston, pilot. Pilot familiarization flight. Mach 0.72. 8g pullout.
May 29, 1947	Bell flight 18, Goodlin. Airspeed calibration flight to Mach 0.72. End of Bell contractor program.

B. NACA FLIGHTS

Sept. 25, 1947	NACA acceptance flight. Capt. Charles E. Yeager, pilot. Number 4 cylinder burned out.
Oct. 21, 1947	NACA glide-familiarization flight for NACA pilot Herbert H. Hoover. Stall check. Nosewheel collapsed on landing.
Dec. 16, 1947	NACA powered flight 1, Hoover. For familiarization. Mach 0.84. No telemetry record.
Dec. 17, 1947	NACA flight 2, Hoover. Same as flight 1. Mach 0.8.
Jan. 6, 1948	NACA flight 3, Hoover. Turns and pull-ups to buffet. Mach 0.74
Jan. 8, 1948	NACA flight 4, Hoover. Turns and pull-ups to buffet. Mach 0.83.
Jan. 9, 1948	NACA flight 5, Howard C. Lilly, pilot. For pilot familiarization.
Jan. 15, 1948	NACA flight 6, Lilly. Turns and pull-ups to buffet. Sideslips. Mach 0.76.
Jan. 21, 1948	NACA flight 7, Hoover. Stabilizer effectiveness investigation. Mach 0.82 at 29,000 ft.
Jan. 23, 1948	NACA flight 8, Hoover. Attempted high-speed run aborted at Mach 0.83 due to drop in chamber pressure.
Jan. 27, 1948	NACA flight 9, Hoover. High-speed run to Mach 0.925 at 38,000 ft. Cylinders 2 and 3 failed to fire.
March 4, 1948	NACA flight 10, Hoover. High-speed run to Mach 0.943 at 40,000 ft.
March 10, 1948	NACA flight 11, Hoover. First NACA supersonic flight. Mach 1.065. First civilian supersonic flight. Nosewheel failed to extend for landing. Minor damage.
March 22, 1948	NACA flight 12, Hoover. Stability and loads investigation. Mach 1.12.
March 30, 1948	NACA flight 13, Hoover. Same as flight 12. Mach 0.90.
March 31, 1948	NACA flight 14, Lilly. Same as flight 12. Plane attained Mach 1.1.
April 5, 1948	NACA flight 15, Lilly. Engine failed to ignite. Propellants jettisoned, completed as glide flight.
April 9, 1948	NACA flight 16, Lilly. Same as flight 12. M = 0.89.
April 16, 1948	NACA flight 17, Lilly. Same as flight 12. Plane's nosewheel collapsed on landing. Moderate damage.
Nov. 1, 1948	NACA flight 18, Hoover. Stability and control. Mach 0.9. Number 4 cylinder failed to fire.
Nov. 15, 1948	NACA flight 19, Hoover. Same as flight 18. Also pressure distribution survey. Mach 0.98.

Nov. 23, 1948	NACA flight 20, Robert A. Champine, pilot. For pilot familiarization. Check on handling qualities and pressure distribution.
Nov. 29, 1948	NACA flight 21, Champine. Check on handling qualities and pressure distribution. Mach 0.88.
Nov. 30, 1948	NACA flight 22, Champine. Same as flight 21.
Dec. 2, 1948	NACA flight 23, Champine. Same as flight 21. Plane exceeded Mach 1 briefly.
May 6, 1949	NACA flight 24, Champine. Check on airplane instrumentation. Mach 0.88 at 40,000 ft.
May 13, 1949	NACA flight 25, Champine. Spanwise pressure distribution, stability and control. Mach 0.91.
May 27, 1949	NACA flight 26, Champine. Same as flight 25. Mach 0.91. Stabilizer found more effective than the elevator during pull-ups at Mach 0.91.
June 16, 1949	NACA flight 27, Champine. Same as flight 25. Rolls and pull-ups around Mach 0.91.
June 23, 1949	NACA flight 28, Champine. Same as flight 25. Rolls, pull-ups, check of stabilizer effectiveness.
July 11, 1949	NACA flight 29, Champine. Same as flight 25. Rolls, pull-ups, check of stabilizer effectiveness. Mach 0.91. Number 2 cylinder failed to fire.
July 19, 1949	NACA flight 30, Champine. Same as flight 25. Rolls, pull-ups, check of stabilizer effectiveness. Mach 0.91. Number 2 cylinder failed to fire.
July 27, 1949	NACA flight 31, Champine. Same as flight 25. Rolls, pull-ups, check of stabilizer effectiveness.
Aug. 4, 1949	NACA flight 32, Champine. Same as flight 25. Sideslips, rolls, check of stabilizer effectiveness.
Sept. 23, 1949	NACA flight 33, John H. Griffith, pilot. For pilot familiarization. Mach 0.9.
Nov. 30, 1949	NACA flight 34, Griffith. Same as flight 33. Mach 0.93.
May 12, 1950	NACA flight 35, Griffith. Same as flight 25. Pull-ups and rolls.
May 17, 1950	NACA flight 36, Griffith. Same as flight 25. Pushdowns and pull-ups. Mach 1.13 at 42,000 ft.
May 26, 1950	NACA flight 37, Griffith. Same as flight 25. Pushdowns, pull-ups, rolls. Mach 1.20. Nosewheel collapsed on landing.
Aug. 9, 1950	NACA flight 38, Griffith. For pressure distribution and stability and control data. Check of stabilizer effectiveness. Mach 0.98.
Aug. 11(?), 1950	NACA flight 39, Griffith. Same as flight 38.
Sept. 21, 1950	NACA flight 40, Griffith. Same as flight 38. Also drag investigation. Pull-ups. Mach 0.90.
Oct. 4, 1950	NACA flight 41, Griffith. Same as flight 40.

April 6, 1951 — NACA flight 42, Capt. Charles E. Yeager, pilot. Flight for RKO film *Jet Pilot*. Slight engine fire but no damage.

April 20, 1951 — NACA flight 43, A. Scott Crossfield, pilot. For pilot familiarization. Reached Mach 1.07.

April 27, 1951 — NACA flight 44, Crossfield. Plane and instrument check.

May 15, 1951 — NACA flight 45, Crossfield. Wing loads and aileron effectiveness. Aileron rolls at Mach 0.90.

July 12, 1951 — NACA flight 46, Crossfield. Same as flight 45. Aileron rolls at Mach 1.07.

July 20, 1951 — NACA flight 47, Crossfield. Same as flight 45. Abrupt rudder fixed aileron rolls left and right, from Mach 0.70 to Mach 0.88.

July 31, 1951 — NACA flight 48, Crossfield. Same as flight 45.

Aug. 3, 1951 — NACA flight 49, Crossfield. Same as flight 45.

Aug. 8, 1951 — NACA flight 50, Crossfield. Same as flight 45. Elevator and stabilizer pull-ups.

Aug. 10, 1951 — NACA flight 51, Crossfield. Same as flight 45. Elevator and stabilizer pull-ups, clean stalls.

Aug. 27, 1951 — NACA flight 52, Joseph A. Walker, pilot. For pilot familiarization. Reached Mach 1.16 at 44,000 ft. during four-cylinder run.

Sept. 5, 1951 — NACA flight 53, Crossfield. Fuselage pressure distribution survey. Number 1 cylinder failed to fire. Stabilizer pull-ups at Mach 1.07.

Oct. 23, 1951 — NACA flight 54, Walker. Vortex-generator investigation. Engine cut out after two ignition attempts; propellants jettisoned and flight completed as a glide flight. Flap actuator failed, so landing made flaps-up. Plane subsequently grounded because of possibility of fatigue failure of nitrogen spheres. Later rebuilt as the Mach 2+ X-1E.

III. X-1 #3 (X-1-3), SERIAL 46-064, FLIGHTS

July 20, 1951 — Bell flight 1, Joseph Cannon, pilot. Glide flight for familiarization. Nosewheel collapse on landing.

Nov. 9, 1951 — Bell flight 2, Cannon. Captive flight with B-50 for propellant jettison test. X-1-3 destroyed in post-flight explosion and fire on the ground. B-50 launch plane also lost and Cannon injured.

IV. X-1A, SERIAL 48-1384, FLIGHTS

A. Bell Contractor Flights

Feb. 14, 1953 — Bell flight 1, Jean Ziegler, pilot. For familiarization. Fuel jettison test. Glide flight only.

Feb. 20, 1953	Bell flight 2, Ziegler. Planned as powered flight, but completed as glide flight following propellant-system difficulties.
Feb. 21, 1953	Bell flight 3, Ziegler. First powered flight. False fire warning.
March 26, 1953	Bell flight 4, Ziegler. Plane demonstrated successful four-cylinder engine operation.
April 10, 1953	Bell flight 5, Ziegler. Pilot noted low-frequency elevator buzz at Mach 0.93, and did not proceed above this speed pending buzz investigation.
April 25, 1953	Bell flight 6, Ziegler. Buzz again noted at Mach 0.93. Turbopump overspeeding caused pilot to terminate power and jettison remaining fuel.

B. AIR FORCE FLIGHTS (After USAF took over remaining Bell program on X-1A, and initiated their own flight program)

Nov. 21, 1953	Flight 7, Maj. Charles E. Yeager, pilot. First Air Force flight. Reached Mach 1.15 on this flight, made for familiarization purposes.
Dec. 2, 1953	Flight 8, Yeager. Mach 1.5.
Dec. 8, 1953	Flight 9, Yeager. First high-Mach flight attempt by X-1A. Mach 1.9 attained at 60,000 ft. during a slight climb.
Dec. 12, 1953	Flight 10, Yeager. Plane attained Mach 2.44, but encountered violent instability above Mach 2.3. Tumbled 50,000 ft., wound up in subsonic inverted spin. Yeager recovered to upright spin, then into normal flight at 25,000 ft.

Fourteen Air Force flight attempts for high altitudes were made in the spring and summer of 1954. Of these, only four flights were successful. The rest were aborted for various malfunctions, including ruptured canopy seal, failure of gear doors to close fully, turbine overspeed, faulty ignition operation. Of the four successful flights, one was Maj. Arthur Murray's checkout flight. The rest were successful high-altitude tries by Murray. The successful altitude flights were:

May 28, 1954	Flight 16, Murray. X-1A attained 87,094 ft., an unofficial world altitude record for manned aircraft.
June 4, 1954	Flight 17, Murray. X-1A reached 89,750 ft. Encountered same instability Yeager had, but at Mach 1.97. Murray recovered after tumbling 20,000 ft. down to 66,000 ft.
August 26, 1954	Flight 24, Murray. Murray attained 90,440 ft. Air Force then turned over the X-1A to NACA.

C. NACA FLIGHTS

July 20, 1955   NACA flight 1, Joseph A. Walker, pilot. For familiarization purposes. Walker attained Mach 1.45 at 45,000 ft. Noted severe aileron buzz at Mach 0.90 to 0.92.

Aug. 8, 1955   Planned as NACA flight 2. Shortly before launch, X-1A suffered a low-order explosion later traced to detonation of Ulmer leather gaskets. Walker exited into B-29 bomb bay. Extent of damage prohibited landing with the crippled X-1A, and the NACA B-29 launch crew jettisoned it into the desert. It exploded and burned on impact.

V. X-1B, SERIAL 48-1385, FLIGHTS

A. AIR FORCE FLIGHTS

Sept. 24, 1954   X-1B Air Force flight 1, Lt. Col. Jack Ridley, pilot. Glide flight, due to turbopump overspeeding.

Oct. 6, 1954   X-1B Air Force flight 2, Ridley. Glide flight, aborted power flight due to evidence of high lox tank pressure.

Oct. 8, 1954   X-1B Air Force flight 3, Maj. Arthur "Kit" Murray pilot. First powered flight.

Oct. 13, 1954   X-1B Air Force flight 4, Maj. Robert Stephens pilot.

Oct. 19, 1954   X-1B Air Force flight 5, Maj. Stuart R. Childs pilot.

Oct. 26, 1954   X-1B Air Force flight 6, Col. Horace B. Hanes pilot.

Nov. 4, 1954   X-1B Air Force flight 7, Capt. Richard B. Harer pilot.

Nov. 26, 1954   X-1B Air Force flight 8, Brig. Gen. J. Stanley Holtoner pilot. (Commander, Air Force Flight Test Center).

Nov. 30, 1954   X-1B Air Force flight 9, Lt. Col. Frank K. Everest pilot.

Dec. 2, 1954   X-1B Air Force flight 10, Everest. Mach 2.3 (approx. 1,520 mph) at 65,000 ft.

B. NACA FLIGHTS

John B. McKay pilot on flights 1-13.

Neil A. Armstrong pilot on flights 14-17.

Aug. 14, 1956   X-1B NACA flight 1. Pilot check; nose landing gear failed on landing, minor damage.

Aug. 29, 1956   X-1B NACA flight 2. Cabin-pressure regulator malfunction causes inner canopy to crack; only low-speed, low-altitude maneuvers made.

Sept. 7, 1956   X-1B NACA flight 3. Speed run to 56,000 ft. and Mach 1.8. Limited heating data gathered.

Sept. 18, 1956	X-1B NACA flight 4. Glide flight, due to erratic engine start.
Sept. 28, 1956	X-1B NACA flight 5. Three-chamber engine run to 60,000 ft. to obtain heating data.
Jan. 3, 1957	X-1B NACA flight 6. Mach 1.94 aerodynamic heating investigation (end of heating program).
May 22, 1957	X-1B NACA flight 7. Control pulses at Mach 1.45 at 60,000 ft. Flight made for instrumentation check.
June 7, 1957	X-1B NACA flight 8. Supersonic maneuvers to Mach 1.5 at 60,000 ft. to determine the dynamic and static stability and control characteristics.
June 24, 1957	X-1B NACA flight 9. Supersonic maneuvers to Mach 1.5 at 60,000 ft. to determine the dynamic and static stability and control characteristics.
July 11, 1957	X-1B NACA flight 10. Aborted after launch, due to indication of open landing-gear door. Propellants jettisoned, completed as a glide flight.
July 19, 1957	X-1B NACA flight 11. Mach 1.65 at 60,000 ft. Control pulses, sideslips, and a 2g wind-up turn.
July 29, 1957	X-1B NACA flight 12. Enlarged wing tips installed to simulate wing tips to be used with reaction controls. Mach 1.55 at 60,000 ft.
Aug. 8, 1957	X-1B NACA flight 13. Stability and control investigation. Mach 1.5 at 60,000 ft., accelerated maneuvers, control pulses, and pull-ups.
Aug. 15, 1957	X-1B NACA flight 14. Pilot check for Armstrong. Nose landing gear failed on landing, minor damage.
Nov. 27, 1957	X-1B NACA flight 15. First reaction-control flight.
Jan. 16, 1958	X-1B NACA flight 16. Low altitude, low Mach reaction-control investigation.
Jan. 23, 1958	X-1B NACA flight 17. Reaction-control investigation. Mach 1.5 at 55,000 ft. Last NACA flight.

VI. X-1D, SERIAL 48-1386, FLIGHTS

A. BELL CONTRACTOR FLIGHTS

July 24, 1951	Bell flight 1, Jean Ziegler pilot. Glide flight for familiarization. Nose landing gear broken on landing. Following repairs, plane turned over to the Air Force.

B. AIR FORCE FLIGHTS

Aug. 22, 1951	AF flight 1, Lt. Col. Frank K. Everest pilot. Launch aborted, but X-1D suffered a low-order explo-

slon during pressurization for fuel jettison. Plane jettisoned from B-50. X-1D exploded on impact with desert. Everest managed to get into B-50 bomb bay before drop. B-50 not damaged, no personal injuries.

VII. X-1E, SERIAL 46-063, FLIGHTS

Joseph Walker pilot for flights 1-21.
John McKay pilot for flights 22-26.

Dec. 3, 1955	Captive flight.
Dec. 12, 1955	X-1E NACA flight 1. Glide flight for pilot checkout and low speed evaluation.
Dec. 15, 1955	X-1E NACA flight 2. First powered flight. Engine running at excessive pressure, four overspeeds of turbopump and two automatic shutdowns. Power terminated by pilot.
April 3, 1956	X-1E NACA flight 3. Mach 0.85 at 30,000 ft. Damping characteristics good; number one cylinder failed to fire.
April 30, 1956	X-1E NACA flight 4. Turbopump did not start; no engine operation.
May 11, 1956	X-1E NACA flight 5. Wind-up turns to $C_{L_{max}}$ from Mach 0.69 to 0.84; also control pulses.
June 7, 1956	X-1E NACA flight 6. Mach 1.55 at 45,000 ft. (approx. 1,020 mph). Longitudinal and lateral trim changes in transonic region found annoying to pilot.
June 18, 1956	X-1E NACA flight 7. Mach 1.74 at 60,000 ft. (approx. 1,150 mph). Damaged on landing.
July 26, 1956	X-1E NACA flight 8. Subsonic because cylinders 3 and 4 would not fire.
Aug. 31, 1956	X-1E NACA flight 9. Mach 2.0 at 60,000 ft. (approx. 1,340 mph). Sideslips, pulses, rolls.
Sept. 14, 1956	X-1E NACA flight 10. Mach 2.1 at 62,000 ft. (approx. 1,385 mph). Stabilizer, rudder, and aileron pulses.
Sept. 20, 1956	X-1E NACA flight 11. Brief engine power only; flight aborted due to unspecified engine malfunction.
Oct. 3, 1956	X-1E NACA flight 12. Only 60 seconds of rocket operation; intermittent pump operation. Flight aborted, and turbopump and engine replaced.
Nov. 20, 1956	X-1E NACA flight 13. No engine operation due to ignition failure and lack of manifold pressure.
April 25, 1957	X-1E NACA flight 14. Mach 1.71 at 67,000 ft. (approx. 1,130 mph). Aileron and rudder pulses.

May 15, 1957	X-1E NACA flight 15. Mach 2.0 at 73,000 ft. (approx. 1,325 mph). Aileron pulses and rolls, sideslips, and wind-up turns. Plane severely damaged upon landing.
Sept. 19, 1957	X-1E NACA flight 16. Planned Mach number not attained due to loss of power during pushover from climb.
Oct. 8, 1957	X-1E NACA flight 17. Mach 2.24 (approx. 1,480 mph).
May 14, 1958	X-1E NACA flight 18. First flight with ventral fins; longitudinal and lateral stability and control maneuvers. Engine airstart made at approx. 70,000 ft.
June 10, 1958	X-1E NACA flight 19. Flight aborted after only one cylinder of engine fired. Plane damaged on landing.
Sept. 10, 1958	X-1E NACA flight 20. Stability and control investigation with ventral fins.
Sept. 17, 1958	X-1E NACA flight 21. Stability and control with ventral fins and a new stabilizer bell crank permitting greater stabilizer travel.
Sept. 19, 1958	X-1E NACA flight 22. Checkout flight for John McKay.
Sept. 30, 1958	X-1E NACA flight 23. Checkout flight for McKay, also check of low-speed stability and control.
Oct. 16, 1958	X-1E NASA flight 24. First flight with elevated chamber pressure; cut short because overcast obscured pilot's view of lakebed.
Oct. 28, 1958	X-1E NASA flight 25. Elevated chamber pressure; good stability and control data gathered.
Nov. 6, 1958	X-1E NASA flight 26. Elevated chamber pressure; low-altitude and low-Mach investigation of U-Deta fuel. Last NASA flight.

VIII. D-558-1 #1, BUAER NO. 37970, FLIGHTS

This aircraft completed 101 flights during its Douglas contractor program. Highlights of the contractor program were:

April 14, 1947	Douglas flight 1, Eugene F. May pilot. For familiarization. Partial power loss forced immediate landing after takeoff.
July 17, 1947	Douglas flight 14, May. Beginning of performance investigations at high Mach numbers. Mach 0.81.
Aug. 20, 1947	Douglas flight 25, Comdr. Turner F. Caldwell, Jr., USN, pilot. Set new world airspeed record of 640.663 mph.

Sept 20, 1948   Douglas flight (?), May. Plane exceeded Mach 1 during a 35-degree dive, only time a Skystreak attained Mach 1.

Douglas delivered the D-558-1 #1 to the NACA on April 21, 1949. NACA never flew it, relegating it to spares support for the D-558-1 #3.

IX. D-558-1 #2, BUAER NO. 37971, FLIGHTS

Howard C. Lilly, pilot
(27 previous flights made by Douglas, Navy, and Marine pilots)

Nov. 25, 1947   NACA flight 1. Pilot familiarization; instrumentation malfunction.

Nov. 26, 1947   NACA flight 2. Landing gear would not lock up.

Feb. 16, 1948   NACA flight 3. Attempted airspeed calibration; instrumentation malfunction.

Mar. 31, 1948   NACA flight 4. Landing gear door would not lock.
                      NACA flight 5. Landing gear door would not lock.

April 1, 1948   NACA flight 6. Landing gear door would not lock.

April 7, 1948   NACA flight 7. Landing gear door would not lock.

April 8, 1948   NACA flight 8. Attempted airspeed calibration; radar beacon failure.
                      NACA flight 9. Airspeed calibration, 30,000 ft.

April 9, 1948   NACA flight 10. Airspeed calibration, 30,000 ft.

April 12, 1948   NACA flight 11. Airspeed calibration, tower fly-by.
                      NACA flight 12. Airspeed calibration, 30,000 ft.

April 14, 1948   NACA flight 13. Smoke in cockpit after takeoff necessitated landing. Smoke due to burning 400-cycle inverter in nose compartment; inverter replaced.

April 20, 1948   NACA flight 14. Sideslips at 10,000 ft. from Mach 0.50 through 0.85, for static directional stability.

April 23, 1948   NACA flight 15. Sideslips at 30,000 ft. from Mach 0.50 through 0.85, for static directional stability.

April 28, 1948   NACA flight 16. Right landing gear would not retract.

April 29, 1948   NACA flight 17. Two speed runs; Mach 0.70 at 41,000 ft., Mach 0.88 at 36,000 ft. Left and right rudder kicks at 10,000 ft.

May 3, 1948   NACA flight 18. Landing gear would not retract.
                      NACA flight 19. Crash after takeoff due to compressor disintegration; Lilly killed.

X. D-558-1 #3, BUAER NO. 37972, FLIGHTS

(Four flights made in early 1948 by Douglas pilots and Howard Lilly)

April 22, 1949	NACA flight 1, Robert A. Champine pilot, for pilot familiarization purposes.
April 28, 1949	NACA flight 2, Champine. Pilot check; dive to Mach 0.87.
Aug. 12, 1949	NACA flight 3, Champine. Handling qualities (rudder kicks, aileron rolls, sideslips); dive to Mach 0.9.
Aug. 18, 1949	NACA flight 4, Champine. Handling qualities; dive to Mach 0.875.
Aug. 19, 1949	NACA flight 5, John H. Griffith, pilot check, handling qualities; trim run to Mach 0.84.
Aug. 23, 1949	NACA flight 6, Griffith. Airspeed calibration using tower passes.
Aug. 24, 1949	NACA flight 7, Champine. Handling qualities; dive to Mach 0.87.
Aug. 31, 1949	NACA flight 8, Champine. Aileron effectiveness investigation; no records taken.
Sept. 28, 1949	NACA flight 9, Griffith. Aileron effectiveness investigations; 16 rolls made, 4 above Mach 0.87.
Oct. 30, 1949	NACA flight 10, Griffith. Beginning of pressure-distribution survey.
Nov. 21, 1949	NACA flight 11, Griffith. Pressure-distribution investigation.
Nov. 23, 1949	NACA flight 12, Champine. Pressure-distribution investigation.
Jan. 26, 1950	NACA flight 13, Champine. Check of airspeed system.
Feb. 15, 1950	NACA flight 14, Champine. Aborted due to engine malfunction.
April 5, 1950	NACA flight 15, Griffith. Pressure-distribution investigation. Mach 0.95 attained.
April 11, 1950	NACA flight 16, Griffith. Pressure-distribution investigation. Mach 0.98 attained.
May 3, 1950	NACA flight 17, Griffith. Vortex generator investigation as part of pressure-distribution investigation. Mach 0.97 attained.
May 5, 1950	NACA flight 17A, Griffith. Vortex generator investigation as part of pressure-distribution investigations.
May 11, 1950	NACA flight 18, Griffith. Vortex generator distributor investigation. Mach 0.87 attained.
May 18, 1950	NACA flight 19, Griffith. Vortex generator distributor investigation. Mach 0.98 attained.

May 31, 1950	NACA flight 20, Griffith. Vortex generator distributor investigation.
June 8, 1950	NACA flight 21, Griffith. Vortex generator distributor investigation.
June 13, 1950	NACA flight 22, Griffith. Vortex generator distributor investigation. Mach 0.98-1.0. Conclusion of pressure-distribution investigation.
Oct. 26, 1950	NACA flight 23, Griffith. Instrument and operational check flight in preparation for the buffeting tail loads and longitudinal stability investigation.
Nov. 29, 1950	NACA flight 24, A. Scott Crossfield, pilot check. Beginning of buffeting, tail loads, and longitudinal stability program.
Dec. 12, 1950	NACA flight 25, Crossfield. Buffeting, tail loads, longitudinal stability investigation.
Dec. 18, 1950	NACA flight 26, Crossfield. Buffeting, tail loads, dynamic longitudinal stability added to longitudinal stability program.
Dec. 20, 1950	NACA flight 27, Crossfield. Longitudinal stability program.
Dec. 26, 1950	NACA flight 28, Crossfield. Longitudinal stability program.
Jan. 5, 1951	NACA flight 29, Crossfield. Longitudinal stability program.
Jan. 23, 1951	NACA flight 30, Crossfield. Longitudinal stability program. (Aborted due to fuel leak.)
Jan. 25, 1951	NACA flight 31, Crossfield. Longitudinal stability program.
Feb. 8, 1951	NACA flight 32, Crossfield. Airspeed calibration, five tower passes.
Feb. 13, 1951	NACA flight 33, Walter P. Jones. Pilot check, but some buffeting, tail loads, and longitudinal stability data taken.
Feb. 20, 1951	NACA flight 34, Jones. Aborted after Jones suffered anoxia due to a faulty O_2 regulator.
May 2, 1951	NACA flight 35, Jones. Buffeting, tail loads, longitudinal stability investigation.
June 1, 1951	NACA flight 36, Crossfield. Buffeting, tail loads, longitudinal stability investigation. Mach 0.84.
June 13, 1951	NACA flight 37, Crossfield. Buffeting, tail loads, longitudinal stability investigation. Mach 0.86.
June 21, 1951	NACA flight 38, Crossfield. Buffeting, tail loads, longitudinal stability investigation. Mach 0.835.
June 28, 1951	NACA flight 39, Jones. Buffeting, tail loads, longitudinal stability investigation. 0.85.
June 29, 1951	NACA flight 40, Joseph A. Walker. Pilot check. Mach 0.82.

July 5, 1951	NACA flight 41, Walker. Buffeting, tail loads, longitudinal stability.
July 17, 1951	NACA flight 42, Walker. Buffeting, tail loads, longitudinal stability. (Cut short, made without tip tanks.)
July 20, 1951	NACA flight 43, Walker. Buffeting, tail loads, longitudinal stability.
July 26, 1951	NACA flight 44, Walker. Buffeting, tail loads, longitudinal stability. Mach 0.83; cut short due to bad cloud formation.
July 30, 1951	NACA flight 45, Walker. Buffeting, tail loads, longitudinal stability. Mach 0.85.
Aug. 2, 1951	NACA flight 46, Walker. Buffeting, tail loads, longitudinal stability. Mach 0.84.
Aug. 7, 1951	NACA flight 47, Jones. Buffeting, tail loads, longitudinal stability. Mach 0.86.
Aug. 10, 1951	NACA flight 48, Walker. Flight cut short due to a fuel leak.
Aug. 20, 1951	NACA flight 49, Walker. Buffeting, tail loads, longitudinal stability. Mach 0.875.
Aug. 22, 1951	NACA flight 50, Walker. Flight cut short due to hydraulic line breaking.
Aug. 30, 1951	NACA flight 51, Walker. Instrument malfunction. Mach 0.86.
Sept. 6, 1951	NACA flight 52, Walker. Buffeting, tail loads, longitudinal stability. Mach 0.86.
Sept. 14, 1951	NACA flight 53, Walker. Buffeting, tail loads, longitudinal stability. Mach 0.84.
Oct. 18, 1951	NACA flight 54, Walker. Buffeting, tail loads, longitudinal stability. Beginning of lateral stability investigation. Mach 0.86.
Oct. 19, 1951	NACA flight 55, Stanley P. Butchart. Pilot check.
Nov. 9, 1951	NACA flight 56, Butchart. Pilot check.
June 27, 1952	NACA flight 57, Crossfield. Beginning of lateral stability and control (aileron effectiveness) investigation.
July 2, 1952	NACA flight 58, Crossfield. Lateral stability and control. Mach 0.85.
July 17, 1952	NACA flight 59, Butchart. Lateral stability and control. Also beginning of a simultaneous dynamic longitudinal stability investigation.
July 22, 1952	NACA flight 60, Butchart. Lateral stability and control. Simultaneous dynamic longitudinal stability investigation.
July 31, 1952	NACA flight 61, Butchart. Lateral stability and control. Simultaneous dynamic longitudinal stability investigation.

Aug. 6, 1952	NACA flight 62, Butchart. Lateral stability and control. Simultaneous dynamic longitudinal stability investigation.
Aug. 12, 1952	NACA flight 63, Butchart. Lateral stability and control. Completion of lateral stability (aileron effectiveness) program.
Jan. 29, 1953	NACA flight 64, Butchart. Dynamic stability investigation.
Feb. 6, 1953	NACA flight 65, Butchart. Dynamic stability investigation.
Feb. 11, 1953	NACA flight 66, Butchart. Dynamic stability investigation.
Feb. 17, 1953	NACA flight 67, Butchart. Dynamic stability investigation.
Feb. 20, 1953	NACA flight 68, Butchart. Dynamic stability investigation. Conclusion of dynamic stability flights.
March 27, 1953	NACA flight 69, John B. McKay. Pilot check.
April 1, 1953	NACA flight 70, McKay. Flight for dynamic stability fill-in data.
April 2, 1953	NACA flight 71, McKay. Flight for dynamic stability fill-in data.
May 7, 1953	NACA flight 72, McKay. Beginning of investigation of tip tanks upon the Skystreak's buffet characteristics. Aborted due to leak in tip tank.
May 12, 1953	NACA flight 73, McKay. Tip tank/buffet investigation. No records taken.
May 13, 1953	NACA flight 74, McKay. Tip tank/buffet investigation.
May 20, 1953	NACA flight 75, McKay. Tip tank/buffet investigation.
June 2, 1953	NACA flight 76, McKay. Tip tank/buffet investigation Also low-speed stability-and-control-in-coordinated-turns investigation.
June 3, 1953	NACA flight 77, McKay. Tip tank/buffet investigation. Also low-speed stability-and-control-in-coordinated-turns investigation.
June 10, 1953	NACA flight 78, Crossfield. Tip tank/buffet investigation. Also low-speed stability-and-control-in-coordinated-turns investigation. Last research flight flown by the Skystreak.

XI. D-558-2 #1, BUAER NO. 37973, FLIGHTS

This aircraft completed 122 flights during its Douglas contractor program. The first flight was on Feb. 4, 1948, by John F. Martin. After initial flight testing, and addition of its rocket engine, Douglas commenced the performance investigation program in the airplane on Oct. 25, 1949. Douglas delivered the plane to NACA on Aug. 31, 1951. NACA sent the plane to Douglas in 1954 for all-rocket air-launch modification, for external stores tests at supersonic speeds. The plane returned to Edwards on Nov. 15, 1955. NACA research pilot John McKay completed a familiarization flight in the plane on Sept. 17, 1956, but subsequently cancelled the remaining planned program on the airplane.

XII. D-558-2 #2, BUAER NO. 37974, FLIGHTS

A. NACA Jet-Powered Flights

Robert A. Champine and John H. Griffith, pilots.

May 24, 1949	NACA flight 1, Champine. Pilot and instrument check, general handling qualities. Mach 0.74.
June 1, 1949	NACA flight 2, Champine. Longitudinal and lateral stability and control, wing bending and twist. Mach 0.85.
June 13, 1949	NACA flight 3, Champine. Longitudinal and lateral stability and control, wing and tail loads.
July 21, 1949	NACA flight 4, Champine. Unsuccessful airspeed calibration due to airspeed/altitude recorder failure.
July 27, 1949	NACA flight 5, Champine. Successful airspeed calibration, using tower passes.
Aug. 3, 1949	NACA flight 6, Champine. Lateral control investigation.
Aug. 8, 1949	NACA flight 7, Champine. Longitudinal stability and control; inadvertant pitch-up to 6g during a 4g turn at Mach 0.60.
Aug. 24, 1949	NACA flight 8, Champine. Longitudinal stability and lateral control investigation during maneuvering flight. M = 0.855.
Aug. 30, 1949	NACA flight 9, Champine. Aborted after takeoff due to fluctuations in engine RPM and oil pressure.
Sept. 12, 1949	NACA flight 10, Griffith. Longitudinal and lateral stability and control. Only partial completion of mission, for one JATO bottle failed to drop.
Sept. 13, 1949	NACA flight 11, Griffith. Longitudinal and lateral stability and control. High engine temperatures.
Oct. 10, 1949	NACA flight 12, Champine. Longitudinal and lateral stability and control, stall characteristics.
Oct. 14, 1949	NACA flight 13, Griffith. Same as flight 12.
Nov. 1, 1949	NACA flight 14, Griffith. Same as flight 12. Inadvertent pitch-up and snap-roll, later pitch-up followed by stall/spin.
Nov. 21, 1949	NACA flight 15, Champine. Lateral stability and control, and directional stability investigation (Aileron rolls), Mach 0.855.
Nov. 22, 1949	NACA flight 16, Griffith. Same as flight 15.

Nov. 23, 1949	NACA flight 17, Griffith. Same as flight 15.
Dec. 7, 1949	NACA flight 18, Champine. Same as flight 15.
Dec. 30, 1949	NACA flight 19, Griffith. Stall investigation with tufts.
Jan. 6, 1950	NACA flight 20, Griffith. Same as flight 19. NACA flight 21, Griffith. Same as flight 19.

B. DOUGLAS AIR-LAUNCH ROCKET FLIGHTS

William B. Bridgeman, pilot.

Nov. 8, 1950	D-558-2 #2 (37974) arrives at Edwards from Douglas via B-29 (P2B-1S) launch aircraft.
Jan. 26, 1951	Douglas flight 1. Air launch at 32,000 ft., climb to 41,000 ft., level run to Mach 1.28. Dutch-roll oscillation, loss of elevator effectiveness noted.
Apr. 5, 1951	Douglas flight 2. Drop at 34,000 ft., maximum Mach of 1.36 at 46,500 ft. Severe lateral oscillation forces Bridgeman to shut off engine prematurely. Rudder lock subsequently installed to control rapid rudder oscillation.
May 18, 1951	Douglas flight 3. Launch at 34,000 ft., maximum Mach of 1.7 at 62,000 ft. Loss of rocket power occurred. Rudder locked at all speeds above Mach 1.
June 11, 1951	Douglas flight 4. Mach 1.79 at 64,000 ft. Low lateral stability, also a lightly damped longitudinal oscillation noted after burnout.
June 23, 1951	Douglas flight 5. Mach 1.85 at 63,000 ft. Violent lateral oscillation necessitates engine shutdown. Wing rolling + and −80 deg. (1.5 radians per second).
August 7, 1951	Douglas flight 6. Mach 1.88 at 66,000 ft. Dynamic lateral instability not as severe on this flight, for Bridgeman did not push over to as low an angle of attack as on previous flights.
August 15, 1951	Douglas flight 7. Altitude flight to 79,494 ft. Unofficial world's altitude record.
August 31, 1951	D-558-2 #2 turned over to the NACA.

C. NACA AIR-LAUNCH ROCKET FLIGHTS

Aug. 31, 1951	Plane delivered to the NACA HSFRS.
Sept. 28, 1951	NACA flight 1, A. Scott Crossfield. Pilot check, Mach 1.2, rough engine operation.
Oct. 12, 1951	NACA flight 2, Crossfield. Stick impulses and rudder kicks, Mach 1.28.

Nov. 13, 1951   NACA flight 3, Crossfield. Mach 1.11. Longitudinal and lateral stability and control, loads data, and aileron effectiveness.

Nov. 16, 1951   NACA flight 4, Crossfield. Same as flight 3. Maximum Mach 1.65 at 60,000 ft.

June 13, 1952   NACA flight 5, Crossfield. Lateral stability and control, vertical tail loads. Mach 1.36.

June 18, 1952   NACA flight 6, Crossfield. Stability and control, loads in low supersonic flight. Mach 1.05.

June 26, 1952   NACA flight 7, Crossfield. Same as flight 6, M = 1.35.

July 10, 1952   NACA flight 8, Crossfield. Longitudinal stability and tail loads. Mach 1.68 at 55,000 ft.

July 15, 1952   NACA flight 9, Crossfield. Longitudinal stability and tail loads. Mach 1.05, engine malfunction caused low Mach.

July 23, 1952   NACA flight 10, Crossfield. High lift investigation at maximum Mach. Mach 1.51.

Aug. 13, 1952   NACA flight 11, Crossfield. Aborted after launch due to lox prime valve remaining open.

Oct. 10, 1952   NACA flight 12, Crossfield. Longitudinal stability at supersonic speeds. Mach 1.65. Pitch-up noted in turns.

Oct. 23, 1952   NACA flight 13, Crossfield. Same as flight 12, Mach 1.10.

March 26, 1953   NACA flight 14, Crossfield. Same as flight 12.

Apr. 2, 1953   NACA flight 15, Crossfield. Lateral stability and handling qualities investigation. Beginning of series of flights to evaluate lateral stability at various angles of attack above Mach 1.

Apr. 3, 1953   NACA flight 16, Crossfield. Lateral stability investigation.

Apr. 21, 1953   NACA flight 17, Crossfield. Lateral stability investigation.

June 9, 1953   NACA flight 18, Crossfield. Lateral stability investigation.

June 18, 1953   NACA flight 19, Crossfield. Aborted after drop; engine running rough, so was shut down.

Aug. 5, 1953   NACA flight 20, Crossfield. Lateral stability investigation. Mach 1.878.

Aug. 14, 1953   NACA flight 21, Lt. Col. Marion Carl, USMC. Unsuccessful altitude attempt.

Aug. 18, 1953   NACA flight 22, Carl. Unsuccessful altitude attempt.

Aug. 21, 1953   NACA flight 23, Carl. Successful altitude flight to 83,235 ft.

Aug. 31, 1953   NACA flight 24, Carl. Maximum Mach flight attempt. Mach 1.5. Violent lateral motions.

Sept. 2, 1953	NACA flight 25, Carl. Maximum Mach flight attempt, to Mach 1.728 at 46,000 ft.
Sept. 17, 1953	NACA flight 26, Crossfield. 1st flight with nozzle extensions. Mach 1.85 at 74,000 ft.
Sept. 25, 1953	NACA flight 27, Crossfield. Lateral stability investigation. Mach 1.8 at 55,000 ft. Severe lateral instability.
Oct. 7, 1953	NACA flight 28, Crossfield. Lateral stability investigation.
Oct. 9, 1953	NACA flight 29, Crossfield. To obtain data on the effect of rocket-nozzle extensions upon the rudder hinge moment parameter.
Oct. 14, 1953	NACA flight 30, Crossfield. Lateral stability investigation. Attained Mach 1.96.
Oct. 29, 1953	NACA flight 31, Crossfield. Lateral stability investigation. No. 2 chamber failed to ignite, and engine shut down prematurely. Subsonic flight only.
Nov. 4, 1953	NACA flight 32, Crossfield. Aerodynamic loads and longitudinal control research flight.
Nov. 6, 1953	NACA flight 33, Crossfield. Lateral and longitudinal stability and control, loads research.
Nov. 20, 1953	NACA flight 34, Crossfield. First Mach 2.0 flight. Plane attains Mach 2.005 in slight dive at 62,000 ft.
Dec. 11, 1953	NACA flight 35, Crossfield. Aborted due to fire warning light. Engine shut down due to frozen valve.
Dec. 23, 1953	NACA flight 36, Crossfield. For rudder-hinge-moment data with rocket-nozzle extensions.
July 9, 1954	NACA flight 37, Crossfield. Dynamic lateral stability investigation.
July 14, 1954	NACA flight 38, Crossfield. Same as flight 37, also structural loads investigation, and wing pressure-distribution survey.
July 21, 1954	NACA flight 39, Crossfield. Same as flight 38.
July 26, 1954	NACA flight 40, Crossfield. Static and dynamic stability and control, loads, and pressure distribution. Mach 1.7 at 60,000 ft.
Aug. 6, 1954	NACA flight 41, Crossfield. Same as flight 40.
Aug. 13, 1954	NACA flight 42, Crossfield. Same as flight 40. Pitch-up encountered in turn at Mach 1.08, plane pitched to 5.8g with heavy buffeting.
Aug. 20, 1954	NACA flight 43, Crossfield. Same as flight 40.
Sept. 17, 1954	NACA flight 44, Crossfield. Same as flight 40.
Sept. 22, 1954	NACA flight 45, Crossfield. Same as flight 40.
Oct. 4, 1954	NACA flight 46, Crossfield. Dynamic lateral stability data to Mach 1.5.

Oct. 27, 1954	NACA flight 47, Crossfield. Same as flight 46. Engine shut down due to pump overspeed during climb.
March 18, 1955	NACA flight 48, Crossfield. For pressure distribution and buffeting data at transonic speeds.
April 29, 1955	NACA flight 49, Joseph A. Walker. For pilot familiarization.
May 5, 1955	NACA flight 50, Lt. Col. Frank K. Everest, Jr. USAF. For pilot familiarization in preparation for the X-2 program. Mach 1.46 at 68,000 ft.
May 6, 1955	NACA flight 51, Walker. For lateral stability and control data at low supersonic speeds.
May 12, 1955	NACA flight 52, Crossfield. For wing and horizontal stabilizer pressure-distribution data to M = 1.75.
May 19, 1955	NACA flight 53, Crossfield. To gather lateral stability and structural loads data to Mach 1.6, but aborted when fire warning indicator came on.
June 8, 1955	NACA flight 54, Crossfield. Lateral stability and aerodynamic loads data to Mach 1.67 at 60,000 ft. Subsequently, nozzle extensions removed from plane.
June 21, 1955	NACA flight 55, Crossfield. Static and dynamic stability investigation to Mach 1.4. This marks end of pressure-distribution program. Recording manometers removed from the airplane.
July 1, 1955	NACA flight 56, Crossfield. Supersonic dynamic stability and structural loads investigation.
July 20, 1955	NACA flight 57, Crossfield. Same as flight 56.
Aug. 3, 1955	NACA flight 58, Crossfield. Same as flight 56.
Aug. 12, 1955	NACA flight 59, Crossfield. Same as flight 56.
Aug. 24, 1955	NACA flight 60, Crossfield. Same as flight 56.
Sept. 2, 1955	NACA flight 61, Crossfield. Dynamic stability investigation. Beginning of vertical tail-loads research program. One rocket cylinder failed to ignite, so plane limited to Mach 1.25 at 40,000 ft.
Sept. 16, 1955	NACA flight 62, John B. McKay. Pilot familiarization, but some data on stability and control and tail loads taken. McKay had to use emergency hydraulic system to lower landing gear on this flight.
Nov. 4, 1955	NACA flight 63, Walker. Dynamic stability and structural loads investigation. Mach 1.34. Following this flight, nozzle extensions were again fitted to the LR-8 engine.
Nov. 10, 1955	NACA flight 64, McKay. Structural heating survey.
Dec. 14, 1955	NACA flight 65, McKay. Same as flight 64, Mach 1.2.
Jan. 24, 1956	NACA flight 66, McKay. Same as flight 64, Mach

	1.25. Structural heating investigation program cancelled after this flight.
Mar. 22, 1956	NACA flight 67, McKay. Plane jettisoned in inflight emergency from B-29 (runaway prop on #4 engine). McKay jettisoned propellants and made safe landing on lakebed. B-29 required extensive repairs.
Aug. 24, 1956	NACA flight 68, McKay. Vertical tail-loads investigation to Mach 1.1.
Sept. 25, 1956	NACA flight 69, McKay. Same as flight 68. This marks end of vertical tail-loads research program.
Oct. 9, 1956	NACA flight 70, McKay. Static and dynamic stability investigation to approximately Mach 1.5.
Oct. 19, 1956	NACA flight 71, McKay. Same as flight 70.
Nov. 1, 1956	NACA flight 72, McKay. Same as flight 70.
Nov. 7, 1956	NACA flight 73, McKay. Same as flight 70.
Dec. 14, 1956	NACA flight 74, McKay. For dynamic stability data at Mach 1.4, and to obtain overall sound-pressure levels in aft fuselage at subsonic and supersonic speeds.
Dec. 20, 1956	NACA flight 75, McKay. Same as flight 74. This was last NACA research flight on D-558-2 #2.

XIII. D-558-2 #3, BUAER NO. 37975, FLIGHTS

15 Douglas flights completed before aircraft modified to air-launch configuration. Pilot Eugene F. May.

Sept. 8, 1950	Douglas flight 16; Bridgeman pilot. 1st airdrop. Flight aborted after launch due to airspeed system malfunction.
Sept. 20, 1950	Douglas flight 17, Bridgeman. 2nd airdrop.
Sept. 29, 1950	Douglas flight 18, Bridgeman. 3rd airdrop.
Oct. 6, 1950	Douglas flight 19, Bridgeman. Airspeed calibration.
Nov. 17, 1950	Douglas flight 20, Bridgeman. Airspeed calibration and air-launch demonstration.
Nov. 27, 1950	Douglas flight 21, Bridgeman. Airspeed calibration and air-launch demonstration. Turbojet engine malfunction, premature rocket shutdown.
Dec. 15, 1950	Plane delivered to NACA HSFRS, designated NACA 145.
Dec. 22, 1950	NACA flight 1, A. Scott Crossfield. Pilot and instrument check, jet engine only.
Dec. 27, 1950	NACA flight 2, Crossfield. Same as flight 1.
March 27, 1951	NACA flight 3, Crossfield. Slat-loads investigation, jet only. Stalls, turns, rolls, to Mach 0.7.

April 20, 1951   NACA flight 4, Crossfield. Dynamic longitudinal stability investigation with slats locked to Mach 0.75; elevator and stabilizer pulses.

May 17, 1951   NACA flight 5, Crossfield. First NACA rocket-jet flight. Jet engine shut off due to flame instability. Mach 0.86 max.

July 17, 1951   NACA flight 6, Crossfield. Jet only, rocket failed to fire due to valve failure. Mach 0.84 max.

July 20, 1951   NACA flight 7, Walter P. Jones. Pilot check, jet only. Mach 0.73.

Aug. 9, 1951   NACA flight 8, Crossfield. Rolls and accelerated turns to Mach 1.14. Jet and rocket.

Aug. 14, 1951   NACA flight 9, Brig. Gen. Albert Boyd USAF. Pilot check. Jet and rocket. Mach 1.05.

Aug. 22, 1951   NACA flight 10, Jones. Jet and rocket, lateral and longitudinal stability investigation. Aileron rolls, elevator pulses to Mach 1.10.

Sept. 18, 1951   NACA flight 11, Jones. Jet only, rocket failure. Longitudinal stability investigation with an accelerated pitching maneuver in landing configuration. Pitch-up followed by spin and normal recovery.

Sept. 26, 1951   NACA flight 12, Jones. Lateral control investigation. Jet and rocket flight to Mach 0.96. Rolls, sideslips, elevator pulses, accelerated turns.

Oct. 18, 1951   NACA flight 13, Jones. Beginning of pitch-up investigation. Evaluation of outboard wing fences at Mach 0.7. Fences markedly aid recovery.

Nov. 9, 1951   NACA flight 14, Jones. Same as flight 13. Mach 0.95. Fences subsequently removed.

June 19, 1952   NACA flight 15, Crossfield. Jet only. Pitch-up investigation with slats locked open. Mach 0.7.

July 3, 1952   NACA flight 16, Jones. Same as flight 15. Mach 0.96.

July 31, 1952   NACA flight 17, Crossfield. Jet and rocket. Slat investigation, aborted in climb due to faulty cabin heating. Some low-speed data.

Aug. 8, 1952   NACA flight 18, Crossfield. Jet and rocket. Same as flight 15. Mach 0.96. Inboard wing fences subsequently removed. Plane now in clean, no-fence configuration.

Aug. 14, 1952   NACA flight 19, Crossfield. Slats still locked open. Flight to check effect of removing wing fences. Removal indicates inboard fences had little effect upon airplane behavior. Following flight, slats moved and locked in ½-open position.

Oct. 8, 1952   NACA flight 20, Crossfield. Jet and rocket. Evaluation of effect of slats ½ open upon pitch-up. Plane pitched to 36 deg. Mach 0.97. Slats subsequently restored to free-floating condition.

Oct. 22, 1952   NACA flight 21, Crossfield. Jet and rocket. Plane in basic no-fence configuration. Longitudinal and lateral stability and control investigation. Pitch-ups encountered during turns. Chord extensions subsequently installed on outer wing panels.

Feb. 27, 1953   NACA flight 22, Crossfield. Jet only. First flight with chord extensions. Mach 0.7. Wind-up turns and 1g stalls. Maneuvers terminated when decay in longitudinal or lateral stability became apparent.

April 8, 1953   NACA flight 23, Crossfield. Jet only, rocket failed to fire due to frozen valve. Wind-up turns, aileron rolls, sideslips, 1g stalls.

April 10, 1953   NACA flight 24, Crossfield. Jet and rocket. Mach 1.03. Same as flight 23. Pitch-up not alleviated by chord extensions, so extensions removed after flight and slats reinstalled on wings.

June 15, 1953   NACA flight 25, Crossfield. Jet and rocket. Slats locked open. Accelerated longitudinal stability maneuvers performed with control bungee installed. Decay in stability noticed at all speeds except at Mach 1. Stiff bungee subsequently installed.

June 25, 1953   NACA flight 26, Crossfield. Jet only. Slats locked open, stiff bungee. Airplane appeared quite controllable at high angles of attack; stability decay less objectionable.

June 26, 1953   NACA flight 27, Stanley P. Butchart. Pilot checkout. Slats locked open and stiff bungee installed. Jet only.

July 24, 1953   NACA flight 28, Crossfield. Jet and rocket. Plane in basic configuration. Transonic lateral and directional stability and control. Mach 1.05.

July 28, 1953   NACA flight 29, Lt. Col. Marion Carl USMC. Pilot check out in D-558-2 #3 before flying all-rocket D-558-2 #2. Jet power only.

July 30, 1953   NACA flight 30, Carl. Jet and rocket. Same as flight 29.

Sept. 9, 1953   NACA flight 31, Crossfield. Longitudinal, lateral, and directional stability investigation, from Mach 0.4 to Mach 1.08.

Sept. 14, 1953   NACA flight 32, Crossfield. Same as flight 31.

Sept. 22, 1953   NACA flight 33, Crossfield. Same as flight 31. Due to malfunction, only two rocket chambers fired.

Dec. 10, 1953   NACA flight 34, Crossfield. Transonic longitudinal stability investigation. Turns, stalls.

Dec. 22, 1953　　　　　NACA flight 35, Crossfield. Same as flight 34. Jet only, rocket did not ignite. Plane subsequently modified for external-stores program.

May 7, 1954　　　　　NACA flight 36, Joseph Walker. Pilot checkout, plane in basic configuration. Jet only.

May 12, 1954　　　　　NACA flight 37, Walker. Same as flight 36. Jet and rocket. Mach 0.97.

June 2, 1954　　　　　NACA flight 38, Crossfield. First flight with external-stores pylons. Jet only. Evaluation of handling qualities to Mach 0.72.

June 16, 1954　　　　　NACA flight 39, Crossfield. First flight with external stores (1,000-lb. bomb shapes). Jet only. No apparent adverse effects. Mach 0.72.

July 8, 1954　　　　　NACA flight 40, Crossfield. Jet and rocket. Stores cause decrease in transonic performance and increase in buffet. Mach 1.0. Stores shapes later removed as being too small.

July 19, 1954　　　　　NACA flight 41, Crossfield. Jet and rocket. Plane in clean configuration. Transonic directional and longitudinal stability and control. Mach 1.05. Sideslips, elevator and rudder pulses.

July 23, 1954　　　　　NACA flight 42, Crossfield. Jet and rocket. Transonic lateral stability and control investigation. Rolls from Mach 0.5 to 1.05.

July 28, 1954　　　　　NACA flight 43, Crossfield. Jet and rocket. Same as flight 42. Mach 1.1.

Aug. 9, 1954　　　　　NACA flight 44, Crossfield. Jet and rocket. Dynamic stability investigation from Mach 0.5 to 1.05. Elevator, aileron, and rudder pulses.

Aug. 11, 1954　　　　　NACA flight 45, Crossfield. Jet and rocket. Same as flight 44.

Aug. 18, 1954　　　　　NACA flight 46, Crossfield. Jet and rocket. Same as flight 44.

Aug. 30, 1954　　　　　NACA flight 47, Crossfield. Jet and rocket. Slats unlocked, flight for longitudinal stability and control and buffet characteristics of the aircraft in this configuration.

Oct. 8, 1954　　　　　NACA flight 48, Crossfield. Resumption of stores-investigation program. Handling qualities with 150-gal. tanks. Jet only. Mach 0.74.

Oct. 21, 1954　　　　　NACA flight 49, Crossfield. Jet and rocket. Same as flight 48. No adverse effects, but pilot noted drag rise and heavier buffet in longitudinal maneuvers. As a result of strain-gauge-loads measurements, stores program again temporarily suspended while Douglas checks strength factor of pylon and wing.

Dec. 23, 1954　　　　　NACA flight 50, Lt. Col. Frank K. Everest, Jr.,

	USAF. Pilot checkout, jet-and-rocket flight in clean configuration in preparation for the Bell X-2 program.
Dec. 28, 1954	NACA flight 51, John B. McKay. Pilot check in clean configuration, jet only.
April 27, 1955	NACA flight 52, McKay. Jet and rocket. Underwing pylons installed. Sideslips, rolls, elevator and rudder pulses. For handling qualities, wing and pylon loads, and buffet data. Mach 1.0.
May 23, 1955	NACA flight 53, McKay. Jet and rocket. 150-gal. stores attached. Same maneuvers as flight 52. Buffet levels higher with stores than with pylons only.
June 3, 1955	NACA flight 54, McKay. Jet and rocket. Pylons only. Same maneuvers as flight 52. Mach 1.0.
June 10, 1955	NACA flight 55, McKay. Jet and rocket. Same as flight 54.
June 17, 1955	NACA flight 56, McKay. Jet and rocket. 150-gal. stores attached. Same maneuvers as flight 52.
June 24, 1955	NACA flight 57, McKay. Jet and rocket. Same as flight 56.
June 28, 1955	NACA flight 58, McKay. Jet and rocket. Same as flight 56.
Aug. 30, 1955	NACA flight 59, McKay. Jet and rocket. Same as flight 56. Plane damaged on landing when tail cone touched lake first.
Nov. 2, 1955	NACA flight 60, Butchart. Jet and rocket. Same as flight 56.
Nov. 8, 1955	NACA flight 61, McKay. Jet and rocket. Same as flight 56.
Nov. 17, 1955	NACA flight 62, McKay. Jet and rocket. Same as flight 56.
Dec. 8, 1955	NACA flight 63, McKay. Jet and rocket. Same as flight 56. This concludes the stores-investigation program. Plane returned to clean configuration.
Feb. 1, 1956	NACA flight 64, McKay. Jet and rocket. To obtain wing-loads data for comparison with external-stores data previously acquired. Lateral, directional, and longitudinal maneuvers. Mach 1.0.
Feb. 3, 1956	NACA flight 65, McKay. Jet and rocket. Rocket engine pump overspeed prevents acquisition of data at Mach 0.9. Flight for same purpose as flight 64, so one more flight scheduled to complete the research program.
Aug. 28, 1956	NACA flight 66, McKay. Jet and rocket. Same as flight 64. Mach 0.96. This completes research program on this aircraft.

BIBLIOGRAPHICAL NOTE

The basic research for this study was conducted at the Historical Office, National Aeronautics and Space Administration Headquarters, Washington, D.C. The bulk of the progress reports, pilots' notes, test-reports, memorandums, and letters come from retired NACA records. Where applicable, the author made use of NACA *Technical Reports* and *Technical Memorandums* prepared on the various research aircraft. The single greatest source of documentation used in this work is a group of retired records obtained from the Federal Records Center at Bell, California. These records are:

NASA/Flight Research Center (FRC) Box 310b, X-1 reports.
NASA/FRC Box 312a, X-1 reports (1955–59).
NASA/FRC Box 361, 1949–57 D-558 series airplanes.
NASA/FRC Box 362, D-558 series airplanes.
NASA/FRC Box 366, D-558 series airplanes.

Some additional X-1 material is interspersed in memorandums and reports found in NASA/FRC Box 321, X-2 reports (1949–56). The material in these containers is not limited to NACA. It also covers participation by contractors and military services.

Supplementary data came from Record Group 255 in the National Archives. Particularly helpful were the papers of Walter T. Bonney and the extensive NACA photographic collection. Useful information also came from the aircraft and personnel files maintained at the National Air and Space Museum of the Smithsonian Institution. Valuable material on the workings of the Research Airplane Projects Panel and the NACA High-Speed Flight Station came from the files of the NASA Langley Research Center. The author obtained additional information on the D-558 program from the Naval Air Systems Command and through individuals at the McDonnell Douglas Corpora-

237

tion. The Air Force Historical Office and the Air Force Systems Command supplied the Edwards AFB semiannual histories from 1946 through 1958. Some material concerning early Army Air Forces supersonic research came from Air Force Museum files.

The assistance of participants in the research aircraft program was vital to this work. Their interviews and correspondence provided little-known background information and personal insights unavailable in written records. They rounded out the work and added new dimensions to the subject.

Contemporary sources furnished data on individuals, national developments, and aircraft. Perhaps more importantly, however, they serve to indicate the framework in which the emergence of the research-aircraft program occurred. The best sources in this vein are the aviation trade journals; however, newspapers and magazines furnish valuable commentary.

The research-aircraft program has not yet received full-length treatment, and there is a dearth of works treating this subject. Those of special value are: Eugene M. Emme, *Aeronautics and Astronautics: An American Chronology of Science and Technology in the Exploration of Space 1915–1960* (Washington, 1961); George W. Gray, *Frontiers of Flight: The Story of NACA Research* (New York, 1948); Edwin P. Hartman, *Adventures in Research: A History of Ames Research Center 1940–1965* (Washington, 1970); William Bridgeman and Jacqueline Hazard, *The Lonely Sky* (New York, 1955); A. Scott Crossfield, *Always Another Dawn: The Story of a Rocket Test Pilot* (Cleveland, 1960); Frank K. Everest, *The Fastest Man Alive* (New York, 1959); William R. Lundgren, *Across the High Frontier: The Story of a Test Pilot— Major Charles E. Yeager, USAF* (New York, 1955).

INDEX